THE RESTLESSNESS OF SHANTI ANDÍA

AND OTHER WRITINGS

Pío Baroja

translated by Anthony Kerrigan

The Restlessness of Shanti Andia

AND

OTHER

WRITINGS

Ann Arbor

The University of Michigan Press

Designed by George Lenox
Copyright © by The University of Michigan 1959
First printing May 1959
Second printing September 1959
Library of Congress Catalog Card No. 59-5063
Published in the United States of America by
the University of Michigan Press and simultaneously
in Toronto, Canada, by Ambassador Books, Ltd.
Printed in the United States of America
by Vail-Ballou Press, Inc., Binghamton, N.Y.

FOR ELAINE

She goes over the cobbles
like a walker on water
taller than the high garden
walls

CONTENTS

The World of Pío Baroja

BY ANTHONY KERRIGAN

The World of Pío Baroja

I.

Pío Baroja was a subtle man of action. His conspirator kinsman Eugenio de Aviraneta had been a nineteenth-century historical and romantic figure: guerrilla in the war against Napoleon, member of the *Carbonari,* soldier in Mexico, an agent with Byron in Greece. Lacking imagination, Aviraneta was forced to live the life of a fictional character amid the irritation of daily living, dependent always on the chance opportunity to act as he pleased, crossing paths and words with aggressive competitors who filled precisely the space he craved to fill. Baroja made Aviraneta the hero of a cycle of books, but he himself, needing only "in summer, a window with a bit of green beyond, in winter, a fire in the grate," stirred Spain more profoundly than any conceivable conspiratorial kinsman.

In old age, in his ancestral home in the Basque town of Vera, he felt much the same mystery in contemplating the medieval church and the smoke over the village rooftops as he had felt at the Etoile in Paris or the Parc Montsouris in his youth. When he was past seventy he could say, with melancholy acerbity, that he still felt, as he had at fifteen, a distant enthusiasm for adventure without believing in it. All the possible moves by contrabandists, soldiers, priests, poets, bomb throwers, prostitutes, thieves, and saints were in his mind like the moves of thousands of possible games in the mind of a chess genius. Whatever chessboards and moves he had not memorized, he could suspect. Like fabulous Mendel the itinerant bookman, he knew the vast bibliography of the worthless titles of the world as well as all the worthwhile.

In sum, Baroja intuited more than Aviraneta—a species of Don Juan of warfare, or compromised Don Quixote—could *do.* Baroja was the antithesis, moreover, of the twentieth-century specialist and of the "social animal" as well; and he was a man of action who did not negate Pascal's dictum that all the trouble in the world was caused by men who could not stay in their rooms.

Baroja made a feint at living in the real world: on the Biscayan coast that had sent out a decisive share of America's explorers, in

3

seething Madrid as a medical student and bakery owner, as a doctor in a Basque provincial town, as an exile in Paris and other parts of France. But he had been born out of time, an anachronistic Basque—among the only people in the West leagued with no one else and still preserving pre-Christian names—and he had inherited the sensitive ear of a buffoon and the memory of a wandering bard.

The raw material of his nearly one hundred novels is all reality —the events of the day for the fifty years during which he wrote, and the immediate history of the century before in his *Memorias de un hombre de acción* ("Memoirs of a Man of Action"), his score of books in the Aviraneta cycle. The crimes, the songs and jingles, the wars, assassinations and citations, the polemical pamphlets, speeches and proclamations, the unchecked rumors and scientific pronouncements are the stuff of his pages.

His most turbulent (and celebrated) novels are those of Madrid low life: the two trilogies *La lucha por la vida* ("The Fight for Life") and *El pasado* ("The Past"). His most generous books are his Basque narratives: *The Restlessness of Shanti Andía, The Legend of Jaun de Alzate, Vidas sombrías* ("Somber Lives"), and *The House of the Aizgorri*. All his other books swing about these two axes of interest, except when they deal with incidental adventures abroad, in Paris, London, Amsterdam, Rome. The Madrid novels and the Basque narratives are diametrically opposed in spirit. The first are tough, anarchistic, and antisocial; their concern with types on the fringes of society is deliberate. "Well, then, what did we expect?" asks the young Ortega y Gasset. "Was he supposed to tell us about senators and commodores, provincial governors, the Dames of the Forty Hours' Devotion, or financiers?" Anyone is more worthy than the "adapted ones," continues Ortega, for in specific societies "adaptation takes on the character of a fall, of a new inertia, of vile submission to slavery." And in a corrupt Spain, Baroja preferred to go to the fringes of society, to the social dump, and portray tramps and fevered gamblers, sponges and wastrels, the farfetched and suicidal. Within ten years he wrote twenty volumes on vagabondage. And he concerned himself with anarchists and radicals as nonconforming individuals, as iconoclasts and rebels, never as the symbols of the mass they thought themselves to be.

There are at least two Barojas: the universal Castilian and the Basque. His Basque novels are intervals of racial affection and tenderness. There are not many of them, but they are distinguished by their poetry and notable for the insight they give us into the strange green land that produced the founder of the Jesuits, Saint Ignatius Loyola; the first global circumnavigator, Juan Sebastián Elcano; the conqueror of the Philippines and founder of Manila, Legazpi from Zumárraga, who removed the archipelago from the Islamic orbit; the Apostle to the Indies and Japan, St. Francis Xavier; and in Baroja's generation, the great heterodox thinker Miguel de Unamuno. If Baroja's Basque sea stories are not as many-faceted or of such moral significance as the sea narratives of Joseph Conrad or Herman Melville, they are nevertheless poetic, evocative commentaries on historic epochs, and have the more direct appeal of the chronicle.

Baroja also wrote seven volumes of *Memorias: Desde la última vuelta del camino* ("Memoirs: From the Last Turn in the Road"), in which, in addition to exhaustive reference to the printed ephemera of his age, he made use of selections from his novels—so close was his fiction to his life and times—as if to prove Unamuno's point that "the novel is the truest history."

Baroja is probably the most widely read of modern novelists in the Spanish-speaking world. In Spain, his fame has been entrenched for years. Nevertheless, in the paradoxical tradition of Spanish letters, he was forced to dodge political recrimination and reprisal more or less continually. He was of the party "of the individual against the State," and denounced Marxism from the times of his first book, but at the outbreak of the Civil War, after being jailed with the village doctor when the Carlists occupied his home town of Vera, it was, ironically, the anti-Marxists from whom he walked away into exile in France, crossing the Bidasoa at Irun, without papers, baggage, or money, clad in rope-soled *alpargatas*. After his eventual return from France, he declared to all and sundry in his home in Madrid that he was "an exile within Spain." During the Republic he had been denounced by the Leftist rulers, and thus his record of enforced nonconformism, like Unamuno's, was impartial: "As writers, we have in Spain not one enemy, but two: the Reds and the Whites." His books have been censored, in whole or in part: from omissions in approved editions of such classics as *Zalacaín, el aventurero* to refusal of approval for works which are, as a result, available only in the expensive *Obras completas*.

Late in 1956, in the opening words of a speech which the censorship passed on condition that the gathering (of university women) in homage to Baroja not be publicly announced, Camilo José Cela, leading Spanish novelist of the post-Civil War generation, reflected a general Spanish evaluation of the Basque writer's underestimated worth: "Two months before his eighty-fourth

birthday, and one week after not having been given the Nobel
Prize, Pío Baroja is dead."

II.   *Homero de la canalla. . .*
                                       —ORTEGA Y GASSET, OF PÍO BAROJA

                                       He chose for his heroes none
                                       but nonconformists, irregulars,
                                       insurgents.

                                       —MATHILDE POMÈS

When his last living comrades brought Pío Baroja's body up the
alley of graves in the Cementerio Civil del Este, the unglorious
and unhallowed civil cemetery of Madrid, they found—something
most of them probably had not known before—that he was to
lie forever in close proximity to Pablo Iglesias and Nicolás
Salmerón. Death, if less facetious than life, again proved equally
as ironic, circumstantial, and just; its justice, hurried and rather
sarcastic, was a poetic justice.

Baudelaire in Paris had been put into the ground alongside his
once hated stepfather, General Aupick, a final irony which did
not lack justice as a commentary on the last repentant days of the
great poet. In the case of Baroja his ultimate neighbors furnished
an equally fitting comment on his life and times.

Pablo Iglesias was the father of Spanish socialism, the leading
Spaniard in the First and Second Internationals. Baroja, far from
being a socialist, was not even a believer in democracy; but he
had written in an *ambiance* partly formed by such men as Iglesias, he had concerned himself principally with rebels and been
the associate of socialist romantics and anarchist conspirators.

Baroja's other neighbor, Nicholás Salmerón, third president of
the first Spanish Republic, was a symbol of republicanism in
Spain, and its drama: a confused well-intentioned tragedy.

The trio in this particular cemetery (where special permission
for admission must be made, a cemetery so exclusive that one had
to be at odds with all of Spain to be eligible: excluded, in effect,
from Spanish society, from the protection of the state religion,
from the circle of national belief and popular myth) represented
the nineteenth century and its aftermath in Spain as well as any
conceivable three men could do. Their chance association in the
ground, through the lack of logic inherent in death, served to
unite them as representative figures just as well as a more
thoughtful selectivity could have done. In addition, given the
historical perspective, it was possible to note characteristic and

fated similarities. Salmerón, an opponent of capital punishment, resigned as President of Spain after only two months in office rather than sign death warrants handed down by the courts against separatist rebels who were fighting to overthrow him— a gesture unmatched in modern political history and inconceivable in the later totalitarian epoch. Despite early Darwinian and Nietzschean pronouncements, Baroja was a man constituted to make a similar gesture; among the various forms of violence which he examined in his novels of action, it was legal violence he came most to suspect; moreover, he believed that "the government which did nothing was the best." For his part, Iglesias had dogmatically, and paradoxically, "declared war against violence."

In an age when idealism was not yet discredited and even politicians, let alone writers, need not be involved, committed, or altogether engaged, Salmerón taught metaphysics at the University of Madrid—in the intervals when he was not in exile, making a sparse living at the law, or failing at politics. And at a little later date, Baroja placed writing as he pleased above any social obligation whatsoever. When Baroja began to write for the first time, in the years that he ran a bakery in a Madrid side street, he contributed to Salmerón's *La justicia,* a utopian paper which attracted writers and theorists of all tendencies, and he heard Salmerón deliver speeches on three occasions: he was most impressed by an address delivered at the same Civil Cemetery.

As regards final purposes, eschatological considerations, the three were again characteristic of their age of overrated reason. In his own way, Salmerón believed in an afterlife, a "heaven of ideas," as he was not too embarrassed to phrase it. The other men were too hidebound and moralizing to believe in any amelioration by easy, supernatural means. In the opinion of Iglesias, it was not enough to die, it was more necessary to love; or, as Baroja had put it, simply "to act decently."

Iglesias, whose name means "churches," was the most puritanical and strait-laced anticlerical in Spain. His bastard father's full-name—Pedro de la Iglesia Expósito—incorporated a laconic summation of his origin: abandonment by exposure outside a church. His life and that of his family was exactly the kind of life that Baroja wrote about in all his early novels of the Madrid *bas fonds.* Dickens wrote of similar types in England, and Baroja read Dickens and never forgot the Englishman's example, but the raw material was in Madrid in vivid form in the life of the man who was at last to be his companion in the ground.

And the life of Baroja's cemetery companion, the founder of socialism in Spain and lifetime president of the Art of Printing

Association (as the printer's union was poetically known in the florid nineteenth century), is worth a moment's glance for an understanding of what Baroja found in Madrid when he went searching about him to write *Red Dawn,* or *Weeds,* or *The Quest,* the trilogy for which he is most famous. It is probable that Baroja knew the details of Iglesias' life, for they formed part of the lore of Madrid; he certainly knew Iglesias himself, and in his *Memorias* he writes of an encounter with the socialist in a print shop, where Iglesias shunned him since Baroja was not on the side of the workers. An account in J. Zugazagoitia's *Pablo Iglesias,* published in 1929, furnishes a vivid picture of the Madrid of his early days: "Mother and son lived narrowly on her washerwoman's wage and from whatever she earned occasionally as a maid. In the houses where she worked she would ask permission to take her one meal home with her, to share with her son. The worst part was the cold. There was no defense in their garret against it. They had a bad time of it indoors, but it was worse in the street. They had no coats and relied on ingenuity to remedy their poverty. Pablo, following the example of the street urchins, clothed himself in long strips of paper torn from theater billboards. He wrapped them around his chest, and then put on a vest and coat—a coat with the brand mark of 'It Fit The Dead Man Better'—and with this covering, set his face against the Madrid winter." This was the Madrid that Iglesias endured and Baroja described.

If the three men had nothing else in common they were astoundingly alike in their virtue, in perhaps the most sacred of virtues: they had been incorruptible in life.

José Ortega y Gasset, surely the outstanding and most remarkable figure of modern Spain, whom Baroja considered "the great Spaniard of my time" and "its greatest writer," was fascinated by the intransigence of Baroja. In a long essay *Ideas sobre Pío Baroja* he stated flatly: "In his anxiety to be sincere and loyal with himself I know of no one in Spain or outside of Spain comparable with Baroja." And Ortega proceeds to speak of a certain incorruptibility which is present in every man. "In general, this ultimate and most individual nucleus of our personality is buried beneath an accumulation of sentimental opinions and mannerisms which have fallen upon us from outside. Only a few men, endowed with a peculiar energy, manage to catch a glimpse, now and again, of the real essence and attitude of the entity that Bergson would call the 'profound I.' From time to time, its secret voice reaches the surface of conscience. Baroja is the extraordinarily rare case, unique in my sphere of experience, of a

man almost entirely constituted of this fundamental incorruptibility and completely free of the 'conventional I' which habitually
envelops it." And he adds that in a man of such breed, nothing
about him can be a matter of indifference. "His ideas may appear absurd to us, but since in him they are pure and spontaneous reactions on the part of what is most inalienable in man,
they gain in valid reality whatever they lack or exceed in logical
consistency." In sum, Baroja "furnishes us an example of genial
independence in the midst of a society like our own, where
everything is compromise and surrender."

III.   . . . a Finnic ogre grafted on
                                        a degenerate Goth.

                                        —DON POMPEYO GENER,
                                        the Francophilic atheist, of Pío Baroja.

If Baroja's life has little but moral bearing on his work, it
nevertheless discloses a good deal about the Spain into which
he was born.

The newspaper obituaries—revealing of current prejudice—
serve as well for the early biography as the entries on Baroja in
any American encyclopedia.

The Madrid *ABC* (Royalist), for instance, for October 31,
1956, carefully noted certain indispensable details. "Pío Baroja
was born in San Sebastián, the 28th of December of 1872, at
Number 6, Oquendo street, in a house built by his grandmother,
Doña Concepción Zornoza." The *ABC* was patently somewhat
ashamed of Don Pío's father, and omits any discussion of him
for the moment, an omission which the more plebian *La Van-
guardia* of Barcelona supplies on the same date: "Don Pío was
the son of Don Serafín Baroja, mining engineer and writer of
popular songs in Basque." The *ABC,* meanwhile, picks a more
respectable ancestor for immediate comment, and, going back
two generations, continues: "One of his great grandfathers
bought a printing press in Oyarzun in about the year 1806;
during the Revolution of 1820 he moved the press to San Sebastián, where his son, Pío, who gave his name to the novelist,
continued the business. The establishment remains to this day.
This grandfather of Baroja was the close friend of many writers
and military men of his time." *ABC* at length comes to the
father: "The father of Pío Baroja was an original man. His career
was in engineering, and he followed it in various parts of Spain.
He was possessed of a Bohemian temperament and was an

amateur writer in Basque and Castilian. He died in 1912. Don Pío's mother—Baroja himself tells us—was a woman with a fund of renunciation and fatalism. She died at Vera de Bidasoa, at the family house, Itzea, in 1935, at 86 years of age."

The mother's name was Carmen Nessi Goñi, and she was of partly Italian descent. Her four children included Pío's brother Ricardo, "later a famous etcher, painter, and writer, dedicated likewise to inventing, who led a very literary life, and harbored dreams of adventure," and Carmen, "who married the publisher Caro Raggio and who was the only one of the family to have descendants."

The Basques among whom Baroja was born are more profoundly divided into coastal and mountain people than they are into French Basques or Spanish. Their nationality has never distinguished one type from the other, but only whether or not they lived by the sea. Pío was born by the sea, and was glad that he had been: "It has always seemed to me an augury of freedom and change." He has written about mountain Basques and seafaring Basques, and his inland novels, such as *Zalacáin, el aventurero,* reflect the redolent mountain terrain depicted with melancholy oppressiveness in Pierre Loti's novel of French Basque life, *Ramuntcho,* while his sea novels, as *The Restlessness of Shanti Andía,* mirror the freedom—the almost aimless, cosmic, vacant freedom—of the sea.

Pío Baroja's first memory was of the Carlist bombing of San Sebastián, which was held by the Liberals. The Carlist wars apart, his memories of his entrance into the "serial story of life" were the poisoning of the upstairs neighbors by the maid, and two mad people he saw capering about as a child. In his later observations the ridiculous was never to be separated from the grandiose. Ortega has pointed out a key word in Baroja's writing that appears and reappears. The word is *farsa:* farce: "And almost all things seem to him a farce, and almost all men farcical." The word may be precisely what Baroja uses to designate lack of honesty: men defending causes they do not believe in, attacking beliefs they do not disbelieve, or even worse, men refusing to defend or practice what they do believe. What is most farcical is that this situation is inevitable. He was born into an epoch notable for woman's use of the bustle rather than for a Pericles or a Marcus Aurelius, "but no one was to blame for this situation."

The Baroja family moved from San Sebastián to Pamplona —where the bulls run in the streets each year during the week of San Fermín—and in 1886 they went to Madrid. They arrived

in the capital a day or two after an attempted republican uprising led by General Villacampa. The family took lodgings on
Independence Street, near the Royal Theater. Baroja's romantic
relative Aviraneta had been born in this quarter, and Baroja
described it in more than one book. The streets and buildings
were heavy with suggestion: the site of the Academy of Human-
ities where Cervantes had studied, the house where the young
playwright Larra killed himself, the balcony from which the
anarchist Morral threw his bomb at Alfonso XIII as the King returned from his wedding, and the tavern where the would-be
regicide, as well as Baroja, drank beer in the evening.

After preliminary studies, Baroja went on, in a rather desultory
fashion, to study medicine, which did not interest him. A
characteristic turmoil prevailed, and Baroja was horrified at the
falseness and mockery of learning; at this time he seems to have
adopted a defensive sarcasm which never left him, and which
represented perhaps a lessening of his powers of understanding.

In later life Baroja hounded the memory of his ex-professors
unmercifully. He apparently hated the lot of them thoroughly,
and if half of what he says in a horrendous chapter on them in
his *Memoirs* is true, he loathed them on good grounds. While the
spectacle of academic stupidity may be repeated endlessly in
other countries and at all times, there is nevertheless a special
nineteenth-century Spanish air of depravity about Baroja's professors that sets them apart. The famous Letamendi was an
arrant plagiarist, and Baroja commenced the practical and
polemical side of his own writing career by running down, for
purposes of ridicule, the originals whence the pedant plagiarized
his observations and anecdotes; in his *Memoirs* he takes credit for
being the one to begin the pulverization of the great man's reputation. The surgeon Rivera was one of the worst: "He was a
mean and bitter Catalan, a little runt with a tenor's voice,
who treated a patient as an enemy. . . He died in a brothel.
After watching him operate, it would have given anyone great
pleasure to operate on him." The professor of therapy was
simply "crazy": since he himself was "sallow, dark, and skinny,
he thought that anyone who did not look the same was made up
to deceive the world." Except for one good man—who was
surely a Jew—the doctors were all either "wild boars," "madmen,"
"humbugs," or "sugary cuckoos." The chief of the syphilis
hospital of San Juan de Dios was a "cruel macaw" in his sadistic
treatment of the woman patients, and Baroja "could not stand
the sadism of that petulant idiot with white sideburns."

These professors taught Baroja a definitive lesson in well-ensconced cruelty and guile. As a medical student he was an anarchist sympathizer—which left him free to avoid joining any organization or from agreeing with anyone else's opinions. From this position he began to veer toward "spiritual nihilism, based on sympathy and pity, without any political solution whatever." This substitute for politics never developed much further.

After Baroja received his medical degree at Valencia, his post-doctoral professors seemed to improve slightly; that is, "the professors I then had to put up with were innocuous enough," as one was "mediocre," another "very solemn, and empty," a third found it "impossible to be pleasant." Baroja wrote a doctoral thesis titled "Pain," which his final examiners "obviously did not read—nor was it worth reading."

For a year or two Baroja practiced medicine in a small town in the Basque country. The provincial town, Cestona, was strange and even interesting, but quarrels with the other doctor in town and the low pay drove him to throw over his inauspicious career, and he never actively practiced medicine again.

In Madrid his brother Ricardo, the artist, was doing his best to run a bakery belonging to the family. To help him out, Pío determined to enter the bakery business, in the thought that he was at least as well suited for this occupation as he had been for medicine.

The bakery was on Misericordia Street, corner of Capellanes. Popular rumor maintained that the cellar of the building connected with the convent of the Unshod Carmelite nuns and with the Royal Palace. Any of numberless Baroja characters could have set such a rumor in motion. The building was owned by Pío's half-Italian aunt, Juana by name; she was an "Old Agrippina" with a highly developed skeptical sense, who believed only in fresh eggs, well-prepared dishes, and fine days.

"Someone would tell me I should get married. But I wasn't in a position to make even a middling impression on a bourgeois family."

"Who is that character?" the mama would have asked, if she had seen me hankering after the girl of the house.

"He's a rare bird. He's a baker."

"A baker? He probably has money."

"No, it seems not. I think he's really a doctor and writes for the newspapers."

"Then he's an idler."

"It looks like it. . ."

Pío also played the stock market systematically.

After six years, a variety of circumstances doomed the bakery;

among the circumstances was a war with the United States. Spain rushed into the Spanish-American War with as much hypocrisy as its transatlantic enemy. The press lied monumentally, the government made false and ridiculous pronouncements, the navy steamed off to its sure destruction. The populace celebrated the lies and official pronouncements with patriotic ardor, anti-American demonstrations, and nationalist songs. The shells from the old Spanish warships reached half way to the American ships which were raking them with fire. The Spanish government, when it heard the news, got ready for a revolution. The populace, when it heard the news, went to the bullfight. It was then that the Academician Silvela, author of *The Literary Bad Taste of the Eighteenth Century,* said that Spain had no pulse.

The disaster in Cuba and the Philippines shocked the intellectuals—if not the authorities or the populace—into a vigorous, and bitter, self-consciousness. This self-consciousness led to an interrogation of the meaning of Spain. The quest for self-knowledge crystallized in the "Generation of 1898."

IV.   *Our only European novelist*
                              —CAMILIO JOSÉ CELA

The significance of the Generation of '98 has so far been largely lost to the world. This group—original, complex, and paradoxically prophetic and forward-looking considering the country of its origin—has a good deal to say to the most technically advanced countries, and even to the more civilized.

The writers and philosophers whom in perspective we group together were nurtured at the turn of the century in Spain's chagrin at suddenly finding itself deceived and thwarted as a nation. The entire modern history of Spain had been mysteriously disastrous. None of the reasons given for her torpor and decline has ever quite sufficed. The writers of '98 began by holding an intellectual wake around the inert body of their country. Next, in the manner of Russian intellectuals, the writers of '98 went to the countryside (literally, for most of them tramped about Spain, through the old cities, the half-deserted towns, the lost hamlets, and the glorious ruins). They went in groups and they went alone. None of the leaders was Castilian, and it was Castile that they rediscovered for themselves and for all of Spain. This mystic landscape of immense plains—offering no sensual solicitation—was all spirit, all soul, and in it they created a new conscience for their race. Their writing recreated the landscape and the country's natural being. They sought, too, to revitalize its history, its primitive classics, its local myth or "intrahistory." They showed an amazing vitality in a prostrate country, amplifying the limits of all things Spanish—it was at this time, for instance, that the forgotten Greek expatriate in Spain, El Greco, was revaluated—and they attempted at the same time to Europeanize Spain, while some of them nonetheless championed its African values.

The principal figures of the Generation of '98—the number is variously enlarged or restricted according to the critic—were Miguel de Unamuno (b. 1864), defender of Spain's quixotic greatness *qua* quixotic and author of *The Tragic Sense of Life;* Ramón del Valle-Inclan (b. 1866), the most exotic figure of his generation; Baroja (b. 1872); and the poet Antonio Machado (b. 1875), who died in flight from the Civil War. Contemporary with the generation, influencing it and influenced by it, were Ángel Ganivet (b. 1865), the earliest to die (he threw himself into the Dwina at Riga, while in the foreign service, in the key year of 1898); Jacinto Benavente (b. 1866), Nobel Prize winner, but the least figure of the group; Ramiro de Maeztu Whitney (b. 1874), of English mother and Basque father, an early Anglophile and later nationalist, shot by a republican firing squad in Madrid in the early days of the Civil War; and Azorín (b. 1873), interpreter of the group's concepts of time and space in his stories and spokesman of their objectives. Younger, though by extension identified with the group, are Ramón Pérez de Ayala (b. 1881), widely traveled exile and Academician, and Ortega y Gasset (b. 1883), doubtless its culminating figure. Working in the same ambiance was the artist and writer José Gutiérrez Solana (b. 1886), perhaps the only Spanish painter of importance in the century to be formed in Spain and to remain there.

The role of the Generation of '98 is one of double paradox: to reject rationalism as an apocryphal tale even before their country had quite accomplished the enthronement of the false god of Reason; and to reject mysticism as an ideal when they themselves were the ones to discover the well-springs of Spain's strength in this very irrationality. More accurately than the thinkers who were followers of De Tocqueville, more incisively than the poets who were followers of Baudelaire, Ortega foresaw the hollowness of progress, the spiritual wastelands of industrialization, the Armageddon of the dinosaurs of materialism. For his part, Unamuno followed Kierkegaard and undermined

Faith so that men might extend themselves for their belief. Like
Kierkegaard, he abominated the bloodless public of an age without passion, and he strove "to sow the seeds of despair." Baroja,
too, would have nothing to do with compromised myth, and,
when he allowed himself any nostalgia, harkened back past
Christianity to the prehistoric Basques and a kind of Celtic
druidism.

If many a post-Victorian intellectual was ahistoric because of
his lack of faith in the past and because of his practical belief in
science, his belief that Science—and not he—would solve all
questions and determine all quests, his Spanish contemporary was
of a totally different mind about himself and his role, and his
generation came to exercise a most important influence in his
country's history. In fact, the concept of the generation in historical interpretation has been notably developed in Spain—most
probably as a result of the dramatic example of the Generation
of '98. Divorced from mere genealogical descent, the theory of
generations, though of an obvious significance, was nonetheless
not examined closely until the nineteenth century; in the twentieth its study is principally by Spaniards, as by Ortega y Gasset,
by Pedro Lain Entralgo (*Las generaciones en la historia*), Julián
Marías (*El metodo historico de las generaciones*), and by Pedro
Salinas ("El concepto de generación literaria aplicada a la del
98").

Since the assertion of the individual, the doubting and disquieted individual, was the most profound statement of these
men, they subordinated at the time any concept of a generation
to that of the individual: they formed no group, nor acted in
concert. It is only a posteriori that they are seen to have been born
under the same sign and to have produced works which, like
German music after the turn of the seventeenth century or
Elizabethan drama at the turn of the sixteenth, are strangely
of a piece.

Within the framework of their similarity, each of the members
of the generation had his own highly individual development,
for example, Ortega's thought can be said to have evolved
through the three phases outlined in José Ferrater Mora's *Ortega
y Gasset*. Baroja's peculiarity was to have sensed and felt much
the same about the world at twenty as at sixty, the more meaningful division in his work being that between the books inspired
by Castile and those on the Basque country.

The individualists of '98 placed the "I" of Ortega, his "I am I
and my circumstance," at the center of all concepts of existence.
There is an absolute necessity for every man to do something

about his "I" at all times—or to abdicate the decision. But he must be always acting, even in his abdicating.

Baroja is the frontiersman of the "I": the activist of the "I," beyond all Nietzschean concepts of the select "I," and beyond all niceties of culture. Ortega wrote of Baroja: "Here is a man who thinks from an instinct of self-preservation, who thinks *against* his environment to avoid being absorbed by it! Baroja bristles his pages around him like a hedgehog bristles its quills."

The "I" of Pío Baroja, the "I" of all his contemporaries, is not the "I" of Oscar Wilde, nor the "I" of Bernard Shaw, nor the "I" of the American twenties; it is neither precious nor brash, neither self-dramatizing or petulant. It may be as medieval as Carcassonne or the walls of Ávila, but it is as honest as short-tempered Diogenes or irascible Paracelsus, or as intransigent as the Spanish heresiarch Servetus, who postulated the circulation of the blood before Calvin had him burned at Geneva.

Unamuno, Ortega, Baroja—each in his manner, but with surprising agreement—believed it necessary for man to take action against his circumstances if he were to *be*. Far from "adjusting," we must *survive* our circumstance. Since our circumstance is never us, to adjust to it is a falsification of ourselves. Life is precisely what we do to avoid being annihilated by our environment. As Ortega y Gasset says in *En Torno a Galileo* (Lección X):

> Life consists in the fact that man finds himself, without knowing how, having to exist in a certain determined and inexorable circumstance. Life must be lived, inexorably, here and now. This circumstance, in which we must exist and maintain ourselves, is formed by our material environment, and by our social environment, the society in which we find ourselves. Inasmuch as this environment, by virtue of being exactly that, is something other than man, something distinct, strange, alien to him, to be in one's circumstance can not mean a passive reclining in it, so as to form part of it. For man does not form part of his circumstance: on the contrary, he always finds himself before it, outside it, and to live is precisely to have to do something to prevent our circumstance from annihilating us.

There is a peculiarly full-bodied quality to the thought and writing of the Generation of '98. Unamuno believed only in the man of bone and blood and not in any abstracted phantom, while Ortega concerned himself with no ready-made man but with the man who was continually becoming what he is. Baroja's preoccupation was with individuals—by preference vagabonds and adventurers—in action, and acting almost always in an antisocial sense; not necessarily against the "interests of society," but in consonance with some individual pattern. Baroja's novels are full of talk about ideas, but his concern is with the purposeful purposelessness of living in a world which is ceaselessly a mystery. In short, in Ortega's thought or in Baroja's novels the very essence of life—and any given man is the totality of what he has made of his life—is the fact that it must be lived. Unamuno's novels lack plot because life has no plot but the one developed as it is lived; Baroja's novels, written in the same anachronistic and paradoxical Spain, typically lack meaningful plot in all but the Basque stories, and we sense that Baroja is letting his characters act out their roles so that he may find out what the plot is, that is, what their life, or any life, might be about.

Baroja, for reasons of his own, categorically denied the existence of the Generation of '98. "I have always affirmed that no Generation of '98 existed. It was an invention of Azorín's." The point of interest in this declaration is that a few pages after making it (in Vol. I of the *Memoirs*), Baroja clearly painted the collective psychological portrait of the nonexistent generation. The Academician Eugenio Montes had written, during World War II, that " the Generation of '98 was—and still is—paradoxically and monstrous as it may appear, a kind of intellectual F.A.I. (Iberian Anarchist Federation), a generation or biological association of anarchists." To which Baroja replies that "if anarchism is subjectivism, the predominance of feeling over concept, of landscape over the city, of the private over the public, of character over reason, then all lyric poetry and the novel are integrally anarchist." In stating his argument in defense of his contemporaries, Baroja had adduced not the qualities of "all lyric poetry and the novel" but precisely those of the poetry and the novel of '98.

V.   *If a machine gun had an opinion,*
                                it might resemble the charac-
                                ters of the City of the
                                Discreet, *of* Paradox, King,
                                or of Red Dawn.

                                                    —ORTEGA Y GASSET

Despite his nearly one hundred novels, there are some grounds for believing that Pío Baroja was not a novelist at all. He began publishing in the first years of this century, and the two books that appeared that year were *Vidas sombrías* (a collection of short stories), and *The House of the Aizgorri* (a "Novel in Seven Acts"—a novel in dialogue form, or play). His last books were the seven volumes of *Memoirs,* and in writing them he availed himself of whole sections taken from his works of fiction, for his novels were of the same stuff as the chronicle of his own history—his lived life or "novel of himself," as Ortega would have called it.

Late in his career, Baroja also issued a first book of verse, *Canciones del suburbio* ("Songs of the Suburb"), a book which Azorín calls a condensation of his originality, and which Cela considers an index of the man and his style and the single best book by which to know him.

Between the first and last books were the dozens of novels. But were they, after all, of any more homogeneous an order than the final *Memoirs* or the first novel in dialogue? Baroja's novels characteristically lack all novelistic development, or argument, or plot. Plot, of course, was something not naturally available to the sensibilities of the Generation of '98. For plot in the usual sense is a conventional schema, an outline or limitation imposed on life, and these writers preferred to trace a course of events which evolve depending on the genius of the characters themselves. Such works as Unamuno's *Abel Sánchez* trace the evolution of an emotional fixation or passion and have a narrowed plot in this sense, but in most novels of the epoch there is neither interplay of motives nor development based on a structural pattern. Characteristically, so alien was the idea of any enforced or arbitrary disciplining that Unamuno thought it would have been defrauding his readers for him to have held back his work once he wrote it down, for his audience must see the bad as well as the good if they were to judge him and his ideas, or better, respond to his stimulus; and Baroja appeared to think that it would have been a deceit and a concession to convenience to make his thought on one day agree with his thoughts of the day before.

In Baroja, the trajectory of a voyage, or a choreographic wandering—transposed from the Spanish picaresque narrative along with the traditional running social criticism—is likely to be the only impelling force. Characters appear and many never reappear. There are stories within the story which dwarf the original narrative. Apart from the predisposition of the Generation of '98 to subordinate the totality of the plot to the peculiarity of the individual, there is in Baroja a willfulness in the characters that makes them act with an omnipotent near-blindness. Only in certain of the Basque stories does Baroja achieve the insight expressed by Antonio Machado, the poet of the generation:

The eye you see
is not an eye because you see it
but an eye because it sees you.

The reciprocity between the characters present in Unamuno in
the form of mutual anguish or concern is absent in Baroja. And
yet the differences between Baroja and the other writers of '98 are
matched by more important similarities.

Baroja's man of action—or often man of activity, for his cease-
less action may be only conversational or at best conspiratorial
(in the words of Ortega, "Thinking can be action, while the
movement and tussle in sports, for instance, are no part of action")—is the fictional counterpart of Ortega's man becoming
what he is by his enforced acting in the world. In Baroja the
struggle of the hero to be, to impose himself on chaos, is the
equivalent of the moral need to act in Ortega. Fulfillment in
action against or in one's circumstance, the conscious transformation of reality, is the climactic point in Ortega's thought and in
Baroja's novels. The stag clearing its way through the woods
as it (almost aesthetically) flees, the hound extending itself as
it pursues, the hunter spiritually "beside himself" in the elec-
trically enlivened landscape: this is the moment of decisive being,
or "vital reason" in Ortega's philosophy, and it is toward this
paradigm that Baroja strives, though he constantly and wryly
lets us see that his heroes are never quite up to their own ideal
of action. And if, as similarly occurs in Sterne's *Tristram
Shandy,* despite endless coming and going the hero is never
fully born or never born to any purpose, there is nevertheless a
verisimilitude of action which serves as well as life to test the
circumstance of would-be heroes.

In the sense of an elaboration, there is no "style" in Baroja,
his style being an attempt to bypass rhetoric in order to reach
the things described. And Baroja is as sure-footed as a goat in
choosing his ground and his stepping stones.

It is with the element of style which is selectivity that Baroja
is most sensitive and most decisive. His dramatic end he achieves
by understatement. What he chooses to say is a résumé of the
unsaid, and his characters are sketched with the rapidity of a
sharp-eyed master draftsman. His visual approach is that of an
artist filling his sketchbook. The Madrid books are triumphs of
a black and white technique; the Basque books have pages of
subtle water color and occasionally the larger composition of a
colorist working in oils.

The poetry of his prose is quickened by his pantheistic feeling for nature; there is a Celtic peopling of the forests and water-courses, a druidical awe before trees and rocks. In *Shanti Andía* the Basque coast is alive with titanic struggle and microcosmic forces, and natural description tends toward verse: "The brackish seaweed forms into skeins like long leashes, and bladderwrack and jellyfish shimmer in the sand." Luis Navascués puts into English a line from *Camino de perfección* which typifies Baroja's naturalism: "What a beautiful poem the bishop's body in a peaceful field!"

His first book, the collection of short pieces, many of which were written while he was a village doctor at Cestona and some of which were published in Salmerón's republican paper, was, like James Joyce's *Dubliners,* both a gallery of frustrated figures and a prelude that stated a number of themes in the compositions to follow. Like *Dubliners,* which was written (though not published) in the same years, the stories were typically without plot, and they were written in the same atmosphere of melancholy stultification. Baroja's Madrid loafer "expects nothing from anyone," and "probably has few friends, perhaps none— a sign of intelligence." The heroes of "The Bakers" bicker and quarrel at the funeral of one of their number. The sky in "The Charcoal Maker" is like a "gray winding sheet waving in the wind," and the charcoal maker himself, high in the Basque mountains, throws stones blindly down into the valley when he hears that he is to be drafted. And "The Master of the Cage," who is God, is deafened by caged mankind. The author records pointless deaths and even more senseless lives with a late-Romantic pessimism and disenchantment. In the Basque stories of this collection, Baroja adumbrated the writing that would deal with nature and men in the land of his birth. In the same year, in *The House of the Aizgorri,* a prototype of his willful Basque hero, of the individual against his circumstance, makes his appearance.

The ironic corollary to Baroja's writing about the Basques as he saw them was that in the end he would be accused by nationalists—most dramatically on the day Carlist soldiers at Vera pointed their rifles in his face—of being an anti-Basque.

VI.

No one is more imaginative than
the Basques of the coast: lovers
of the impossible, followers of
danger into the abyss and across
the sombre seas of the two Poles.

—MICHELET

The fatherland is the landscape,
the color of the fields and sky.

—BAROJA

The Basques have a language and a tradition, but they have no history. Baroja wrote that a people without cities cannot make history, and Unamuno before him reasoned that since the Basques are historyless, even their language—a rural tongue at best—must disappear in the face of a superior culture.

By the twentieth century, being a Basque is less a matter of language than of tradition. The Basques are a mysterious quantity in anthropology, ethnology, and linguistics. The race, anthropologists agree, has become indefinable, whether or not it can be linked with Cro-Magnon man, or antedates all other tribes in Spain and is the living descendant of the primitive Iberians of Berber stock, modified by Lapp and Finn. In 1821 Wilhelm von Humboldt reaffirmed the theory that the distribution of Basque-root place-names in Spain proved the language had once been spoken across most of the peninsula. Basque linguistic patriots have long held that Basque was the first language of Spain, and Julio Cejador, a professor at the University of Madrid, in a book published in 1906 held that Basque was the basis of all languages—fundamental to Latin and Spanish and others as well—and he presumed that Adam and Eve spoke Basque. The Basque language in Spain is in much the same cultural position now as Gaelic in the British Isles, though in an inferior status, since there is no important literature in Basque. And Basque nationalism just as Irish nationalism—the two phenomena have many points in common—has had to do without the support of the outstanding men of its land. The attitude of the "movement" toward men of letters in both countries, who naturally refused to write in a stilted language, has been roughly similar. When the Irish author George Moore died in 1933, his compatriot Joyce ordered a wreath sent him, "but excluding ivy absolutely"—since ivy was the emblem of Irish nationalism—and he noted later that at Moore's funeral nobody, of course, was present "from beyond S. Patrick's Canal, or should I say, Canaille." This incident and Joyce's gesture express the attitude of the two outstanding Irishmen of an epoch, and express nearly as well that of the two outstanding Basques of the same epoch toward a very similar social manifestation. Two years before Moore's death and Joyce's wreath, Unamuno delivered an address as deputy in the Constituent Assembly of the Second Republic, in which he attacked the "nationalism of resentful *señoritos,*" defended the official preference given Castilian over other languages spoken in Spain, and relegated Basque to the philology museum. Unamuno made a point of speaking the three regional languages of Spain—Galician, Catalan, and Basque—and in the course of his address he made poetic use of all three, evoking intense partisan interest in his auditors over poetry, unusual in a parliamentary body. For his part, Baroja paid little attention to Basque beyond quoting folksongs and local phrases.

The provincial linguists have admired Basque for its complexity, which makes it similar, said Unamuno, to the languages of American and African tribes, at the opposite extreme from English, which with combinations of a few elements obtains the same results as a multitude of complicated forms gives the more complex and primitive tongues. Above all, Basque could not serve in the Europeanization of Spain, for while it was adequate for field workers, it could not be used to discuss art or science, or even for legal documents—so that even the famous Basque laws and special privileges (the *fueros*) are in Castilian. Baroja and Unamuno, in short, were never tempted to use their mysterious native language for literary purposes.

In an article dated as early as 1901, Baroja charged that the attempt to make Basque serve as a literary vehicle was a narrow-minded political maneuver behind which Carlists, wearing the masks of linguists, concealed themselves. And yet, even though Hegel could never be translated into Basque, Baroja hoped the country folk would be left free to sing their ancient songs and use their rugged tongue, if only to avoid the uniformity and monotony of one language for all of Spain.

Both Unamuno and Baroja were true to their Basque natures, and both were most tender toward their land and its people. Though the body is dying, said Unamuno of Basque, it dies so that the soul may better live on. And Unamuno celebrated his marriage by the Guernica Tree, the famous tree of Basque liberty, where the ancient governing councils once sat, while Baroja "in his head and eyes" loved the humid climate and the green meadows of the Basque country above all other Spanish terrain, even though a high dry climate with scant vegetation significantly allowed him to think clearer.

If the Basques could make no history as a nation, still their tradition stretches back before history began. In prehistoric times, living in a barbaric state, they inhabited a larger area than their present mountain and coastal fortress. They left behind no traces of any civilization whatsoever.

When the Romans came, they found a loosely matriarchal society (precedence of the eldest daughters) among the Basques, whose principal staple was acorn bread, aided by a primitive agriculture at the hands of women, and whatever wine the men could plunder from the vineyards to the south. The hair of both sexes was long and flowing, and washed in urine, a custom brought back with the wine, though the Eskimos practice the same hygiene. As ancestors of Spaniards, they were splendid horsemen; as good warriors, they practiced poetry. They were particularly religious on nights of full moon, worshiping that orb, whose name was ineffable. Some towns were nearly atheist, but others sacrificed he-goats and men to an unknown deity, drinking the blood of sacrificial horses beforehand. Before the Conquest, cremation was current, and the natives worshiped the mountains, the god of the Black Rock, Gorri (the Red), the woods and trees, the sun and the stars. They were good irregular cavalrymen, but were lost on open ground and a prey to the Romans. Among the conquerors they maintained their fame as augurs and haruspices; given to soothsaying, they also bewitched, and were specialists in poison, which they used frequently on themselves in the face of the vanquishing Romans.

Once conquered, the vanquished became involved in the politics of Rome. The Basques—by situation conservative—sided with Pompey and the *ancien régime* against Caesar.

Under the Romans, the Basques held to their local cults more firmly than did the rest of Hispania. The Romans, always tolerant, admitted the local Basque deities to their own pantheon, while the Basques martyred early Christians—mostly Roman soldiers—who appeared among them. In the fourth century, the Basques took the field against the cities built in the image of Rome to the south of them, and kept their independence intact until the time of the first medieval kingdoms.

By the early eighth century (the time of the Visigothic King Witiza), they were still not Christians, and there were no more surnames among them than there were Christians, as Baroja tried to prove to an "aristocratizing" aunt, in the course of trying to demonstrate that their famous ancestor Teodosio de Goñi, the Navarrese dragon fighter, was a sun myth.

Baroja states in his *Memoirs* the belief that the country people were not yet Christians even by the fourteenth century. At Alzate, named for ancestors of Baroja and depicted by him in the *Legend of Jaun de Alzate,* there was probably no church until the fourteenth century.

When the Basques in the cities were Christianized, probably in the eleventh century, they then clung to the peculiarly Latin Christianity of their converters, and in the most obscure epoch of the Middle Ages it was they who (paradoxically, after having resisted the Romans) maintained the last vestiges of the spirit of Christian Rome.

Their religiosity was never again questionable. Even their legendary bad men—legends that disclose a nation's conscience —are blasphemous, and not simply amoral or weak. The terrible conquistador Lope de Aguirre, the despoiler of Peru and the Amazon and the greatest of Spanish desperadoes—whom Baroja makes the ancestor of Shanti Andía, and who was in fact a distant ancestor of Unamuno—the infamous Lope de Aguirre, "The Traitor," as he signed himself, whom Unamuno wanted to defend as Giovanni Papini defended the Devil, or Jorge Luis Borges defended Judas, was a good prototype of Basque religiosity, for he never denied, but always blasphemed, in certain belief of a heaven and hell and of his own eventual perdition. At a far remove from the attitude of the Calvinist elect and yet touched by their doctrine, the mystically bedeviled Lope de Aguirre believed in his own hellish destiny. Unamuno points out that his relative was a true desperado (from Spanish *desesperado:* "devoid of hope"), as surely desperate as Lucifer, and of a Luciferian temper—which is to say, angelic—and a total believer, given over to religious despair. Lope de Aguirre strove to amass bad works, since good works would be of no avail, so that his name should resound "even in the ninth heaven," and he expected to reside in hell with Julius Caesar, Alexander, and other great captains, as Unamuno tells us in a fine essay full of compassion. "The Traitor's" confused religious wrath was such, however, that he had two confessors hung in a row when they refused him absolution, as Baroja records in *Shanti Andía.* After the Basque criminal had killed himself at Barquisimeto, Venezuela, his skull was locked up in an iron cage and placed in the church, and properly so. For he had lived and died, if terrifyingly, in his religion, an example on the negative side of Basque religiosity.

Catholic as the Basques have shown themselves to be, it was nevertheless a Huguenot who stands out in their brief literature: the second book to be translated into Basque, and something of a standard for the written language, is the Protestant version of the New Testament made by Jean de Lizarrague (or Juan de Lizarraga), printed at La Rochelle in 1571.

Pierre Loti's *Ramuntcho*, a classic of romantic pessimism, deals with the Basques across the border, in the *pays basque*. Loti reflects much more accurately than Baroja—who was not an adherent of the religion of the vast majority of Basques—the religion of daily living among the mountaineers.

The church bell in Basque mountain villages, at least in Loti's day (he signed *Ramuntcho* in 1896), interrupts and measures life as the chant of the muezzin does in the Orient. Even the smugglers regulate the rhythm of their work by church time. On leaving for the border with an illicit cargo, Ramuntcho is thinking of the next day's mass, and on returning falls asleep dreaming of the feast of All Souls'; and the Angelus bell stops all human movement within sound. On one occasion Ramuntcho's mother, Franchita, questions her son:

"What are you taking?"

"Bales of silk and velvet."

"And who are you going with?"

"The same as usual: Arrochkoa, Florentino, and the Iragola brothers. Like the other night it's for Itchoua [the church warden]. . . Goodnight, mother. . . We won't be out late; I'll be back in time for mass." Itchoua, the chief has the best voice in the parish; he had killed a man, but since the victim was a *carabinero*, a border guard, no one held it against him. For, as the fine Irish Hispanist Walter Starkie explains the Basques' stand (in his *The Road to Santiago*, 1957): "Smuggling is not a vice but a clan or tribal virtue, and just as it is lawful and praiseworthy, according to clan standards, to rob the next clan which is that of the enemy, so should the state be robbed, which is the enemy of all the clans." Moreover, the justification is now habitual, for the Basques had always had free trade among themselves, and the present French-Spanish border between them is an artificiality. In effect, the customs frontier of Spain has traditionally begun only at the Ebro River, well into Spain.

The Basques are religious, with the fervor of converts—since they are comparatively late-comers to Christianity—but they were never able to imagine God for themselves. Ortega points out this paradox, and the concomitant language difficulty:

"They forgot to include a sign to designate God in their vocabulary, and it was necessary to resort to *Jaungoiḳoa,* "Liege Lord of the Height." Since it has now been centuries since the authority of liege lords disappeared, *Jaungoiḳoa* today signifies, directly, God. But we have to imagine ourselves in the epoch when it was incumbent on one to think of God as a political or worldly authority, to think of God as a Civil Governor or something of the sort. It is precisely this situation that reveals to us that, lacking a name for God, it was hard for the Basques to think of Him. And thus they were late in converting to Christianity, and their word suggests why it was that the police had to intervene to drive the pure idea of divinity into their heads."

This paradox is one of the theses of *The Legend of Jaun de Alzate.*

The Basque language proved unable to raise itself to the degree of abstraction demanded by generic concepts, and the words for thing, time, and so forth, also had to be borrowed from Latin.

If the absence of abstract concepts among the Basques was a point of weakness, perhaps it was also a source of strength. They were at a disadvantage in dealing with European time, physics, and the idea of things, but they were thus kept from capitulating to these concepts; they were never made feverish by the Western sickness of time, nor was their spirit gnawed by the metaphysical need for things: they could not need what they could not name. Their love of particularity, of what was palpable and all around them, within reach of their senses, made them long content with their life in the valleys and free among their mountains and along their sea frontier.

Moreover, as the poet Edward Dahlberg wrote: "Jehovah confounds the tongues of men that each nation may have its own myths and names."

The Basque countryside has always been filled with demons and powers. The people of the fields have been haunted by witches and witches' Sabbaths, by he-goats and old men of the wood. A fine and divine frenzy overtakes them in their wild festivals and processions. "Mystical and sensual, they refresh their prayers with hard cider," writes Ortega, "and form religious processions which dissolve into dances of primitive choreography." Baroja, especially in *Jaun de Alzate,* is sensitive to the most farfetched folk belief, and he could echo the populace's fears with his "No Flies Republic." For sorcerers and malevolent beings work through demons, who assume the shape of flies, and evildoers carry the demons in a sheath, as anglers do their casting flies.

Baroja shared with the atavistic country people "the Celtic conception of religion," as he called it: a vague apprehension or dread of nature, "a dread of the great caves, of the black and inert swamps, of the groves, of the founts of clear and mysterious water."

Julio Caro Baroja, one of Spain's leading and most gifted writers on ethnography and Pío Baroja's immediate heir, has pointed out that racism—the idea of blood purity—is more prevalent in the Basque provinces than anywhere else in Spain. In an essay ("Sobre ideas raciales en España," 1956), Caro Baroja distinguishes Basque racism as sharply and surprisingly different from classic Spanish *hidalguía*. The racism of Basque nationalists is "equalitarian and democratic" (Ortega calls it "metaphysical democracy and transcendental equalitarianism"), and, in a country where the mark of the true noble, of the hidalgo, is the refusal to do manual work, the Basque provinces are peopled by "noble shoemakers, noble charcoal makers, noble tailors, noble carpenters." For Basque blood, as the Jesuit nationalist Larramendi declared, makes its possessor a man "who always has been noble, always is noble, and always will be noble."

Whatever the anomalies of his small fatherland, Baroja thought the rest of the world in a far worse state. The Basque countryside he considered to be the purest and most authentic corner of Europe. It was the farthest away in spirit from the false civilization of the cinema and cement. The Basque countryman worked within the magic circle of nature: he was perhaps the only true man of the countryside left in Europe, and certainly he had no counterpart or equal in America. There was a moral aristocracy, devoid of all spurious theory, in the very blood of the country people. The tradition of the Basques was worthy of vitalization: "Whoever can plumb our ancestral obscurity, which still envelops us, back to prehistory, back through our traditions and superstitions, will have accomplished a lasting labor." While in exile in Paris, Baroja once said that he had never presumed to be an international writer, or even a national one, but merely to write novels in a Basque tone, critically and independently.

Baroja ridiculed provincial claims, but, though he was neither a Basque nationalist nor used the Basque language to voice any of his own thought, Baroja the Basque was Spain's chief contribution to the European and world novel in the first half of the twentieth century.

Palma de Mallorca, 1958

NOVEL:

The Restlessness of Shanti Andía

Drawings by the author,
courtesy of Miguel Pérez Ferrero
and *Papeles de Son Armadans*

BOOK ONE

Childhood

I. SHANTI MAKES HIS APOLOGIES

The circumstances of present-day life are responsible for the fact that most people are dull. Nowadays, almost no one has anything happen to him. The generality of men swim about in a sea of vulgarity. Neither our love affairs nor our adventures are of sufficient interest to warrant communicating them to others. Our society is committed to making our life, our ideas, our aspirations more and more uniform. At a certain period of my life, I passed through some difficult moments, and it was the recollection of these moments that awakened in me the desire to write.

I had not the slightest intention of turning over the results to the printer; but when the *Lúzaro Courier* began to appear, all my friends urged me to publish my memoirs in it.

It was up to me to collaborate in the cultural life of the city, they said. I was one of the pillars of Lúzaro's civilization. At home we laughed a bit over these eulogies, but I began to publish my diary in the *Lúzaro Courier* and to pay periodically on the printer's bill.

I went away from Lúzaro for a week to take my second son to school, and on returning from my trip I found that the *Courier* had gone to a better life, so that my memoirs were left hanging, precisely at the point that I considered most exciting. Despite the effort I had put into the writing, no one seemed interested in finding out what followed, an attitude which served to pique me in my self-esteem as a literary man.

And now, my friend Cincunegui has insisted on seeing the complete diary into print. Lúzaro needs a great man; it must put forth a figure presentable to the eyes of the world. Ever since the death of Don Blas de Artola, the retired naval lieutenant, the position of illustrious man has been vacant in our town. Cincunegui arouses my ambitious instincts; he seeks to raise me to the heights, he desires to exalt me; according to him, I must seek the pinnacles of glory.

To tell the truth, glory does not really interest me. Glory is not for rainy countries; to have a statue on the shores of the Mediterranean, in some city of Andalucia, of Valencia, or Italy,

is all very well; but what would be my fate if, as a reward for
this book, a statue were erected to me in Lúzaro? I would simply
get a shower of rain down my back forevermore.

No, no; I am too rheumatic, and even in effigy I would not
want to be out in the open like that.

Need I tell my readers that I have no literary pretensions whatsoever? They will see it, if they but leaf through the pages of
my book. These pages are written in different epochs of my life
and in different frames of mind. The sentiment has been sincere; the form, unskilled. My public will not censure me, I am
sure, for lack of nicety. Besides, I write for my friends of the
Loafing Place of the Long Wharf.

I am merely a seaman, possessed of little culture, a rude
mariner, as they say in serials, and there is no need to expect
from me the literary flourishes of a professor of rhetoric.

II. THE ANCIENT SEA

I have had a reputation for being indolent and optimistic, indifferent and apathetic. One need only have a reputation of any
kind, good or bad, to enable one's friends and acquaintances to
add their stone to the monument—whether it be dedicated to
valor or cowardice, to ingenuity or to brutality.

This spontanous collaboration constitutes the adornment of
great deeds and of great characters. One man insinuates: "It
could be . . ."; another puts in: "They say . . ."; a third adds:
"It was this way . . ."; one last man assures: "I saw it myself. . ." In this fashion is the story built up, a serial romance
for serious people.

According to authorities in our town, my indolence and cold-
bloodedness were truly extraordinary: neither squalls, tempests,
thunder or lightning could move me from my habitual passivity.
Anecdotes concerning my coldness and indifference were manufactured and spread about. Once, they say, in the Philippines,
a fanatic ran at me, his hunting knife raised to strike off my
head, and I gazed at him in annoyance and yawned with irritated
boredom.

I do not deny that my basic laziness, my natural indolence,
have furnished the ingredients for these tales. And my pan-
egyrists and my detractors alike would be astonished to know
how often I regret my nature. But, is it my lack of energy that
I regret, the absence in me of the spirit of enterprise? Not at all.

Quite the contrary. No doubt this is a proof of my cynical and immoral character. But the truth must out.

The majority of men are very proud of their constancy, of the steadfastness of their plans. They are as consistent as the steel in a broken or rusted compass. They know where they are going, and where they came from. Each step along the way of life has already been counted and calculated.

If we listen to them, they will tell us: "Let's not dally to look at the stars or the sea; it's best not to get distracted. The road is waiting. We run the risk of not getting to the end."

The end! What an illusion! There is no end in life. The end is a point in space and time, and no more transcendental than the point that preceded or follows.

The astonishment of these discreet, perspicacious, sensible men must be great when they behold those who, without any special concern over the windings in the road, are carried by the wings of chance along the same highroads as themselves, and who (shamelessly!) have the satisfaction not only of achieving their ends but of gazing about them on either side of the road, and of watching how the sun comes up or goes down and how the stars appear in the sky on cloudless nights.

The preoccupation with achieving an end makes all of us, even the most fearless, even the most indolent, constantly uneasy, and I, for my part, would have liked to have lived each hour, each minute even more than I did, free of any nostalgia for the past or any anxiety for the future. This desire is the consequence of my basic epicureanism and of the exaggerated indolence for which I have been so much reproached, qualities that the life of a sailor probably brings out and develops.

In all truth, the sea annihilates a man, consumes him; it exhausts his imagination and his will. Its infinite monotony, its infinite changes, its immense solitude draws him into complaisance. Those rolling green waves, that whitish spray, rock the pupils of our eyes, consume our soul, wear away our personality, until we are altogether compliant, until we are one with nature.

We want to understand the sea, and we cannot; we strive to find a reason behind it, and we do not. The sea is a monster, an incomprehensible sphinx; though dead, it is a laboratory of life, though inert it is the representation of constant restlessness. Often we seem to detect some symbol in it, some lesson; at moments we think to have deciphered its mystery; at other times, its purpose escapes us and is lost in the reflection of its waves and the whistling of the wind.

All of us, without knowing why, assume that the sea is a woman; all of us attribute to it an intuitive and shifting personality, enigmatic and perfidious.

In nature, among the trees and over the plants, a vague shadow of justice and goodness seems to fall; over the sea, there is nothing of the sort. The sea smiles at us, caresses us, threatens us, crushes us, all with equal capriciousness.

If the sea takes hold of one as a youth, as it did me, it molds one in a definitive way, and makes one a seaman forever. Whoever hands himself over with a candid heart, with a virgin intelligence, is forever enthralled.

For the fisherman, for the ignorant and simple man who can not depend on scientific knowledge and foundations for support of his thoughts and ideas, the sea is a tyrant; it deceives him, it adulates him, it seduces him, it drowns him. For the poor mariner, the sea is the *summum* of interest, of enchantment, of variety. Those miserable workers whose life is one continuous battle, and at all times a gigantic effort, are often happy, and the sea, their enemy the sea, the incomprehensible monster, fills their existence and constitutes their happiness.

For those of us who are seamen on the high seas, the sea is first of all a route, almost exclusively a road. But what a road!

I shall never forget the first time I crossed the ocean. The sailing ship was still everywhere dominant. What an epoch it was! I don't say that the sea was better then, but it was more poetic, more mysterious, more unknown.

Today, the sea is getting industrialized. The sailor, in his iron ship, knows when he will be moving, when he will stop; his days and hours are all counted out. In those far-off days, it was not that way. One proceeded by benefit of chance, good luck, a favorable wind.

At that time, the world was still unknown to a large extent; it was still crossed only by the traditional routes, and there was an immensity of open sea as yet unvisited by man. As a man walking in the desert follows the tracks of another, the seaman on the high seas followed the routes of the ancient mariners. And so, those who set out for the Cape of Good Hope, on reaching the Cape Verde Islands, headed for Brazil, obeying routine and the prevailing winds, and then recrossed the Atlantic once more.

In most of the ships, the position was determined more by conjecture than by calculation. The navigational instruments used by mariners were sometimes off by entire degrees. It is true that in London and Liverpool admirable sextants had al-

ready been developed; but many sea captains did not know how
to use them and navigated in the old fashion.

The variety of vessels and riggings was extraordinary. In all
ports one could still see, interspersed among the everyday brigantines and frigates, Turkish caravels, Greco-Roman saics, Ve-
netian polacres, Dutch hookers, Tunisian *sindalos,* and Tuscan
galiots.

There were still pirates abroad in the world, there were still
slavers; all of them evil—who would deny it?—and all of them
menaces that obliged the mariner to adopt heroic measures in his
own defense. The immediate perils expanded the imagination,
inspired courage, and stimulated the will to overcome them.

The barbarity of the sea was matched by the barbarity of its
seamen servants; the brutality of the saline element was equaled
by the brutality of the human.

In those days, a sailor would return to his corner of the world
with an earring in his ear, a bracelet around his wrist, and a
cockatoo or a monkey on his shoulder.

A seaman was something extrasocial, almost extrahuman; a
seaman was a being to whom morality offered a face different
than the one offered other mortals. "You'll be asked *how much*
you've done, not *how* you've done it," fathers would warn the
sons who were about to launch into the sea adventure. And the
sons would hurl themselves into the abyss of this intense life,
without scruples or preconceptions. Blind chance would lead
them along unknown paths; Destiny, in its mysterious mold,
would melt down the former character of a man and cast up
intrepid mariners or ferocious slavers, audacious explorers or
traffickers in Chinamen. For all these men, morality depended
on the latitude. The sea, in short, was the scene of all kinds of
human crime and violence.

Now the sea has changed, and the ships have changed, and
the seamen have changed. All that is left of those graceful spars
and masts that fired our enthusiasm are short sticks to hold
block and tackle; of the complicated classic maneuvers nothing
is left.

The sailing ship was like a divine creation, something like
a religion or a poem; the steamship is something that changes
from day to day, as science does, a piece of machinery in constant transformation. The captain was formerly a wise man, a
tyrant with unlimited power, a man who had to be sufficient unto
himself; today he is a specialist grafted to a bureaucrat.

Nowadays it is the machine, an exact, mathematical, measured
force, which drives the ships; before, it was the wind, something

capricious, impalpable, outside and beyond man. "We're carrying our Guardian Angel in the canvas of our sails," Don Ciriaco,
a very intelligent and picturesque old frigate captain, used to
say to me. Nowadays a captain might say: "Our strength is in
our fuel tank." Fuel, that minor though useful god, has replaced
the wings of the poetic Guardian Angel which we carried in our
sails, and all the conditions of the sea have changed.

The sea used to be our divinity, the capricious queen-goddess,
haughty and cruel; but now she is a woman whom we treat like
a slave. We old seamen were more gallant, and celebrated her
as our queen, instead of admiring her as our slave. No doubt the
sea was not as well-behaved as it is today, nor as peaceful; but
it certainly was more beautiful, more picturesque, a little bit
younger.

The spiritual map of the universe of that epoch was like a
variously colored chart, wherein not only the strong contrasts
are obvious but even the lightest shadings are made clear. But
the shadings have been lost. The world is tending to confuse
and carelessly mix its colors. The Japanese man of today is a
civilized gentleman dressed in European style; a Polynesian
goes to Mecca as a tourist, traveling aboard a magnificent fifteen-
thousand-ton passenger liner. The muse of progress is speed;
what is not fast is condemned to die.

All this is to the good; who can doubt it? It indicates more
civilization; but for whoever still retains in his mind's eye the
sight and memory of the ancient sea, for such a man modern
leveling and amorphousness is a lamentable spectacle.

Oh, proud masts, white sails, graceful frigates with bows
raised and figurehead clear on the cutwater! Rounded hookers,
swift-sailing brigs! How sad it makes me to think that you
will disappear! Lovely siren, who rose above the blue waves to
gaze at us with green eyes, you will be seen no longer!

Oh, days of calm! Oh, moments of idleness!

How many hours have I spent in a hammock, contemplating
the sea, calm or tempestuous, green or blue, red at sunset, silver
under the light of the moon, and filled with mystery under a
sky thick with stars!

III. I MUST SPEAK ABOUT MYSELF

I must speak about myself: it is inevitable in memoirs.

In addition to my being apathetic and indolent, qualities

exaggerated in a certain measure by my neighbors in Lúzaro in order to make me out to be an odd type, I am also a sentimentalist and dreamer.

I love to look, and have a certain avidity in my eyes; I could spend hours on end watching clouds floating by or a fountain spouting water. Perhaps if I had lived on land I might have developed a musical sense, as is common in many of my countrymen; but at sea it was my optical sense which was amplified and extended. Often I have thought of myself as two staring eyes, a mere mirror or camera obscura reflecting nature.

According to what my family says, I am rather given to telling tales and have a highly developed sense of curiosity. But what is curiosity—I ask by way of defending myself—but a desire to know, to understand, to comprehend what is unknown? I like to see; and if any complication or danger arises in the course of satisfying my curiosity, I do not shrink from facing it.

In my own way I am also a patriot. I do not know the history of Spain, and in reality I do not care too much about it; if I were asked who Wamba or Atanagildo were, I would be brought up short; and yet, though I know nothing or almost nothing of my country's history, I have always felt profoundly stirred when at the end of a long voyage I sighted the coast of Spain.

The memory of my fatherland, and especially of Lúzaro, this corner of the Basque coast where I was born and where I live, has always been alive in my soul. I do not consider this to be of special merit, for I do not share the exclusivist tendencies of my fellow Basques. In short, the land is for the farmer, the sea for the mariner, and to argue which of the two is the best seems to me a piece of foolishness. Lúzaro pleases me, but the fact that I was born here, or that my family has lived here for many years, constitutes no special mark of superiority as far as I am concerned.

I feel the same way about all patriotic sentiments as a Mason I once knew in Liverpool. This Mason had reached the thirty-third, or forty-third, or some such degree—in any case, the very highest. On holidays, this man would don his best clothes, tie on his Masonic apron, put on a quantity of badges and triangles, and go off to the lodge, from where he would eventually return completely drunk. At home, everyone thought he was a great man, and the good gentleman, who was very simple, said to me: "My father had me join the lodge when I was a very young man; now I'm sixty-five and I've reached the highest degree. People see a great deal of merit in this, but I, if the truth be told, don't find it at all remarkable."

He was simply an honest man, this honorable Mason.

And just as in the case of this bricklayer belonging to the celestial order of bricklayers, I find it scarcely remarkable that my family has lived in Lúzaro for a long, long time. On the other hand, neither is this fact an obstacle to my being more at home in my own town than anywhere else.

Often, as I lay in my bunk, sailing on the Atlantic or the Indian Ocean, and thought of Lúzaro, I would suddenly have a powerful vision of a mountain, or of a great coastal rock, or of a beech grove. In my imagination I could see Lúzaro rising from the sea, and the river which cuts into its flank, and the woods on one side and the cornfields and oak groves on the other.

At such moments I would sing to myself the *zortzicos* and tabor beats of the Basque country; hearing them I could imagine myself walking about the narrow streets of my town, smelling the hay, seeing the rocks of Izarra as the sea dashes on them, the pale blue sky furrowed by white clouds.

My enthusiasm for Lúzaro is understandable; I come from here, and from here comes my entire family. And then, my life can be divided into two periods: one spent in Lúzaro, where the most wonderful and pleasant events of my life have happened to me; the other, the period spent at sea, where nothing much happened to me, at least nothing good, and where I lived with a cold heart and a retina filled with strong impressions.

My family has come from Lúzaro, and they have been a seagoing race; this is particularly true of my mother's side, the family of the Aguirre, whose maritime genealogy is abundant and endless.

My father, Damián de Andía, was also a sea captain. He died at sea, in the English Channel. One night, off the coast of England, the corvette which he commanded, the "Mary-Rose," went down with the loss of nearly all hands: only one seaman was saved.

Although I was a very young boy, I remember my father quite well. He made a virtue of indifference, and was rather a scoffer. He had an expressive face, gray eyes, aquiline nose, and a trim beard. According to what I have gathered, we must have a strong resemblance, with a certain predisposition for the tedious life of the sea; he was in no wise a sad man, however, but on the contrary had a strong tendency toward the satirical. He felt great admiration for the northern races, for the Norwegians and Danes whom he met at sea; he spoke English well, was very liberal, and he could laugh at women. He seemed, in short, to have been born to mock everything and shrug his shoulders at everybody. Still, his satirical vein held no venomous intent; he laughed without bitterness and without chagrin.

My father was one of those Basques who leave behind all their dead weight of intolerance and fanaticism when they set foot aboard their first ship. He had taken soundings in the abyss of human stupidity and badness, and he knew what to hold to.

My grandmother did not get along well with him, and she prompted her daughter, my mother, to go against him. No doubt she was blinded by her instinct as mother-in-law. He would give in, laughing all the while, and my grandmother would grow furious.

Whenever my father would put into Lúzaro, he would get together with other pilots, mariners, and fishermen to talk; sometimes he would sing and carouse in the streets in their company.

Everyone who knew him testified to his greatheartedness. For my part, I have always regretted not having known him better, for I am sure we would have been good friends.

My grandmother, Doña Celestina de Aguirre, had no love for my father; after the lapse of many years, I have heard her still speak badly of him. It is very sad when the rancor and hatred of people can extend even to the dead; but then, who does not have some rotten instinct in his heart?

My grandmother's motives for not loving my father were somewhat farfetched. My father had been born in Elguea, a rival town to Lúzaro. As far as my grandmother was concerned, the three and a half miles of coast which lay between Lúzaro and Elguea irrevocably separated two worlds: the serious-minded people of Lúzaro and the insolent, voluble, and fatuous inhabitants of Elguea.

Another cause of Doña Celestina's enmity toward her son-in-law was the fact that his mother, my paternal grandmother, was the daughter of a Swiss hardware dealer who had established himself at Elguea. Doña Celestina had known the daughter of another hardware dealer in her youth, when they were both single, and apparently a great antipathy had developed between the two.

Doña Celestina was convinced that the blood of the Swiss hardware man had ruined me: in all truth, the shop with its hoops and its rubber balls has somewhat held back the forward motion of the stern sailing vessel with its rigging and anchors. She often told me when I was a boy that I had turned out like my father. I could not at that time comprehend the awful judgement and accusation that was concealed in this likeness.

My grandmother always harbored great secret ambitions, a
pride of name, and an extraordinary attachment to her lineage.
For her, the family of the Aguirre constituted the most select
element of the race, and the mariner's profession, because it
was the most usual among the men of her caste, was the most
aristocratic and highly distinguished.

Doña Celestina, in her inmost heart, apparently thought that
the other families of Lúzaro, with the exception of two or three,
had sprung up like mushrooms in the grass, or perhaps that
the individual members were formed from river mud.

It was not easy to convince my haughty grandmother that it
was not precisely a fact of transcendental importance whether or
not an Aguirre had appeared in Lúzaro in the fifteenth century.
Doña Celestina felt that anything having to do with the Aguirre
family was of capital importance, and she did not mind lying if
it were for the greater glory of the family.

Were she alive today, how the good lady would be scan-
dalized by the ideas of the young doctor who has come to
Lúzaro! This doctor is the son of a comrade of my childhood,
the mate José Mari Recalde.

Our young doctor amuses himself these days with measuring
craniums; he has begun to poke around in the boneyard at the
cemetery, and there he busies himself, assisted by the gravedigger,
loading birdshot into the skulls of our venerable forefathers and
weighing the results, and committing other such devilish
abominations.

Young Recalde has talent; he has been to Germany and is
very knowledgeable; but I, personally, do not put much faith
in his assertions.

According to him, there are only two types within the white
race: the round head and the long head—Cain and Abel.

The round head, Cain, is violent, proud, restless, somber, a
miner and burrower in the earth, fond of music. The long head,
Abel, is tranquil, placid, intelligent, agricultural, a mathemati-
cian, a man of science. Cain is savage, Abel civilized. Cain is
religious, fanatical, and a reactionary idolizer of the gods; Abel
is an observer, progressive, does not idolize but studies and
contemplates.

For Recalde I was the opposite of what I was for my grandmother. According to him, the blood of the Aguirre had undone
me and ruined my nature; without the nefarious influence of this
violent Cain-like race of round heads, I would have been a man
of an admirable type; but that restless blood had been crossed
with my better half.

"You are one of the few truly European types we have in Lúzaro," the doctor tells me. "Your grandfather, the Swiss, must have been a blond dolichocephalic type, purely Germanic, without any admixture of the Celt or of Alpine man. The Andía are among the finest stock in Elguea, the most select Iberian type. It is a shame that they ever mixed with those round-headed Aguirres!"

"Don't fret over it," I tell him with a laugh.

"Why shouldn't I fret!" he replies. "If you were one of those round-headed barbarians, like my father, for example, I wouldn't say anything to you; but since you're not, I want to recommend that you exercise care in regard to your children: you must not let them marry round-headed individuals."

It really would be the height of comedy to forbid one's son to marry some good girl because she had a round head; and it would be just as comic to set oneself against a marriage because the grandfather of the bride or the groom had been in his time a shoemaker or a hardware dealer. In these questions youth usually possesses a better instinct than old age, for youth pays attention only to its feelings and instincts.

A maid in our house, La Iñure, used to tell of a rich ex-slaver, returned from America to her village, who was very upset because his son wanted to marry a poor girl, and who warned the girl in the following manner:

"If I were you, I would never marry my son. Don't forget that I have been a slaver, a trafficker in Negroes, and there have been people in my family who were hanged by the hangman."

"That doesn't matter to me," the girl replied. "Thanks be to God there have been many in my family who were hanged by the hangman."

In all truth, this girl discoursed very well.

IV. OUR HOUSE AND MY GRANDMOTHER'S HOUSE

My mother and I lived in an isolated house at the side of the road, fifteen minutes walk from the village. The house had balconies on three sides. From the house we looked over the entire city, the port as far as the point with the watchtower, and the sea. We could see, far off, the small boats as they came and went; and the Elguea stagecoach went by our house, after stopping at the nearby inn.

It was in the closed central porch of this house that the first years of my infancy were spent. On stormy days it was more like a boat than a house; the doors and windows rattled fiercely, the wind howled through the openings and in the chimneys, wailing fantastically all the while, and gusts of rain furiously lashed the window panes.

There were three of us living in the house: my mother and I, and the old woman who had been my mother's wet nurse whom we called La Iñure. I can almost see that old woman at this moment. She was thin, wizened, toothless, her face covered with wrinkles, her eyes tiny and lively. She always dressed in black, with a kerchief of the same color on her head, knotted so that the corners of the kerchief pointed upward, as is the custom among widows of this region.

I do not believe that La Iñure could say two words in a row in Castilian; on the other hand, she expressed herself in Basque at a dizzy rate, in the tone of a person saying his prayers.

La Iñure had a sister, La Josepha Iñashi, who was at the same time wife to the sacristan and candlewoman to the church. La Josepha Iñashi lived in an old, black house next to the parish church and forming a dependent part of it. Since the sacristan was a dim-wit, the candlewoman arranged all the altars and laid out the chasubles. She was constantly consulting the ecclesiastical almanac. Whenever I would go to La Josepha's house with La Iñure, we would customarily go into the kitchen and make sacred wafers, large and small, putting some water and flour on a metal sheet, and cooking them over the fire.

My mother spent most of the day with my grandmother; but she did not want to go and live with her, for she knew Doña Celestina's authoritative and domineering character.

My grandmother's house was called Aguirreche, which in Basque means the House of Aguirre; it was then, and still is, one of the finest houses in the town. It had the severe aspect typical of those great old stone mansions of the Basque country: black in color, overhanging roof, a line of balconies spaced at wide intervals, all the ironwork very florid and ornate; there were small windows on the top floor, and a great escutcheon over the entrance. The house, set in the lower part of Lúzaro among numerous black cottages, was surrounded by winding, damp, narrow streets.

At the time when my grandmother was still alive, Aguirreche almost always gave the impression of being closed up, so that it had a sad look, but this was somewhat mitigated by the multitude of flowers that brightly bloomed from the balconies.

On entering the house, one would be overcome by a sense

of oppressive darkness. The entrance way, painted blue, was murky, the walls peeling and saltpetrous; the stairway, of chestnut wood, was warped and worm-eaten; on the principal landing, in a wall niche, there was a Virgin painted in relief on a background of gilded wood. My grandmother's house had many rooms with paneled doors that never opened. The walls in these rooms were whitewashed, the ceilings beamed, the wide, dark planks of the floor warped by time, and all of them were empty.

My grandmother and my Aunt Ursula were possessed by a mania for polishing the floors, and the two of them, aided by a girl, made a habit of waxing and rubbing until everything was like a mirror.

In the drawing room—that synthesis and recapitulation of everything most select in Aguirreche—the luster was something sacred. This room could have been called the high altar of the family; no object was given the honor of being allowed there unless it had some history: the red damask chairs, the two or three lacquered pedestal tables, the mirror, the framed title attesting to the lineage of the Aguirre, the chest. . . About each of these things my grandmother, or my Aunt Ursula, could talk for half an hour.

From the roof of this drawing room there hung suspended an ebony and ivory frigate, complete with all the masts, sails, and cannon that corresponded to it.

In the place of honor, above the sofa, hung what looked like a colored drawing. It represented a vessel battling the waves in the fury of a tempest; the captain was depicted tied to the mainmast, screaming out orders, while the wild sea surrounding the ship was strewn with planks and casks. The ship was "La Constancia," a frigate for a long time under the command of my grandmother's father.

The drawing bore the following inscription beneath it: "The Spanish frigate 'La Constancia,' under the command of her captain, Don Blas de Aguirre, at dawn of the third day of February, 1793, at the meridian of the island of Rodrigo, beset by heavy seas from Northeast and Southeast, in the course of a hurricane, on the voyage from Manila to Cádiz, during which all the hencoops on the poop deck, all glassware, casks, and various planks of the gunwale were washed overboard./ Painted by Ant.º de Iturrizar."

I used to believe, thinking of the exaggerated claims of my grandmother, that this picture had some value; but then later I found that it was merely an engraving of the epoch, to which it was the custom to add a legend at the bottom, and which then served endless numbers of Basque seamen as votive offerings when they went to the church at Begoña, or the church of the Virgin of Guadalupe, or Our Lady of Iciar.

On either side of "La Constancia" were two engravings in color with their respective legends: "Ship of the Line, Spanish, Lying To and Saluting," on one; and, on the other, "Spanish Ship of 112 Cannon, at Anchor, View Amidships." These two engravings keep company to this day with "La Constancia," where my great-grandfather remains tied to the mainmast, in the moments before he will surely promise a candle to the Virgin of Rota.

There was also a group of English engravings, framed in mahogany, representing a naval engagement between the English frigate "Eurotas" and the French "Clorinde" in 1814. There were three in the series: the first showed the two ships, their sails unfurled, approaching each other; the second fixed forever the exact moment that the battle was at its height; and in the last, the two ships were seen utterly shorn of their masts and on the point of going down.

Another colored picture, which enjoyed a great reputation in the house, was one that featured a mariner's compass card in the center, while the flags, banners, and mariner's register of the world were depicted along the sides.

In an even higher category of esteem were two large scapularies which had been given to my great-grandfather by the nuns of Santa Clara of Lúzaro, and which the captain had framed in Cádiz and taken with him on all his voyages, including his trip around the world.

My grandmother endowed all these objects with such extreme veneration and assigned them such importance that I thought they belonged to the common domain, and that the feats of my great-grandfather were as well known as those of Napoleon or Nelson.

In addition to the furnishings and pictures, the drawing room boasted a compass, a barometer, a thermometer, a telescope, and various pale daguerreotypes of distant cousins and other relatives. I recall a heavy, very large and ancient octant, made of copper, whose scale for marking the degrees was of bone.

On the console table there were usually two boxes of China tea, a cup carved from a coconut, and various conch shells of the type common in the Indian Ocean, with mother-of-pearl volutes from the inside of which one seems to hear the echo of the waves.

The most attractive objects in the room, and the ones I most admired, were a pair of little Chinese figures, each inside a bell glass, whose heads could be made to move. They both had expressive porcelain faces, and they were quite elegant in their manner and dress. The man, with pointed black mustaches and crossed eyes, held an ostrich egg, painted red, in his hand; the woman wore a blue tunic and in her hand held a fan.

As one came near them, the footsteps on the floor would cause the couple to bow and salute gracefully, and they seemed to vie with each other in the amenities.

Whenever we were allowed to set foot in the drawing room, I would watch them endlessly, and call out: "Grandmother, now they're saying yes, now they're saying no. Now yes, now no."

My grandmother also owned a parrot, "Paquito," who was a master of dialogue and monologue.

We would ask him:

> Little parrot, are you married?

And he would answer:

> And in Vera Cruz veiled
> A ha hai, and also regaled!

His constant monologue was made up of a string of nautical cries, in the manner of any harbor parrot:

> On the port! On the starboard!
>
> Bon voyage! Bon passage!
>
> Fire! Hurrah, Pol!

I always felt there was a certain hidden irony in everything the parrot said, and it annoyed me. La Iñure told me a story of how, a long time before, a parrot kept by a seaman from Elguea informed on him: it was through his bird that it became known that he had been a pirate.

Despite his aptitude and the cleverness of his kind, which he possessed in large measure, Paquito was hateful to me; he never would answer when I was the one to ask if he were married, and one time he almost carried off my finger by a vicious bite. Ever since this incident I looked on him with horror and hatred, and if I could have had my way, I would have stuffed him with parsley until he went off to tell his tales in the paradise of parrots.

There was also a music box in my grandmother's house; it was ancient, and contained a cylinder covered with sharp points which was supposed to be wound up; but it was broken and did not run.

V. MY AUNT URSULA

I was quite late in starting school. I had taken a fall on my knee when I was very young, and, whether from the treatment given it by the town healer—who applied only poultices of flour and wine—or for some other reason, the fact is that I suffered from a painful arthritis for a long time.

It may have been for this reason that I grew up rather sickly at first, and the doctor advised my mother to keep me out of school. My early childhood was thus very solitary. I had some old toys to play with that had belonged to my mother and to my uncle. Toys that pass from generation to generation carry with them a sad air. The Noah's Ark that had belonged to my Uncle Juan was a melancholy ark; one of the horses was missing a hoof; one of the elephants lacked a trunk; the rooster had lost his crest. It was a Noah's Ark that somehow resembled an invalid's refuge.

My Aunt Ursula, elder sister to my mother and a romantic maiden lady, set about teaching me to read. If Doña Celestina was like the spirit of tradition in the Aguirre family, Aunt Ursula represented fantasy and romanticism. Whenever my Aunt Ursula came to our house she would sit in a low chair to bring her down to my height and tell me a string of tales and adventure stories.

In her room in Aguirreche, Aunt Ursula had surrounded herself with pictures and books illustrated with French and Spanish plates, telling of naval battles, piracies, famous escapes, and the voyages of the great navigators. These books must have been in a cave for a long time, for they gave off an odor of humidity and their bindings were turned up at the corners. It was doubtless from these books that my aunt derived her inspiration.

My Aunt Ursula had a habit of relating the most insignificant things with a solemnity that dazzled me. She succeeded in filling my head with visions of shipwrecks, desert islands, and pirate ships.

She knew more than the generality of women, especially the generality of women of the Basque country. It was she who explained to me how, in the old days, the Basques had gone to the whale fisheries in the northern seas; how it was the Basques who had originally discovered the Newfoundland Banks; and how even up to the last century they were building great frigates in the shipyards of Biscay and Guipúzcoa provinces, at Orio, Pasajes, Aguinaga, and Guernica.

She also told me, with great pride, of the Basque mariners and sea captains: of Elcano, and his voyage around the world; of Oquendo, victorious in more than a hundred combats, and who, beaten at length in his old age by Admiral Tremp, died of sadness; of Blas de Lezo, one-eyed and one-legged, constantly fighting, and defeating, with his few ships, the powerful squadron of the English Admiral Vernon at Cartagena of the Indies; of the wise and heroic Churruca, of Echaide, of Recalde, of Gaztañeta. Frequently she would conclude her narrations with the following verses found in Concha's *Art of Navigation:*

> Over land and above the whirl
> A Basque of stout and willing heart
> With a compass and a chart
> Made a circuit of the world.

And, whether or not these verses bore any relation to the tale my aunt had just finished telling me, the solemn tone with which she pronounced them made them seem to me a very fitting end to any tale whatever.

In that far-off epoch of my childhood I knew no other children of my age but some second cousins. These children lived in Madrid and would come to Lúzaro to spend the summer. When they were at my grandmother's house, we would go together to a country house owned by the family. There we were always given cottage cheese. My Aunt Ursula would divide it up, and each of us would watch to see if any one of the others was getting more, ready always to protest.

My cousins would tell about the theaters and circuses which they had seen in the capital city, but, in truth, I was never much seduced by these tales. What attracted me was the sea. I would gaze with envy on the boys who went barefoot about the wharfs. I would have liked to have been the son of a fisherman, so that I could run on the breakwater and play about the barges and scows.

My Aunt Ursula possessed, in addition to her library of illustrated French novels of adventure and her sea stories, another source from which to draw the moving and dramatic tales which fascinated me.

Deposited among many other ancient and respectable objects in the great chest in the Aguirre drawing room was a manuscript volume of enormous thickness. On the parchment cover one could read, in letters grown faded and pink: *History of the*

Aguirre Family. Since almost all the members of this family
and of those related to the Aguirre clan had been mariners and
voyagers, the yellowing pages of the book were stuffed with
old navigational charts, very unusual and now very rare, inserted here and there to help explain the voyages described. In
these old charts and maps the sea is symbolized by a whale
spouting water, a galleon, and a number of dolphins; towns
are represented by small houses; forests, by trees; and savage
countries, by Indians with feathers on their heads and carrying
bows and arrows. There were also charts to indicate the presence
and flow of currents and winds, and drawings of sounding
lines, primitive compasses, and astrolabes. The entire book was a
series of land and sea adventures.

My Aunt Ursula would put on her spectacles and begin to
read any one of these accounts with attention and care; then
she would add her comments. Most of the accounts were short,
but they were written in a style so full of mannerisms that I
could not, unaided, make any sense of them. One of the most
entertaining, nevertheless, was the story of Domingo de Aguirre,
called the Basque, who had formed part of the expedition of
Gonzalo Jiménez de Quesada during the Conquest of America.
Domingo de Aguirre had witnessed the firing of Iraca, which
must have been of great importance, to judge by the description.

As soon as I knew how to write, my Aunt Ursula got the
idea of dictating entire paragraphs from the family history, and
I still preserve, by some chance, a sheet of untrimmed paper on
which my unpracticed hand had written in uneven letters:

"The ship's captain, Martín Pérez de Irizar, en route home
from Cádiz after loading his galleon with merchandise there,
on the high sea encountered the French corsair Jean Florin,
whose name inspired terror in all who sailed. The vaunted
Frenchman had two well-armed ships under his command.
Whomever he caught at sea, large ships or small, men or women,
he stripped of everything they had; as a result he was very rich.

"As soon as he saw the galleon under the captain from
Guipúzcoa, the pirate attacked fiercely. Irizar defended himself
courageously. The blood ran red on both sides. The battle was
soon over, and Martín Pérez de Irizar captured Jean Florin, his
vessels, and his men.

"The pirates lost; thirty men killed, and more than eighty of
their number were wounded. Jean Florin offered Captain
Irizar 20,000 duros as ransom; but his offer was in vain, for a
man of good sense and understanding will always prefer his
honor to all the money in the world.

"With ninety prisoners and the two captured vessels, Captain Irizar returned to Cádiz, as was proper in a man of his fine and true loyalty.

"The emperor, Don Carlos, our lord, ordered that Jean Florin be hung, and that Captain Martín Pérez de Irizar incorporate in his coat-of-arms, for eternal memory, an image of the galleon and banner won in the encounter."

I remember that as I wrote all this down from my aunt's dictation I asked her various questions relating to the customs and kind of life led by pirates. Despite her attempt to magnify the awfulness of the knights of fortune, it seemed to me that being a pirate, and going about the seas, boarding ships and seizing their treasures, and marooning people on desert islands, was something altogether marvelous.

As a result of all these tales of family adventure I learned to read and write. One strange fact, I noticed, kept recurring: there was always some adventuresome Aguirre whose end was not known. One was lost among the Indians, another was reported to have joined the pirates.

It seemed as if a fatal destiny pursued some members of the family, through time and down the generations.

VI. LOPE DE AGUIRRE, THE TRAITOR

The family book concerned itself mainly with numbers of captains, mariners, adventurers and priests; but, among all those histories, the most extraordinary, the most farfetched in its reality was the story of Lope de Aguirre, the madman, also called Lope de Aguirre, the Traitor. More than once I read through the astonishing adventures of this man, related with full detail in our manuscript.

Domingo de Cincunegui, the author of the *Historical Recollections of Lúzaro,* has repeatedly asked me to look through all the odd corners of Aguirreche in search of the old manuscript; but the folio has never turned up; doubtless it was lost at the death of my grandmother; or perhaps it has served one of the seamen who now live in the old house as a means of lighting a fire. The account given of Lope de Aguirre by Cincunegui in his *Recollections of Lúzaro* is taken from a history of Peru and of Venezuela.

It is from the *Recollections* that I take the following data, by way of giving an idea of my frightful ancestor:

"Lope de Aguirre was born in the first third of the sixteenth century in Biscay, though in which town is not known. In the sixteenth century there were three important houses of Aguirre: one at Oyarzun, another at Gaviria, and the other in Navarre. "Lope de Aguirre was surely from one of these three houses.

"Lope arrived in Peru in the middle of the sixteenth century, and he joined the forces of Gonzalo Pizarro in the latter's rebellion. He served with Pizarro for some time, but then turned traitor to his chief and committed acts of inhuman cruelty against his former comrades.

"Lope was a man of restless and turbulent temperament, hard-faced and ill-featured. Condemned to death in the course of one seditious uprising, he escaped and became a horsebreaker. It was a good occupation and outlet for his barbarous energy. Among the military Lope was known as Aguirre the Madman.

"In 1560, the viceroy, Don Andrés Hurtado de Mendoza, entrusted Captain Pedro de Ursúa, a Basque, with an expedition to explore the banks of the Marañon River for gold. Lope was one of the leaders of this expedition.

"One night, the restless Aguirre incited the expeditionary soldiery to mutiny, and he himself stabbed to death Captain Ursúa and his woman companion, Inés de Atienza, daughter of the conquistador Blas de Atienza.

"Lope also assassinated Ursúa's lieutenant, Vargas, and he issued a manifesto to the rebels, calling on them to follow him; and they did so. The mutineers proclaimed Fernando de Guzmán general and prince of Peru, and Lope de Aguirre field marshall.

"When General Guzmán remonstrated with Lope over his unnecessary cruelty, the ferocious Basque, who tolerated no recriminations, took swift vengeance and assassinated his chief. Next, he committed a series of crimes and outrages.

"At the head of his men, who were held in leash by terror (he had hung eight of them, who had seemed of dubious loyalty), he descended along the Amazon River, and for months and months followed along the endless course of this great waterway. He finally reached the Atlantic, and quickly attempted to put to sea.

"Lope had only a few small vessels, all of them barely useful for river navigation; but he was not a man to be stopped by difficulties, and he was soon at sea. Lope de Aguirre was every inch a man.

"Near Ecuador, he weathered two terrible storms in his tiny ships, and next he sailed along the coasts of Brazil, the Guianas, and Venezuela.

"Wherever he put in, Lope looted and sacked, burning everything in front of him, carried along by his wild and crazy fury.

"A friar in the flotilla ventured to supplicate his captain against being so cruel. Aguirre listened to him politely, and politely ordered him hanged.

"Feeling some remorse in his hard heart over this act, he summoned a missionary priest from Parrachagua so that he might make his confession; when the good priest refused to grant him absolution for the crime, he ordered this holy man hanged as company for the other one.

"Those among the band of adventurers who proved lukewarm to his person suffered the same fate with monotonous regularity.

"Of the four hundred men who had set out with Ursúa, there were soon only some one hundred and fifty left to Lope, and of this number many were deserting daily. When Aguirre saw that he was left without sufficient crews for his ships, he set fire to them, and then he sought refuge, along with his daughter and a handful of loyal companions, in the vicinity of Barquisimeto, in Venezuela.

"There, in the country, while living in an abandoned house, Aguirre wrote a report to Philip II, justifying his excesses, and, in order to lend force to the document, he signed it in the following bold, cynical, and farfetched manner: 'Lope de Aguirre, the Traitor.'

"The troops of the king, joined by some of the deserters from Aguirre's force, commenced to hunt down the Basque captain as if he were a wild beast, with the intention of killing him.

"A broken man at last, and completely surrounded, Lope, when he saw he was lost, took out his dagger and plunged it to the hilt into the heart of his daughter, who was still a child. 'I will not allow her to grow up to be a bad woman,' he said, 'nor ever to be called the daughter of the Traitor.' Then he commanded one of his loyal soldiers to fire on him with a harquebuse. The soldier obeyed. 'Bad shot!' yelled Lope, as the first bullet whistled over his head. And when, at the second shot, he felt the bullet piercing his chest and taking away his life, he yelled out, saluting his killer with a fierce joy: 'That's a good shot.'

"In all truth, Lope de Aguirre was every inch a man.

"Following his death, they cut off his head and quartered his body, locking up the skull in an iron cage in the church at Barquisimeto."

Thus ran the account given by Cincunegui in his *Historical Recollections of Lúzaro*, and, more or less, it is the same as was written in the manuscript book in my grandmother's house, though the manuscript included many more details and copious commentary.

Reading these adventures of Aguirre gave me the same feeling that children get when they see Guignol beat up the policeman and hang the judge. Despite all his crimes and atrocities, Aguirre, the Madman, was almost a sympathetic figure.

VII. THE FUNERAL OF MY UNCLE JUAN

One of the strongest impressions of my childhood was the funeral held *in absentia* for my Uncle Juan de Aguirre. For a long time the whereabouts of my mother's older brother had constituted a mystery, until it was learned that he had died. I had always sensed, with that kind of understanding typical of children, that the family had great, great reservations in connection with my Uncle Juan; neither my mother, nor her sister Ursula, nor my grandmother had any desire to speak of the missing man; this mystery and this reserve stimulated my fantasy.

Our maid, La Iñure, who was very superstitious, assured me that Uncle Juan had not died at all.

"Well where is he?" I asked her.

"He's far from here."

"And why doesn't he come?"

"He can't come."

"But why?"

Finally, after exhorting me not to repeat to my mother anything she was about to tell me, La Iñure related that my Uncle Juan had turned pirate and had been carried off to a prison in England, where he was being held with chains about his feet and certain letters branded on his back with a hot iron. For all these reasons, he could not return to Lúzaro.

La Iñure's tale excited me all the more. At night I seemed to see my uncle in his dungeon jail, naked and lamenting, the letters branded on his back glowing hideously.

At this time, and as if to fix even more vividly in my mind the memory of my uncle, his funeral, *in absentia,* was celebrated in Lúzaro. My grandmother had apparently received a letter from the Spanish consul in some Irish city informing her of the death of Juan de Aguirre. But, was it true? La Iñure assured me roundly that it was not.

I recall the day of the funeral very well. It is, in fact, engraved on my memory.

My mother woke me up at dawn; she was already dressed in black; I dressed quickly, and the two of us set out, with La Iñure as company. It was an autumn morning; the town was beginning to awaken; the mist was rising up the flanks of Mount Izarra, and from the harbor mouth a schooner was slowly emerging.

We arrived at Aguirreche and waited a moment, and then my grandmother, Aunt Ursula, and my mother, all now draped in black mantillas, with La Iñure and me in the rear, set out toward the church.

The high nave was dark and deserted; in the middle of the church, in front of the high altar, the candlewoman and the sacristan were dressing a catafalque with black cloth; the floor was littered with a collection of diverse objects—blocks of wood in which the yellow wax candles are rolled and baskets with bits of black cloth.

My grandmother, my mother, and my aunt joined the candlewoman at her work, and the four of them went from one side to the other, arranging all manner of things.

La Iñure wanted me to sit down in one of the benches near the mortuary platform, where the relatives who would be the principal mourners were to sit, but I was frightened at the idea of sitting there by myself.

I followed my mother around, holding on to her skirt, hindering her from doing anything, until old Irizar came up, in his black suit, his top hat in his hand, and I was forced to sit next to him in the central bench.

One by one women dressed in mourning began to come in; they would kneel down, spread out black cloths on the floor, unroll yellow candles and light them.

The tapers on the high altar began to burn, and in their light the whole Churrigueresque altarpiece, gilt and twisted, with its Solomonic columns and racemes of grapes, shimmered and shone.

High above in the transept hung the sailing vessel, which rocked smoothly, as if it were sailing toward the golden splendor of the high altar.

A bell began to toll, and people started to arrive, at first slowly and then, all of a sudden, in a rush; the two benches reserved for the relatives and friends of the deceased were soon filled; and the mass began.

I was frightened; I knew that there was no one inside the

mortuary platform, but it seemed to me that somewhere inside Uncle Juan must be crouching with the chains around his feet and the ignominious letters burning on his back.

From time to time the organ sounded, and its harmonious voice rose into the high vault. I continually stared around in every direction, until old Irizar strongly recommended that I pay more attention to my devotions.

What fervor the women displayed! Kneeling on their black cloths, they prayed with all their souls. A number of them were the widows of sea captains and pilots, and as they thought of the dead man lost at sea, they sobbed.

Following the mass, the priest turned toward the faithful and said a prayer for the dead man and for all those who had been buried at sea. The sobs thereupon redoubled. Next, the priest approached the catafalque to pray, and he sprinkled the empty platform various times with holy water.

I was completely terrified by this time. As we went out of the church the pale sun lit up the atrium. Irizar and I were left standing at the entrance. All the women in their black shawls went by in front of us, trooping in a procession to my grandmother's house; behind them came the gentlemen with their top hats, and then the seamen and fishermen in their coarse wool clothes, their hands stuck in the pockets of their pants.

That night, La Iñure assured me once again that my Uncle Juan was not dead at all. Sooner or later, I would meet him.

Her convictions became mine. I was certain that some day I would see a man with the aspect of one of the seamen in my Aunt Ursula's books, with side whiskers, high boots, frock coat, and an oilskin hat with straps hanging down. I would speak to this man, and it would turn out that he was my Uncle Juan.

For a long time, the mystery of Juan de Aguirre made me uneasy. And I associated this mystery with the funeral in the church, with the clouds of incense floating in the air, and the sailing ship hanging from the transept, which looked as if it were sailing toward the golden fire of the high altar. . .

The Christmas festivities gave me the same feeling of mystery. In this season of holiday the air, the light, everything seemed different.

There was a tradition at Aguirreche of assembling a very large crèche in a room on the ground floor. A half-crazy old woman named La Curriqui, dressed in a flowered skirt and a white headdress, was in charge of explaining what took place in Bethlehem. In one hand she carried a little pointer with which to identify the figures in the crèche, and in the other she held a

tambourine with which to accompany herself when she broke
into a carol. She knew two or three monotonous tunes, and a
handful of monorhymed verses to go with them. Among the
figures in the crèche there was one ragged woman, who was
doubtless the classic buffoon, the butt of jokes. I remember the
song that La Curriqui used to address to her. It went thus:

> Orra Mari Domingui
> Beguira orri
> Gurequin naidubela
> Belena etorri.

(There stands Marie Dominque. Look at that ridiculous figure!
And she wants to come with us to Bethlehem!)
     And then La Curriqui would continue:

> Gurequin naibadezu
> Belena etorri
> Atera bearco dezu
> Gona zar hori.

(If you want to come to Bethlehem with us, you'll have to take
off that ancient skirt.)
     The public, made up of fishermen and youngsters, were very
happy with these naturalistic details.
     On the Day of the Kings—Twelfth Night—La Curriqui, wear-
ing a white cape and a brass crown, would return to her stage
at Aguirreche to sing us more songs. On this day, some of the
shepherds from the hills would come down into town and
would sing carols in their sharp, hoarse voices, accompanying
themselves with tambourines and country drums. If the lady
of the house would give them some coins, they would add a
verse to their carol saying that she resembled the Virgin; on
the other hand, if she gave them nothing, they would call her
an old witch.

VIII. FORAYS OF BOYHOOD

I had heard so much about the evil ways of the other children
that when I was led off to school I felt like a lamb being led to
the slaughter.
     I was prepared to fight, like Martín Pérez de Irizar, against
any Jean Florin who ventured to attack me, even though my
forces were not very great.
     At first the teacher placed me among the most backward stu-

dents, a move which filled me with shame; but I soon was able to gain a place among those of my own age.

The teacher, Don Hilario, was an old Castilian who strove to teach us to speak and pronounce well. He hated the Basque tongue as if it were a personal enemy, and he believed that to speak Castilian as it is spoken in Burgos or at Miranda del Ebro conferred such superiority on an individual that any person of good sense, before learning how to earn a living, or even to live, must learn to pronounce correctly.

All the boys thought it ridiculous to give the importance to terrestrial matters that Don Hilario did. Instead of talking to us about the Cape of Good Hope or the Newfoundland banks, he spoke to us of the vineyards of Haro or the wheat fields of Medina del Campo. All of us feared him and looked down on him at the same time.

He understood our disdain for everything that he held dear, and he instinctively reacted by hating the town and everything Basque. He habitually beat us furiously. I was often saved from these beatings because my mother had made a special point of making it known that I was not to be beaten, inasmuch as I was still sickly.

As soon as I understood the benefits to be derived from being sick, I complained often of a pain in my chest or stomach, and thus escaped punishment. I saved myself from the blows of the teacher, but at the same time I lost my reputation as a tough. "This boy isn't worth a thing," everyone said; and this opinion has persisted to this day.

One has to laugh remembering the subterfuges and dodges of childhood; and yet, when one thinks back to those days, it is impossible not to recollect that the first days of school are among the most somber and lamentable of one's life. Later there are always sorrows and crises to be overcome—and who has not had to overcome them? But by then one's sensibilities have been blunted; one dominates one's nerves as a pilot dominates his boat. No, it is not easy for anyone of my age, in thinking back to his childhood, to remember kindly the schools and the teachers who embittered the first days of our existence. The memory of the cold, dank school, where one's feet grew numb, and where one received, without well knowing why, a rain of recriminations, hard words, blows and punishments, this memory is among the ugliest and most hateful of an entire lifetime.

It is strange that a truth which savages have understood, namely that a child, since he is weaker and more tender, war-

rants more care and even more respect than a developed adult,
it is strange that this truth is something that civilized man does
not comprehend; among us, a man who would be incapable of
doing harm to a fellow adult is capable of martyrizing a child,
and of getting the full consent of the parents to do so. This is
merely one of the many barbarities to be found in our so-called
civilization.

Within a few days of entering school, I had formed friendships with two boys who have continued to be my friends to
this day: one was José María Recalde; the other Domingo Zelayeta.

José Mari, as he was called, was the son of Juan Recalde the
Brave. His father was thus called because he had repeatedly
demonstrated his extraordinary valor. José Mari was proceeding
along the same road: he had already proved himself impetuous
and bold.

The other lad, Chomin, as he was known, was the son of a
turner and seller of tackle on the wharf.

Chomin distinguished himself for his liveliness and his ingenuity. His father was an unusual type, a man of great energy,
of strong character, and rather sullen, who found strange motives for everything he did.

"Why don't you get married again, Zelayeta?" someone asked
him.

"No, no; what for? I'd only have to make the house bigger,
and that wouldn't suit me at all."

Once some people of the town wanted to make him a councilman, but he opposed the move with all his strength.

"But, *hombre,* why don't you want to be a councilman?"

"I'd rather be killed than be forced to wear a coat with a
swallow's tail." The abominated swallow-tail coat to which he
had reference was merely the formal wear which on certain
solemn occasions the councilmen of Lúzaro traditionally donned.

Zelayeta, the father, despite all his eccentricities and rough-
ness, was a man of progressive tendencies; he liked to sign up
for books to be delivered by subscription, principally so that his
son might have them to read.

For the first few months of school, my mother used to send
La Iñure to fetch me when I came out, and, although the old
woman was not very severe with me, I was forced to march
along at her side while my comrades went off by themselves in
whichever direction they chose.

After much begging and complaining on my part, I succeeded in gaining the right to come and go to school without

an escort. My mother declared that I could go where I wanted, except to the pier, which was like telling me that I could go everywhere and nowhere. Despite her warning, the moment I left school I set out toward the pier, running all the way to the steps leading to it.

Some of the other boys, generally those of terrestrial families, preferred to go to the courts to play Basque pelota, or *jai alai*. The rest of us, those of seafaring families, among which were Recalde, Zelayeta, and myself, headed toward the sea.

We would watch the small boats come in and out of the harbor; we would gaze at the boys who were ducking naked in the water off the long wharf, which in Basque is called *Cay luce;* and at the pole fishermen exercising their patience. These fishermen all knew us well.

What a surprise it always was to find an octopus, dangling at the end of a fishing pole, with its myopic eyes, round and stupid, its owl-like beak, and its horrible arms covered with suckers! It was scarcely less exciting to pull out one of those long twisting eels, fighting valiantly for its life, or one of those sea toads, inflated, black, and horribly repulsive.

When no one was watching us, we would slip down the mooring ropes and run along the barges and launches, jumping from one vessel to the other.

In this matter of childhood independence one gains ground rapidly, and I advanced along this road with such speed that within a short time I boasted of complete liberty.

Often Zelayeta, Recalde, and I would skip school. The teacher, Don Hilario, would send notes to the house, saying that on such and such a day I had failed to appear; but my mother always made up an excuse for me, and since she saw that I was growing strong and robust, she pretended not to notice my escapades.

On Sundays and on the weekdays on which we skipped school we used to go to the sand dunes, where we would take off our shoes and stockings and run about barefooted.

We would gather shells, pieces of meerschaum, razor clams, and small yellow, black, and pink stones, polished and shining.

At dusk, the green sand flies would begin to jump and the round holes in the coral rock would throw up bubbles when the thin film of water washed over them from a wave.

Sometimes we would succeed in unearthing one of those mollusks which in Basque we call *deituba* and about which we say, for some reason, that it chokes itself to death. In order to lure it out of its hiding place, we threw a little salt on it.

The luckiest of the three in making discoveries was Zelayeta; it was he who always found the starfish or the rare conch; he it was who sighted the octopus between the rocks or the dolphin swimming among the waves. He was forever busy examining everything; because of his perpetual searching about, his father called him the Border Guard.

My mother began to let me go off with my comrades even on Sundays, after giving me a long list of warnings and recommendations. On these days, since we had plenty of time at our disposal, we did not content ourselves merely by going to the sand dunes, but instead climbed up Mount Izarra, and then down to the rocks nearby. The practical purpose of our trips to the rocks was to capture those large, dark crabs which we call *carramarros,* a marine crab with spotted scales. Once we had grown used to clambering around the rocks, the beach seemed insipid by comparison.

Mount Izarra, on one of whose flanks lies Lúzaro, forms a kind of peninsula, separating the port from a rather wide inlet which lies between two points, one of which is called Lighthouse Point and the other Souls' Point. Mount Izarra is a slaty promontory formed of sloping slabs splashed by the sea. The schists of the mountain, standing out one from the other like the leaves of an open book, advance into the sea, where they form reefs, black rocks continually washed over by a restless tide, and they come to an end in a high, black rock, mysterious in its isolation, which is called Frayburu.

To go on our expeditions we would gather very early in the morning on the dock, walk out past the Convent of Santa Clara, up a steep street which had four or five flights of stairs, and finally emerge on a narrow lane bounded on either side by the walls of orchards. Then we cut across maize fields and vineyards to emerge higher up in the rocky open fields covered with beech trees and ferns.

At the top of Izarra there must formerly have been an artillery emplacement; the remains of a stone bulwark and of cannon emplacements could still be seen. Nearby was a weed-choked cave, which we liked to explore. This cave was really a hole built into the rock, no doubt burrowed at some former time by the soldiers attached to the battery to protect themselves from the rain; it served us as a place to play at Robinson Crusoe.

Old Yurrumendi, a strange inventor of fantasies, told Zelayeta that this cave was the grotto where a great winged serpent, the "Egan-suguia," took shelter. This serpent had the claws of a tiger, the wings of a vulture, and the face of an old woman. At night, it wandered about drinking the blood of children and committing other abominations; its very breath was poisonous.

After we had heard this tale, the cave took on a new meaning for us and gave us pause. Still, my suggestion was that we burn the weeds that filled the interior. If the "Egan-suguia" was in there, it would burn, and if it wasn't, then nothing would happen. Recalde did not approve the idea. Thus are superstitions entrenched.

The heights of Izarra were truly imposing. At the very edge of the sea a rocky path wound along on top of a cliff whose base was formed of perforated rocks. The waves flowed in among the crevices of the slate, into the heart of the mountain, and looking down one could see them break and jump, white and foam-tipped, like fountains of snow. Some boys did not dare climb those heights for fear of getting dizzy, but the precipice exerted a fascination and attraction for me.

Down below, at some places, the tiered stones formed what looked like the rows of seats in an amphitheater. As the sea withdrew from the tiers of this natural coliseum it left behind round puddles of clear water on the seats, like resplendent eyes reflecting the sky.

It was Yurrumendi again who asserted that, according to Zelayeta, the tiers of seats were put there to provide the sirens with accommodations from which they could see the dolphin races and the battles of the marine monsters that pullulate in the restless empire of the sea.

The water, green and white, leaped furiously among the rocks; the waves broke in a rain of foam and advanced like herds of wild horses, their manes flowing in the wind.

Far off, a half-mile from the coast, like a sentry over those reefs, the rock of tragic aspect, Frayburu, raised its head. The fishermen said that in front of Frayburu there was a great cavity in the side of Mount Izarra, an enormous and mysterious cavern.

Once this section was passed, Izarra was cut into a smooth-faced rock cliff of black slate, grained with white and red veins, in whose junctures and level places grew bushes and wild grasses. On this side the sea, very deep, was less agitated than in front of the reefs.

As one followed the road down, the beach near Souls' Point came into view beyond Lighthouse Point, which was nearer to Izarra. Over the beach drifted sand dunes hung with green, and in the middle of it all the scattered houses of the neighboring district of Izarte sent smoke up their fireplace chimneys.

When we got near Lighthouse Point we would strike away from the road and scramble among the rocks. In this area there were holes the size of chimneys that led down into the water. At the mouths of some of these openings a wind could be felt rushing up, making the flowers growing around the aperture sway. At the mouths of others the din of the sea could be clearly heard.

We leaped from rock to rock, and would go on to the farthest outlying reefs; but as soon as the tide began to rise we would be forced to flee the waves, and often we were caught by the water and would have to take off our shoes and wade. At low tide, one could see in between the lichen-covered rocks the quiet puddles which the retreating water had left behind. Many the hour I have spent gazing into these little seas with the greatest interest and enthusiasm.

Under the transparent water lay the pock-marked rock, covered with holes and barnacles. At the very bottom, in among the green lichen and the multicolored stones, were red sea-urchins, whose soft tentacles would contract when we touched them. On the surface bits of seaweed steeped and swayed in the water and would metamorphose into little branches of silvery filaments, seagull's feathers, or traces of cork. A little silver fish would dart by like an arrow, crossing the tiny ocean, and from time to time a crab, monster denizen of these deeps, would emerge from his secret cranny, and treacherously propel himself sidewise, while his enormous eyes inspected his domain in search of a victim.

Some of the puddles boasted canals communicating them with others, and their own inlets and gulfs as well; seeing them in this way, I imagined that they represented on a small scale the great oceans of the world.

I used to like to sit in the shelves of the rocks, where the algae piled up and dried in the sun; the strong odor of the sea flooded my senses and excited my mind like the aroma of a choice wine.

The hours spent among the rocks flew by for all of us; and I was almost always late getting home.

Sometimes on Sunday the weather went against us; it would rain down disastrously, and my mother would not let me out. I would have to go with her to Aguirreche, where we would have the noonday meal in my grandmother's company and then spend the afternoon in the house. What a disappointment! There would be a gathering of respectable ladies, among whom there were three or four widows of sea captains and pilots, and at nightfall chocolate would be served. And I would listen to the continual chatter in Basque of my grandmother's friends, and watch in despair the continual and monotonous falling of the rain, and listen to the noise of the water as it streamed down the spouts and on to the sidewalks.

IX. YURRUMENDI, THE FANCIFUL

In my time, the long wharf at Lúzaro (the *Cay luce*), was not as wide nor as well paved as it is now; it was bounded by a small wall, and instead of a breakwater as a final limit, it ended on the open rocks.

All along the wharf, in that epoch and in this, the same aspect was presented: there were fishermen's houses with wooden balconies and windows, all of them hung and adorned with clotheslines bearing red shirts, blue stockings, yellow sou'westers, tackle, and cork floats.

There was always clothing hanging from these houses, which was a reflection both on the instinct of cleanliness in the fisherfolk and the difficulty of drying things soaked by sea water.

In among the houses along the *Cay luce* pier there were before, as there are now, some charcoal shops and a string of taverns in which the fishermen gathered—and still gather—to drink and talk, and from which wafted, especially on Sundays, a strong odor of fried sardines and tunafish and onion stew; these were accompanied by the sound of accordion music.

The taverns included the "Telescope," the "Belle Siren," the "Dutchman," the "Morning Star," and, most famous of them all, the *Guezurrechape de Cay luce* (the "Loafing Place of the Long Wharf"), which was owned by Joshe Ramón.

On this wharf, a few paces from the Loafing Place, the father of Zelayeta had his workshop. The window of the house had been converted into a store window and in it were laid out such things as wooden pulleys, lanterns, fishing poles, and a lifesaving belt. Zelayeta's father worked at his lathe with his apprentice helper, and while he worked some of his friends would stop by and sit in the doorway to chat with him.

I had become an intimate friend of Chomin Zelayeta. Chomin was very skillful and very patient. He succeeded in domesticating a small seagull, for instance, and when he got bigger the bird used to fight all the cats in the neighborhood. On stormy days, the bird would hide in some dark hole, and would not emerge until the storm had blown over.

Zelayeta felt, as I did, a great enthusiasm for desert islands and pirates, and since he had talent, he drew plans for the ship that was to take us sailing and charts of the unknown islands where he would work out our apprenticeship as Robinson Crusoes.

Our adventurous inclinations, which already reflected the atavistic restlessness of the Basque, was spurred on by the tales told us by the pilot Yurrumendi, the old and fantastic Yurrumendi, friend and conversational comrade of Zelayeta's father. Eustasio Yurrumendi had traveled widely; but he was a chimerical man, whose chimeras and fantasies overcame his sense. All of us possess and live with an ensemble of lies which serve to cloak us from the coldness and sadness of life; but Yurrumendi overelaborated his cloak.

He was an enormous man, broad-shouldered, big-bellied, his great hands always stuck in the pockets of his trousers, which were on the point of slipping off him, so low did he hitch them. He had a handsome face, noble and red; his hair was white, his side whiskers short, and his eyes small and bright. He dressed very cleanly: in summer, some suiting of blue linen, which was completely faded from much washing; and in winter, a jacket of coarse black cloth, which seemed as well-caulked as a barge. On his head he wore a knitted cap with a tuft in the center. He was a single man who lived alone with an old landlady, smoked a pipe a great deal, walked with a rolling gait, and wore a gold earring in his ear.

Yurrumendi had been a member of the crew of a slaver; he had also sailed on French ships armed as privateers and had spent some time in prison as a suspected pirate. In short, Yurrumendi was a sea wolf. He knew the Atlantic from Iceland and the Lofoten Islands to the Cape of Good Hope and Cape Horn. He knew what the tempests of the Pacific were like, as well as the typhoons of the Indian Ocean.

Yurrumendi had seen a great deal, but he would rather talk of what he imagined than of what he had seen. He succeeded in driving both Chomin Zelayeta and myself wild with his tales. He would tell us that at the bottom of the sea, just as above it, there are forests, plains, deserts, mountains, volcanoes, islands of white coral, ships, uncounted treasures, and a watery sky much the same as the airy one. To whatever was true he added the most farfetched elaborations. "Sometimes," he would say, "the sea raises up like a wall, and in the middle there will be a hole which seems to be filled with pearls. There are those who say that if you can get into this hole, you can walk about as on land."

"And where does this hole lead?" one of us would ask anxiously.

"This can't be told, even when it's known," Yurrumendi would answer solemnly; "but there are those who assert that a woman can be seen inside."

"Some siren," Zelayeta's father would interrupt dryly.

"Who knows what it is!" the old sailor would reply.

Whenever Yurrumendi spoke of himself, he did so as if he were talking of a stranger, a third person. Thus he would say: "Then Yurrumendi understood . . . Then Yurrumendi said such and such. . ." He seemed to hold certain doubts in regard to his own personality.

Yurrumendi was possessed of a truly extraordinary imagination. He was the greatest inventor of chimeras and wild stories that I have ever known. According to him, behind Mount Izarra, a little beyond Frayburu, there was a bottomless abyss in the sea. He had often dropped his sounding lead there; but he had never touched sand or rock. If we told him that his sounding lead was simply too short, he replied that even if it were a hundred miles long, it would never find bottom.

In regard to the cave in Izarra, in front of Frayburu, he did not wish to relate the details of the thousand extraordinary and supernatural things with which it was filled. It sufficed for him to say that if a man were to emerge from there, assuming that it were possible for a man to emerge from there alive, he would be nearly crazy, from seeing the things that were to be seen inside. It was quite enough to say that sirens, marine unicorns, and sea horses moved about in there like flies, and that a giant with red eyes maintained a mysterious dwelling there.

This giant was apparently the brother, or a least the cousin, of another giant, whose proportions were unknown, but whose eyes were certainly red, and who, in an age of greater belief and greater fear of God, used to appear at Donosti, amid the rocks of Zurriola, with a fish in his hand; and this giant would be asked

> Onentzarro begui gorri
> Nun arrapatu dec array hori?

(Onentzarro, of the red eyes, where did you catch that fish?)

And the poor giant of the red eyes, instead of disdaining the impertinent question of his interlocutor, would answer amiably:

Bart arratzean amaiquetan
Zuniyolaco arroquetan.

(Last night, at eleven, among the rocks of Zurriola.)

I am not certain in what category Yurrumendi placed his giant with the red eyes; but I believe that he did not consider him on the same level with the "Egan-suguia," the great winged serpent of Izarra, with its vulture wings, its face of a sinister old woman, and its poisonous breath.

Yurrumendi spoke also of gigantic octopuses with immense tentacles which were able to sink a frigate; of the Saragosso Sea, where ships sail over land which opens up to allow passage for the vessels; of lands where it snows feathers; of dophins, endowed with an obscure sympathy for men, a sentiment hard to explain; of the sentimental whales, whose tragedy lies in knowing that humanity thinks more of their oil than of their melancholy hearts; of the two thousand hump-backed and extravagant dwarfs on the Norwegian coasts; of the sea serpents which pursue ships, barking all the while; of the spider of the Kraken in the pine tree at Portland, England; and of that terrible monster of the Maelstrom, whose fauces swallow the sea and any imprudent vessel, making them disappear into its gigantic entrails. He also assigned a great deal of importance to the *Curcushada,* the Horns of the Moon, which bore an intimate relation with the life of men, in his opinion.

Another of Yurrumendi's favorite themes was the Isle of Fire, where he had been. At the top of this inaccessible mountain there was a fire which burned intermittently, lighting up every night, and extinguishing itself with the day. One might have thought that he was simply talking about a volcano, whose flames were not visible in the light of the sun; but Yurrumendi assured us that the bonfire was kindled afresh every night by the souls of Captain Kidd's famous crew, who were there guarding an immense treasure they had buried.

Another one of the fascinating things to be seen at sea, according to Yurrumendi, was a phantom ship, whose crew was captained by a Dutchman. This condemned man, a drunkard, blasphemer, and cynical pirate, coursed the seas with his devilish crew committing all manner of crimes. If the cursed Dutchman sailed close to a ship, the wine aboard turned to vinegar, the water grew cloudy, the meat rotted. If the Dutchman sent one a letter it was best not to read it, for the person addressed could go mad from the lies it contained.

Yurrumendi told of how he had seen the cursed Dutchman,

only once, at a distance; fortunately, however, the Dutchman
had not approached any nearer.

On certain occasions, the old mariner would tell us a series of
stories recounting horrible cruelties: of pirates who would cut
off the tongues or hands of whomever fell into their power; of
others who threw their enemies into the sea in a cage or after
digging out their eyes. His tales made us tremble, but we listened to them. There is a fundament of cruelty in all men, and
especially in children, which is darkly satisfied when human
barbarity is brought to the surface.

Almost always when he spoke of piracies and the brutalities
of slavers, a certain Basque song would be brought to Yurrumendi's mind.

"This song," he would say, "used to be sung by Gastibeltza,
a countryman of ours who was mate of a slave ship on which
I sailed as cabin boy. Gastibeltza would sing it as we turned the
windlass to raise the anchor or to hoist some cargo."

"What was the song like?" we would ask, although we knew
it by heart. "Sing it for us!"

And he would sing, in his hoarse seaman's voice that had been
formed by the fogs and cold, by alcohol and the smoke of his
pipe:

> Ateraquiyoc
> Emanaquiyoc
> Aurreco orri
> Elduaquiyoc
> Orra! Orra!
> Cinzaliyoc
> Itsastarra oh! oh!
> Balesaquiyoc

Which meant: "Pull it! Haul it! Grab the one in front. That's
the one, that's the one. Hang it up, sailor; oh! oh! Now you can
relax."

No one could have sung that song like Yurrumendi; every
time I heard it, I could imagine a boarding party of pirates coming alongside, climbing the ladders of a ship, with knives between their teeth.

For Zelayeta and for me, Yurrumendi's tales were a revelation.
We made up our minds: we would become pirates; and after
endless adventures, looting great ships and brigs, and making
mock of the English, after selling our ounces of ancient Mexi-
can gold and the treasure of precious stones which we would
have stored on a desert island, we would come back to Lúzaro to
recount our feats, like Yurrumendi. If we happened to have

brought back a parrot, and he gave signs of informing on us, like the one La Iñure told of, we would tie a stone around his neck and throw him into the sea.

Zelayeta drew up a plan of the kind of house we would build outside town, on a height, when we returned to Lúzaro.

Yurrumendi was our model for everything in those days. We even walked like him, with a rolling gait, our legs bending beneath us, our fists closed; we tried smoking a pipe, though for my part, after the first two draws, I was unable to overcome a feeling of nausea.

When our friend, the old sea wolf, was gayer than usual, he spun sea stories. These stories were not much different from the histories which he proclaimed to be true. There was one among these stories which he used as a theme and elaborated variously.

The theme was basically simple: a sailor, who though a heavy drinker was a good man, would meet an old beggar, ragged and dirty; the old man would humbly ask a small favor; the sailor would help him, and the old man would turn out to be none other than St. Peter, who would then show his gratitude by giving the sailor some important gift. The gift varied according to the stories: in some it was a purse, from which everything desired poured out as soon as certain sacramental phrases were uttered; in others, it was a marvelous seed, from which a giant tree sprang, yielding enough wood for ten or twelve frigates and a like number of brigantines—with a little left over.

When he recounted these stories, Yurrumendi liked to make use of an extreme particularity, as "One time, in Liverpool, at the travern of the Red Dragon. . ." Or: "We were in the Atlantic, at the latitude of Cape Verde. . ." When a ship was involved, he always felt compelled to go into the details of its class of rigging, its tonnage, and its seaworthiness.

Finally, at the end, the winged serpents, the sirens, the witches, and *La Curchushada,* in combination with old age and alcohol, disordered his mind a bit. I, who ever since boyhood had had a certain influence upon him, attempted to tell him that though he might well consider the world of fancy to be the true one, if he so desired, he should on no account assign it too much importance.

He would reply, in the most solemn manner: "Shanti, you know more than we do, because you've studied; but others, older than I am, and wiser, too, have seen these things."

"That's true," some old friend of his would put in.

Poor Yurrumendi! I would give anything to see him again

in Zelayeta's tackle shop or in the *Guezurrechape de Cay luce*
spinning his tales; but the years do not come and go in vain,
and it is a long time that Yurrumendi has been sleeping his
eternal sleep in the graveyard at Lúzaro.

X. SHACU'S INDIGNATION

Recalde, Zelayeta, and myself entered Nautical School. We
would have preferred to go out fishing, as did the dock boys,
with some old fisherman, but we could not. We were victims
of our elevated social position. If we wished to be deep-sea mariners, we had to study, and for us, to be navigators on the high
seas constituted the highest superiority.

After a course with Don Gregorio Azurmendi, who explained
mathematics to us dressed in full-dress coat and white tie, the
summer vacations luckily arrived. I could not hope to carry out
great escapades, for I was too closely watched, but I did go out
a few times with a fisherman to fish for squid and cuttlefish beyond the points. My mother became so alarmed that she made
me lose all my enthusiasm.

"I don't know what you're going to do when I finally ship
out," I said.

"When that time comes, we'll see."

Since I met with so many difficulties in going out in a small
boat, Zelayeta and I decided to buy a toy ship with which to
make maneuvers, and we went to the house of Caracas, who
was the master builder of that type of ship. We boys considered
Caracas an admirable naval architect, and thought that he could
have constructed a large frigate as easily as a model.

Caracas had his shop at the far end of the pier; it was a black
hole, hollowed into the wall, where he sold tar, wax, casks, nails,
caulked wood, nets, and hooks of all types. The back of his
little cave was adorned by a ship's figurehead, painted and
gilded, taken from some old ship.

Besides being a tradesman, Caracas was a master carpenter;
from time to time he received an order to make a ship's model
to hang in the church of some nearby town; once it was finished
and painted, his fishermen friends would troop by his little
shop to see the masterwork. He also made models for some of
the seamen to use as votive offerings. For, as is well known, one
of the ways of placating a divinity is to bring a ship's model
to a hermitage.

The brother of this Caracas had been, until he died, one of

the greatest schemers in town; there were those who asserted that he had left behind more than a dozen widows in different parts of Spain and America, as well as a series of fabulous bequests in his will, all inheritances which existed only in his overheated imagination.

There was a pair of conversationalists usually to be found inside Caracas' cave at all hours of the day. One was a drunkard called Joshepe Tiñacu, and another was a semi-idiot, wearing a blue shirt and red cap, who guarded the small boats and was nicknamed Shacu.

By reason of our coming and going to see when Caracas would have our ship ready, Zelayeta and I became very friendly with these two, and with others who dropped in.

Joshepe Tiñacu was one of those idle and drunken seamen who pass their life in port with their hands in their pockets. He would ship out very infrequently, and then very soon be back in Lúzaro. He wandered continually from tavern to tavern, from cider press to cider press. When he was drunk he drew such circles as he reeled through the streets that, as Yurrumendi said, it was worthwhile inviting him to drink just to see him walk.

When he reached his house, Joshepe Tiñacu would halt and, in a soft and insinuating voice, call up to his wife: "Anthoni, bring out the candle." His wife would lean out a window with a light, and the drunkard would then walk straight through the door.

When Caracas finished our little vessel, Zelayeta and I went to the dock ramp and launched our craft; the boat, as if it had been tired, lay down on the water and wet its sails.

For all our efforts, we did not succeed in sailing the ship Caracas had built for us. As a decoration, it was certainly splendid; to hang from the transept in some church, it was fine; but it did not go in the water. Thus are many of the objects of life.

In order to make up this failure, Shacu was sent to see us, under instructions from Caracas, to offer us the loan of a launch belonging to Zapiain, watchmaker and commercial traveler. This launch, which was in Shacu's care, was named the "Cachalote."

At first we would give the watchman some coins to keep him happy, but later we used to take the launch without saying a word to him. When he saw us getting into the launch, Shacu would pretend he noticed nothing, but the moment we went past the hole in the wall belonging to Caracas, Shacu would run forward and begin clamoring with all his might:

"Get out of that launch, you rascals!"

We would pay no attention, but continue rowing, and he, apparently growing more furious, would shriek: "Thieves! Pirates! Corsairs! I hope you drown!"

Then Zelayeta, who was often cruel, would yell: "We're going to sell your launch. Cry, Shacu!"

And Shacu would be seized with such despair that he would stamp the ground, throw his red cap down, and almost break into tears in his rage.

In the "Cachalote" we did not go out of the harbor, or the estuary; we dared not cross the bar in such a light launch because a wave of any unusual force would have turned us over.

If the port itself had nothing special to recommend it to the eye, the estuary was very pretty. One of its shores was formed of clayey sand and it was here that Shempelar's shipyard was to be found. At low tide, eels could be fished off this bank, and there was always a row of black boats lying there. The other shore was wild country and extremely rocky; between the rocks and bushes there were caves, where, according to popular tradition, arms were hidden during the War of Independence. We—Zelayeta, Recalde, and myself—once found a large bronze cannon in one, but the three of us took an oath not to tell anyone of our find. A little beyond, there were corners filled with bullrushes and elderbushes and a small grotto from which spring water poured.

At our return from these expeditions, we would find that Shacu's fit of anger had passed. Sometimes, however, he would grumpily warn us against taking the launch again. The very next Sunday we would steal it once more.

One day we made up our minds to go over the bar, and after that we lost our fear and came and went about the port in the "Cachalote" even when the waves were running high.

XI. THE WRECK OF THE "STELLA MARIS"

One autumn morning, when I was fourteen or fifteen, Recalde stopped Zelayeta and myself as we were going into the Nautical School. A schooner had just run aground behind Mount Izarra, near the rocks of Frayburu.

Recalde the Brave, father of our comrade Joshe Mari, and another skipper, named Zurbelcha, had gone out with some others in a two-masted *trincadura* to pick up survivors. Zelayeta, Recalde, and I made up our minds at once to skip school and,

setting off at a run, we headed for Mount Izarra. Before long
we had clambered to the crest.

The weather was dark, the sky leaden, and a purple bar lay
along the horizon; the wind blew furiously on the summit, and
the gusts carried traces of rain. Dense masses of mist scudded
through the air. We took the path along the cliff; down below
the waves battered against the mountain, seeming to shake it.
Fog was sweeping over and covering everything; at intervals
the sea appeared, pale but clear in a light that irradiated the
water.

We watched the gray curtain of mist with rapt interest. Suddenly, on the heel of a furious gust of wind, the sun came out,
illuminating a cadaverously clay-colored sea covered with foam.

In that eclipse-like clarity, we saw, between the waves, the
rescue vessel attempting to reach the grounded schooner.

"Is your father the skipper?" I asked Recalde.

"No, Zurbelcha is," he answered.

Zurbelcha, in his sou'wester, was bending forward, handling
the oar that served as rudder; he was an expert seaman who
knew these reefs and the coast better than anyone. One false
move, and the launch would break against the rocks. Zurbelcha
had nerves of steel, and the precision of his hand was mathematical.

The oars dipped and rose rhythmically; occasionally the rowers
took a backward stroke, doubtless to avoid a rock. Waves high
as mountains and clouds of spray hid the valiant men for long
stretches of time.

On the deck of the grounded schooner, two men and a woman
gesticulated and yelled; we could hear their voices on the wind.

The launch gradually approached the schooner's side; it remained alongside for the merest moment, and then it cast loose
violently from the doomed ship and sank itself between the
waves. The two men and the woman had disappeared from the
deck.

We thought that the launch had been lost. We waited with
drawn breath, searching the horizon. There it was! We made
it out through the fog. Zurbelcha was still bent over his oar, and
the rescue craft was advancing toward the port.

Another difficulty remained: the passing of the bar. Recalde,
Zelayeta, and I had meanwhile reached the extreme point of
the pier. The lookout, supporting himself on the rocks, was
shouting instructions to Zurbelcha through his megaphone, and
the *trincadura* passed over the bar without difficulty.

Very soon afterward, the victims of the shipwreck were on

dry land. One of the men was tall, old, with a fringe of whiskers; he was dressed in black and wore a cap; the other was small and dark. The woman carried a child in her arms.

Zapiain, the watchmaker and commercial traveler, was able to communicate with them. They were Bretons, and spoke only their own language and some French.

The schooner was called the "Stella Maris" and was out of Quimper. The survivors were unable to explain what had happened to the members of the crew. Doubtless the sailors, aware of the danger before their captain, took to the lifeboat, which must have struck a rock and gone down.

Days later, when the storm had abated, an attempt was made to float the "Stella Maris" out from among the rocks; but it proved impossible. The keel was driven in among the sharp crags of Frayburu, and there was no way of pulling it out or of floating the vessel.

The seamen experienced at this sort of thing finally desisted in their efforts, and they advised the Brittany captain to save the cargo and abandon the ship.

This he did. As soon as the weather was steadily good, a handful of men unloaded the ship and dismantled it. Two weeks later, a corporal of the local infantry regiment stationed at the Elguea highway post reported to the Lúzaro commandant that at the foot of the cliff known as Leizazpicua the body of a man of about forty had been washed up by the waves.

The dead man was dressed in sailor's clothes—knit wool shirt, pants, and jacket with yellow buttons. He had only one shoe on, the one on the right foot; his hand on the same side was missing, and his face was all torn. Later, I much regretted going out to see him, because for a long time the image of him kept appearing in my mind.

XII. OUR GREAT ADVENTURE

When I saw the "Stella Maris" totally abandoned, it occurred to me to go out and reconnoiter it. I had the illusion that, by some chance, it might still be made to float. When I explained my plan to Zelayeta and Recalde, they were at first overawed but later enthusiastic.

We decided to wait until the rains stopped and as a result we waited through the entire winter. The fantasies we built up around the "Stella Maris" had no end: we would float it, take aboard the cannon hidden in the cave by the river, and sail away from Lúzaro amid our own cannonade.

One day in March, on a Saturday afternoon when the weather was fine, we set the following day for our expedition out to the wreck. That night I casually observed to my mother that I was going with my friends to Elguea and that we would not return until nightfall.

Sunday at dawn I got out of bed, dressed, and hurried toward the town. Recalde and Zelayeta were already waiting for me on the dock. Zelayeta said that it might be better to postpone the expedition to another day, because the sky was cloudy and the sea rather choppy; but Recalde asserted that the weather would clear.

Our minds made up, we bought some cheese, bread, and a bottle of wine from the *Guezurrechape* on the pier; we descended to the corner of the *Cay erdi* where Shacu kept his launches, we untied the "Cachalote" and headed out to sea. We carried a small four-pronged anchor, tied to a rope, and a wood-handled scoop for bailing water.

Two of us were to row, and the other would handle the rudder; we would switch about for relief. The horizon was cloudy, but broken here and there to allow patches of blue sky to show through. As we crossed the bar, the "Cachalote" danced over the waves like a happy whale, and we began to round Mount Izarra well out from the reefs.

I remembered Yurrumendi's imaginative tales about the abyss that was supposed to lie at this point in the sea, and I imagined myself plunging down into the unfathomable abyss at a speed of twenty-five miles per minute.

Despite Recalde's assurances, the sky was not clearing; on the contrary, it was getting darker, and very few fishing boats or launches were outside the harbor. The wind began to blow in violent gusts. The waves battered the rocks of Izarra and threw spray over them with a frightening din.

We passed in front of Frayburu, the great black rock, elder sister to the rocks of Izarra. From the sea, Frayburu looked like a fortified tower in ruins.

We began to approach the "Stella Maris." It was a sad and painful sight to see the schooner fallen over on its side, its masts broken, like an animal that has been wounded to the heart.

The sea broke upon the rocks and over the ship's side, making a violent noise like thunder, and the seagulls began to circle around us, uttering wild cries over our heads.

We were very excited; Zelayeta and I, I am sure, would have

gladly returned to Lúzaro, but we said nothing. Recalde was not the type to turn back. Difficulties and danger only spurred him on. If we had suggested going back, we would not have convinced him, and so, tacitly, the two of us determined to follow him. Stubborn and never carried away by fits of temper, Joshe Mari was a skillful seaman by instinct.

He knew there was a narrow channel four or five fathoms deep among the shoals, and he planned to use it in approaching the schooner. We made several attempts to get into the channel, but every time we started to go in we were forced to veer away.

Recalde would yell to us to hold with our oars. And we would dip our oars into the water, holding for all we were worth.

There was a moment when we could not hold against the push of a great wave, and then we suddenly found ourselves hurled into the channel, grazing the rocks as we came in, enveloped in clouds of foam, in danger of being dashed to pieces.

All around us the sea was white; in contrast, farther out it all looked completely black now. The waves dashed up over the rocks with such force that as the foam fell back in white flakes like liquid snow it soaked us to the bone. The more we advanced into the channel, the smoother was the sea; the green water, almost immobile, was covered with silver scrollwork.

Once we saw we were safe, we looked around with satisfaction. Zelayeta took a position in the bow with the boat hook in hand, and with Recalde and I sometimes rowing and sometimes pushing off from the rocks, the boat advanced slowly. All of a sudden, Zelayeta shouted, while he pressed down with the boat hook: "Hey! Stop!"

"What's the matter?"

"We have to stop. We're losing depth."

Our boat was scraping bottom. We halted some twenty paces from the schooner. I could see a brace of rope hanging from the poop. I leaped from rock to rock and began to scale the "Stella Maris" hand over hand.

As I climbed over the side, a flock of birds and seagulls rose on the wing and frightened me so much that I almost fell back into the sea. Some of the birds whirled above me with shrill screams and seemed about to attack me with their beaks. But I defended myself with the length of rope and drove them off.

"What happened?" yelled Recalde.

"Nothing," I answered. "It's only birds. You can come on up."

"Throw down the rope."

I threw the rope down, and they tied the "Cachalote" to it.

Then, leaping as I had done, from rock to rock, they finally got aboard.

We took solemn possession of the "Stella Maris." It was a shame that we did not have the cannon from the riverside cave with us to mark our first conquest with a cannonade of salvoes.

Next we started a search of the ship. The "Stella Maris" was down by the bow and raised in the air aft. The decks were all rent from the fall of the masts and tackle. The part that stood clear of the water was heaped with bird excrement, seagull bones, and feathers; near the bow, which was warped, undone, and soaked by the tide, the ship's boards were covered with seaweed and rockweed and as slippery as a greased pole.

The damp and the sun were beginning to open up the wood joints and cause the caulking to run; all the iron work and the iron rings were eaten with rust. The ship's wheel still spun about, creaking. It was impossible to find anything that was not crumbling, and cords of rope were rotting where they were coiled.

Recalde forced open the hatchway on the poop and disappeared within.

"Can you walk around down there?" we asked.

"Yes. There's a lot of water, but I can walk around."

The three of us descended and rummaged through the master cabin, the pantry, and the hold, all of which were flooded. We discovered nothing. Zelayeta found a prayer book, in French, printed at Quimper, and he kept it.

The excitement and the exercise had given us an appetite. We took out the bread and cheese and seated on the poop, devoured it all.

After we ate we discussed our plans for the afternoon and decided to go to Frayburu and explore it. From the sea, on the sheltered side, this great rock has a different aspect than that presented toward land: it has a small beach bordered by underbrush growing from between the rocks.

The weather was clearing, and as the tide was beginning to rise, the waves, green and lapping, gradually covered the rocks and came closer around us. The water was coming in through the openings in the prow of the "Stella Maris," and it ran along the incline of the deck and fell back with a soft murmur. Occasionally, the violent slap of a wave would shake the whole ship, and the iron work and the iron rings, the wheel and the gunwales would grate out a kind of bad-humored protest.

"Will we be able to get away without going through the channel we used to get here?" I asked.

"In this high tide it will be a lot easier," answered Recalde.

At this moment there was a sudden unexpected crackling sound.

"What is it?" we asked each other.

It was impossible for us to comprehend what had happened.

XIII. THE IZARRA GROTTO

We peered over the side of the "Stella Maris." The "Cachalote" had sunk, tied to its line. Doubtless it had smacked sharply against a rock and opened a hole. What were we to do? How could we get back to Lúzaro?

Zelayeta proposed climbing what remained of the tallest mast and trying to summon aid by attracting the attention of any fishing launch that chanced to pass, but this was a slow and ineffective solution. And then, this procedure must have struck Recalde as rather humiliating, for he announced grimly that we must raise our boat.

Between the three of us, pulling on the line to which the boat was tied, we succeeded in raising the submerged craft. But we lacked the strength to raise it all the way to the deck of the "Stella Maris" and instead hauled it around to the side away from the waves, between the schooner and Frayburu.

The boat was now sustained by the tightened line, though it was still half submerged in the water. Recalde took off his clothes, let himself down a rope until he found footing on the rocks, and while he pushed, Zelayeta and I pulled, and gradually we got the boat above the water.

The "Cachalote" had a rent in its ribs about eight inches long.

"Throw me some lengths of rope," Recalde called.

We threw him all the rope we could find, and he kept stuffing it into the aperture until he had it completely closed up. As the ropes were impregnated with tar they served very well. Once the hole was filled, Recalde called: "Throw me down my clothes."

We threw down his clothes, and he slowly dressed.

"This boat won't hold more than two," he announced; "one to row and the other to bail and to watch that the hole doesn't open up. We'll come back for the one that stays. . . Which of you is coming?"

"You decide," Zelayeta answered, without much enthusiasm.

"All right. Shanti, you come. Where's the bailing scoop?"

"It should be in the boat; unless it's gone into the water," I told him.

"Without the scoop we can't do anything," murmured Recalde.

We looked about for it and saw it floating a short distance away.

"Come on down," Recalde said to me.

I slid down, somewhat overcome by excitement. The possibility of going down into the great black depths of which Yurrumendi spoke was beginning to loom large and ominous. I could see myself like the sailor from the "Stella Maris" whom the sea had tossed up under the cliff, with his face gone and a hand missing.

"You row until we get past the rocks," Recalde told me. "I'll steer."

I began to row; I watched the bottom of the boat, which was filling with water, in terror. Recalde steered; the tide was at full; we passed over the reefs without the slightest trouble. Leaving Frayburu to one side we headed for Izarra.

As we came out from among the rocks, where the waves broke, we changed places.

"Now I'll row," Recalde said; "don't you do anything but bail."

It was high time, for the boat was filling with water; our feet and pants were already wet. I set to work with the bailing scoop, and, working furiously, I succeeded in lowering the water level in the boat.

We planned to double Mount Izarra and land at Lighthouse Point. When Recalde got tired rowing I took his place. I did not want to look toward the land and find out the distance which lay between us. Besides, we were now in front of the grotto of Izarra, of which Yurrumendi had spoken so often and so vividly, and we felt a certain tremor.

When we changed places the next time, something happened: I do not know what we did; the plug in the hole must have shifted, and the boat began to fill up again. Recalde bent down and worked to close the opening, but he could not. I stopped rowing.

"Give me your handkerchief," he yelled.

I gave him my handkerchief.

"Give me your beret."

I gave him my beret, and meanwhile I began bailing, and tried not to think of our desperate situation. Recalde would plug up the hole on one side, and then it would open up on the other. He was sweating, without getting any results.

"Do you know how to swim?" he asked me, beginning to get scared.

"Very little," I answered, with a sinister stoicism.

Recalde persisted in his efforts, and at length succeeded in preventing the boat's sinking further. We were some two hundred yards now from the Izarra grotto.

"We'll have to head straight for the cave!" I said.

"The cave! What for?" asked Recalde in astonishment.

"We have to. There's no choice. If we don't, the 'Cachalote' will open up on us before we get to Lighthouse Point."

"Yes, you're right. Let's head for Izarra."

Once again, I commenced to row, slowly, carefully, making the least movement possible, so that the plug would not be dislodged. I stared at Recalde, and Recalde stared at the enormous hole in Mount Izarra, which kept increasing in size as we approached.

I could see the terror reflected in the eyes of my companion. Before us the chasm opened its great spume-filled mouth. I forced myself to speak quietly to Recalde and to try to convince him that all the phantasmagoria associated with the cavern was something to frighten children.

But when I myself turned around, I was shaken at the sight. The grotto looked like the door to an immense cathedral, an irregular cathedral built up out of the water. Two great slab-rocks of slate stood at either side of the entrance. We continued to approach, and our stupefaction increased.

We skirted the large rocks that seemed like weird, fantastic sentinels at the entrance to the cave. Recalde, basically much more superstitious than I, tried not to look. When I urged him to look around the interior he answered rudely: "Leave me alone!"

As I gazed at this natural setting I began to lose my fear, and I looked about me with redoubled curiosity. The moment of our actual entrance was a solemn one. The inside of that black grot was white; it looked as if the bones of a megathere, long extinct and big as a mountain, had been stored in that cavity, for some of the rocks had the shapes of tibias and metacarpuses, of vertebraes and sphenoids; others resembled solitary spires, obelisks, chimneys, pedestals upon which rested the profiles of a man or a bird; still others, hollowed and fretted, looked like a kind of stone lace formed by the sea.

As the clouds scudded across the sky, darkening or lightening the mouth of the cave, they changed the shapes of things inside. It was a scene from a nightmare, or from feverish delirium. The sea boiled up in the interior of that black hole and the waves detonated like cannon shots, causing the entrails of the mountain to quiver and shake. Recalde was terrified, his face white.

"It's the door to Hell," he muttered in Basque, in a low voice, and he crossed himself several times.

I told him not to be afraid, that nothing would happen to us. He stared at me, astonished at my calmness.

"What shall we do?" he murmured.

"There must be some place to tie up, don't you think?" I said.

The walls of the cavern, up to a considerable height, were all smooth. Recalde, who was gazing at them in desperation, suddenly discovered a kind of platform which ran along like a ledge, forming a cornice, some ten feet above the water.

We rowed under it.

"Let's see if you can jump up there when we get close enough," Recalde said.

It was impossible; there was no projection to take hold of or step on, and meanwhile the boat moved about.

"Suppose we dropped anchor?" my companion said.

"What for? It must be terribly deep here," I said.

I was remembering the tales of Yurrumendi.

"What'll we do, then? Shall we leave this hole?" he asked.

Recalde was ready to leave.

"Throw the anchor up there, let's see if it will hold," I said, pointing to the balcony-like ledge.

We made the attempt, and on the third try one of the hooks caught among the rocks. I climbed up to the platform with the aid of the rope, and then Recalde followed. We unhooked the anchor, in case we needed to use the rope again, and then we sat down to rest and think.

We were on a ledge of coral-like rock, filled with holes and covered with barnacles, which sloped down gradually towards the interior of the cave. Some paces further in, a tree trunk lay alongside the outside border of the ledge, and this caused me to believe that the cornice had been used before as a path and therefore must lead somewhere. The "Cachalote," abandoned now, filled up with water and was already beginning to sink to the bottom of the grotto; suddenly it hit up against a jagged rock and went down quickly.

I walked ahead for a few yards.

The tree trunk, then a line of tree trunks, rotting and worm-eaten, bordered the cornice all along the edge.

"Let's see if there's a way out along here," I said.

"Let's go," said Recalde nervously.

In sober truth, if we were not to find a way out, our situation, instead of improving, had considerably worsened. We advanced with caution, feeling for each step; at first we could see well enough, but then the darkness became more intense. The waves swept in, making everything tremble; they roared furiously, with a hoarse voice amid the darkness, and the sea din seemed like some infernal uproar of lamentations and clamor.

After some thirty or forty paces in the darkness, we commenced to sense a pallid clarity somewhere in front of us. Then, in this uncertain light, we began to make out the sharp pyramids of the rocks, the white stalactites hanging from the ceiling, and, down below, the sea, boiling up in foam so that it looked like an agglomeration of silver monsters revolving in a whirlpool. It was really extraordinary. The collisions of the waves made the rocks tremble, and the noise of it all rebounded and reverberated in all the holes and passages of the grotto.

"Look, look," I said to Recalde.

My friend tremulously murmured:

"Shanti, let's go back."

"No, no," I answered. "There must be an opening up front from where that light is coming."

The tree trunks bordering the cornice indicated that someone in the past had used this way. We continued to advance and soon emerged beneath a slanting chimney formed between two slabs of slate. The outlined remains of a flight of steps could be made out. Recalde, who was more agile than I, scaled the steps to the top, and I followed, using the rope which Recalde let down.

We found ourselves among the rocks of Izarra. Only a few yards away was the cliff road. Recalde confessed that he had experienced some moments of awful fear in that cursed hole. I tried to convince him that there was nothing out of the ordinary in there, nothing beyond the play of light and shadow.

The tree-trunk border on the cornice must have meant that illegal arms shipments or smuggling activity had been carried on there in former times.

We descended Izarra and came out between the rocks to Lighthouse Point. Recalde knew that in a small anchorage among the rocks of the promontory where the tower stood there was usually a small boat used by the lighthouse-keeper for fishing; we looked for the opening and found the boat, but it was chained.

We went up to the lighthouse and called, and an old woman came out and told us that the lighthouse-keeper had gone to Elguea. The person who had the key to the lock on the chain on the boat, however, was a man who lived in the first house as one entered Izarte.

"That man should be on the beach at this hour. If you walk along the sand, you'll probably find him."

We went along the sand of what is known as the Beach of Souls. The first man we encountered was tall, red-faced, and wore short side-whiskers. We explained to him what we were after, but he did not seem to understand us.

This man led us down the beach for a little way, to where an older man and a girl were sitting. We once more explained our situation, and the second man stood up and took the tall man aside and spoke to him. Then the two men, the girl, Recalde, and myself walked back to the small anchorage at Lighthouse Point; the man released the chain which held the boat, and then he and the tall man got aboard.

We started to get in, too, but the older man said:

"You two wait here."

The older man took his place by the rudder, the tall man hoisted the sail, and the launch set out toward Frayburu at a good speed. An hour later they were back bringing Zelayeta with them.

The older man asked us our names, and when I told him mine he gazed at me fixedly.

We three adventurers, reunited again, returned to Lúzaro, weary and crestfallen.

At home, I was unable to conceal anything. I had to tell it all. My mother and La Iñure kept crossing themselves.

"What a boy! What a boy!" the two of them repeated.

From that day on, Joshe Mari Recalde began to treat me with special consideration. The fact that I had not been as frightened as he in the Izarra cave doubtless seemed to him a mark of great superiority.

"Don't you believe it," he used to say to our fellow students. "You wouldn't think so, but Shanti is very brave."

Oftentimes, after all these years, I dream that I am entering the Izarra cave aboard the "Cachalote" and that I cannot find any place to land, and the thought of it gives me such a fright that I wake up trembling and bathed in sweat.

I. MY FIRST VOYAGES

Our adventure resounded through Lúzaro. Everyone knew of it, and we had to pay Zapiain, the watchmaker and commercial traveler, for the lost "Cachalote."

For us it was nothing to be ashamed of; all the other boys admired us. I recounted my sensations in the Izarra cave with a thousand variations and pointed out that there was nothing miraculous inside, beyond traces of contrabandists who had passed that way.

My grandmother and my mother apparently did not want to give me the chance to get conceited from all this popular interest, and, after the examinations at the Nautical School, they put me in the hands of Don Ciriaco Andonaegui, captain of a frigate in the trade between Cádiz and the Philippines.

Don Ciriaco had begun his career at sea in a similar manner, under the aegis of my grandfather, and it was only right that he should do for me what a member of my family had done for him.

My grandmother and Don Ciriaco decided to send me to sea as a first supernumerary. After the voyage of initiation I would accompany Don Ciriaco on the run between Cádiz and the Philippines; then, after this voyage—which would last a year, or a year and a half—I would go to San Fernando to conclude my nautical studies.

My trip as supernumerary was made between Liverpool and Havana, in the brigantine "Caridad," under Captain Urdampilleta. The voyage lasted more than two months, for we did not take the direct route, but dropped down to the Canaries and from there set out for the West Indies.

From Cuba we returned to Manchester, and from Manchester went to Cádiz.

Aboard that brigantine I spent a terrible apprenticeship. There was never enough to eat, nor was it possible to sleep or to change one's clothes. On the other hand, when the weather was good, it was a delight to be at sea; we played cards and spun tales of witches and pirates. The seamen, nearly all of them Basque, got along well and there were no squabbles.

On my return from this trip, I embarked with Don Ciriaco at Cádiz, on board the "Bella Vizcaína." This frigate seemed like a salon to me, so clean and neat was everything.

Like his ship, Don Ciriaco was also very well turned out and handsome. He almost always wore a straw hat and a white suit. He spoke with an accent between Basque and Andalusian, with an admixture of Philippine words. An old-fashioned mariner, he knew his run superbly, but had only slight knowledge about anything else. But still, he had studied in Vergara, and he knew three things infrequently known among merchant mariners: Latin, how to dance, and how to make verses. He liked social life and the city.

Don Ciriaco wanted to complete my education, and on various occasions he asked me if I felt no inclination toward poetry, or no taste for dancing; but apparently my aptitudes did not lead along this road.

We set out from Cádiz. The idea of opening up the isthmus of Suez had not yet been thought of, and the voyage to the Philippines was made via the Cape of Good Hope. We sailed down the coast of Africa looking for the trade winds, traversed the equatorial calms, and made a halt at Cape Verde. Then we continued south, until we found the winds from the west and were able to skirt the calms of the Tropic of Capricorn. We doubled the Cape and proceeded by making a great circuit of the Indian Ocean toward the Sunda Strait.

I spent my first Christmas Eve aboard ship in the Indian Ocean. The afternoon had been suffocating. By day the sea had been like an immobile plain of sun-fused crystal, but the night was splendid, thick with glittering stars.

The majority of the crew was Chinese, and they did not celebrate this day. But we Spanish—Basques and Andalusians—drank and sang until the night was well advanced.

Once the Sunda Strait was traversed, we were very near our goal. We had made the trip in only five months, and inasmuch as this represented in those days a navigational triumph for Don Ciriaco, we entered Manila Bay shooting off fireworks.

The days spent in Manila sped by; everything was new and filled with interest. I was young and had no cause to be anything but happy.

We left the Philippines in March, and instead of returning through the Sunda Strait we sailed before the southwest monsoon until we entered the Molucca Sea and then proceeded through the Strait of Gilolo, Pitt's Pass, and the Strait of Ombai.

From there we set our course so as to reach the region of the trade winds as quickly as possible; we expected to pick up these winds toward latitudes 18° or 20°, but we had no luck.

As soon as we had rounded the Cape of Good Hope we were forced to battle a violent storm that nearly dragged us to the shoals off the continent of Africa, and throughout the rest of the voyage we ran into squalls and foul weather.

When I stepped ashore at Cádiz, I felt the most profound pleasure. I would have liked to have gone on to Lúzaro, but the nautical course was about to begin, and Don Ciriaco was of the opinion that not a single day of class should be missed. The captain introduced me at the San Fernando school and then took me to the house of a woman, a friend of his in that city, where I might board.

I would graduate from the San Fernando school a first mate, next I would make a couple of sea voyages, and then Don Ciriaco would retire, leaving me his command of the "Bella Vizcaína."

II. THE HISTORY OF THE "BELLA VIZCAÍNA"

On the first Saturday of the course, in the afternoon, Don Ciriaco appeared at my house in the town of San Fernando and said to me: "Come sleep on board. Tomorrow we have to go into Cádiz. I'm going to present you at the home of the Cepeda family. Wear your new suit."

Don Matías Cepeda was the leading partner of the Basque-Andalusian shipping company, Cepeda and Associates, proprietors of the frigate commanded by Don Ciriaco, and of many other ships as well.

We went to the ship, I slept in my cabin, and the next morning I was awakened by two knocks on my door.

"Eh, Shanti!" Don Ciriaco called. "It's time to get up. You sleep like a baby."

I got up and dressed, grooming myself as best I could. A group of sailors in Sunday dress were waiting for us in the ship's launch; Don Ciriaco and I got in the craft, and it headed for Cádiz. En route, the captain explained to me in Basque that the principal object of our visit was to meet the wife of Cepeda, a countrywoman of ours, who had first been married to Fermín Menchada and was married now to Don Matías Cepeda, warehouseman and originally partner of the first husband.

We landed on the dock, passed La Puerta del Mar, and went along a street which ran under the city walls. We were near the

Customs House when Don Ciriaco stopped in front of a large house with bay windows.

"This is it," he said.

We entered through a very high-roofed hallway, paved with marble. We crossed it and the captain knocked at a door. A servant opened the grate in the door and then passed us on to a courtyard. It was roofed with glass, and there was an arcade to separate it from the corridors; all the floors were of marble.

Preceded by the servant, we climbed a monumental flight of stairs, and, after walking the length of a corridor, arrived in an immense salon, hung with great mirrors and medallions.

We waited briefly, and the lady of the house appeared. Her name was Doña Hortensia; she was an opulent woman, and extremely beautiful.

She received us with great amiability. Don Ciriaco was very courtly in his treatment of her. In truth the old sea captain was a man of the salon. Exaggerating here and there, Don Ciriaco spoke to Doña Hortensia about my family, of our manorial house in Lúzaro, of my ancestors. . . When she heard the details of our illustrious lineage, the amiability of the beautiful lady increased. Doña Hortensia displayed a weakness for the pre-eminences of nobility. And then it turned out that, as is not so rare among Basques, we had a surname in common.

"We must be related," she said.

"That's very possible," I replied.

"Well then, if we are somehow related, don't be shocked if I address you familiarly, for you seem no more than a boy, in any case."

I was confused and embarrassed, but I managed to say that I was happy at this demonstration of confidence on her part.

We were still conversing when Doña Hortensia's daughter, Dolorcitas, a girl of fourteen or fifteen, a lovely thing, entered the room accompanied by an old serving-maid. Don Ciriaco acted like an ancient gallant from the court of Versailles with her. Dolorcitas resembled her mother, only she was smaller of stature, with blacker eyes and darker skin. There was great mobility in her expression, and she was very graceful and bright in her speech.

Need I say that in her presence I was utterly torpid, uneasy, embarrassed, a complete fool? No, it is not necessary. I was at the age of the goose, I had never dealt with women before, and I was by nature timid.

Doña Hortensia told the manservant:

"Tell the master that we are waiting lunch for him."

Half an hour later, Don Matías Cepeda appeared, and I was introduced to him. Señor Cepeda was scarcely a sympathetic figure, far from it; he had a hard face, protruding cheekbones, a flat nose, narrow forehead, and a short, bristly mustache.

Señor Cepeda was very attentive with Don Ciriaco, and even made the attempt to be witty. He did not look at me. In the eyes of Don Matías, not to be fifty years old was no doubt a form of impertinence. He addressed only one phrase to me, and this phrase made me smart. "Be careful," he told me, "because here, in Cádiz, they're going to make a fool of you."

After lunch, Don Matías and Don Ciriaco withdrew to talk business, and Doña Hortensia and Dolorcitas were inspired to show me the house. It was something that flattered their vanity.

The house was enormous, a veritable delirium of grandeur. Imagination had been allowed to run riot: the floor was of marble, the halls were vast, the ceilings painted with historical scenes; the bay windows were as wide and spacious as if they had been added rooms. Mirrors spread the full length of walls, and the corridors were lined with statues and alabaster fountains. At that time I had still not seen anything of the world, and did not know the difference between luxurious ostentation and good taste, and so I marveled and was impressed.

After going through the house, we ascended to the roof and stood contemplating the bay of Cádiz, inundated with sunlight and filled with frigates, brigantines, and schooners. Dolorcitas brought a telescope and we looked through it at Puerto de Santa María, Rota, and Puerto Real. I related, as best I could, my voyage with Don Ciriaco. Then several girl friends of Dolorcitas appeared. I remained talking with Doña Hortensia, who was very amiable with me.

At midafternoon, Don Ciriaco called me.

"Let's go, Shanti."

The mistress of the house observed to me that I had a permanent invitation to dine with them every Sunday and holiday. If I did not appear, she would inquire after me and see to it that I was brought to the house by force.

I took my leave of everyone and went off with Don Ciriaco in a glow of enthusiasm for my new friends. The old captain took me to a sea-food restaurant on the same street with the Customs House. He summoned the owner, a fellow highlander and friend of his, and ordered a selected menu, a meal for people who understand the transcendental nature of devouring food. The owner of the restaurant and Don Ciriaco discussed the various plates, the sauces, and the wines in great detail.

"I need an hour to prepare all this," the highlander said.

"Very well," said the captain. "We'll give you an hour."

"You have time to take a turn, if you like."

"No, no. What for? Bring us a bottle of Sanlúcar manzanilla and some olives."

The two of us drank; and then Don Ciriaco said:

"Look, my boy, I've introduced you to Hortensia and Don Matías because they might be of use to you."

"Thank you very much!" I responded.

"Wait a bit. You've got to stay here a year; you don't know anybody, and in case of necessity it's just as well that you have someone to whom you can turn; but first I'm going to tell you the history of Hortensia, so that you'll know what to go by."

"What the devil! Has she got a history?"

"You'll see. Hortensia is Biscayan, from a town near Bilbao. Her father was a man known as 'the Greek.' Probably that's what he was; some adventurer who came to town and got married there. The young Hortensia had pretensions, for she was very beautiful, and did not want to marry just anybody. At this point, a friend of mine, Fermín Menchada, a ship's captain who had set up as a merchant in Cádiz, came to town, where his father, who had been skipper of a launch, had just died. Menchada saw Hortensia and fell in love with her. He was not ready or disposed to get married, nor was he disposed to give up Hortensia. He showered her with gifts and jewels. She said no to everything. She would either be his wife or nothing. Menchada promised to make her his wife, and Hortensia yielded. The day of the marriage, Menchada, who was a changeable man, fled town and left Hortensia pregnant.

"Finding herself abandoned, the girl, who was not at all timid, sold the jewels her lover had given her and soon presented herself in Cádiz with her daughter. Menchada was in the Philippines; Hortensia went to the Philippines; she found Menchada, and forced him to marry her.

"Menchada was a hot-headed man, very daring, had inspired ideas and was capable of doing good things and bad. But he was not mature; he upheld, as if it were an article of faith, that simple-minded belief that women must not be taken seriously. It's an old man that tells you this, Shanti, an old bachelor who has adored women, but you must never believe anything women tell you or anything that people tell you about women. And don't ever think that a woman, just because she is a woman, is weak or timid or of slight intelligence. The sex of a person is a very general and vague indicator of what they are, and the variations are infinite. If you want to know what a woman is like, the first thing is to avoid falling in love with her; then, study her with tranquility, and when you get to know her well . . . then you'll find that she no longer means anything at all to you."

"I'll attempt to follow your advice."

"If you can, my boy, if you can. . . Well, as I was saying, despite the fact that Menchada could have easily seen for himself that Hortensia was a woman of character, he did not, or would not, see it. Menchada had allied himself with this Don Matías Cepeda whom you met; a strange association from the point of view of affinities, for Menchada was a daring man, full of initiative, and Cepeda, on the other hand, was the vulgar and ordinary type of apprehensive merchant who goes along in a routine way on the basis of hard security. Cepeda is an Asturian who came here with nothing in his pockets and today he has a great fortune."

"That's not something a fool could do, Don Ciriaco."

"But, do you know what it was about Cepeda that made his fortune?"

"No."

"Well, it was his physique, nothing more."

"His physique? That's very funny."

"Yes, his physique. You'll say that he's no Adonis; but ugliness in a man is almost never an obstacle. Cepeda arrived in Cádiz, straight from his Asturian mountains, and took a job as an employee in a large sugar, coffee, and cocoa warehouse on Customs House Street; then he married the woman who owned it, and she, on her death, left him sole heir, a wealthy widower.

"Cepeda was by nature timorous with his money. Menchada pushed him into ventures, and the two of them made millions. One complemented the other. Menchada was the man of initiative, who thought up the projects and was full of enthusiasm; Cepeda settled the details and the practical difficulties.

"As soon as Menchada established himself in Cádiz, he set up a house for a girl from Puerto Real, and had the nerve to parade around with her in a coach and make her presents of clothing and jewels.

"It was then that the talk went around that Hortensia had begun an affair with her husband's partner, Cepeda. I never believed it. Menchada was, as I've told you, a hot-head, almost a madman, and when he heard that his wife was deceiving him, he fell in love with her all over again. Menchada was already well along in years. He was probably fifty, and a fifty-year-old man in love is like a runaway coach horse. Menchada abandoned the girl from Puerto Real and began to keep watch over his wife.

"She had been deeply hurt; he, jealous and gloomy, did not choose to ask for explanations or admit his own fault, considering any inquiry or any admission of guilt beneath his dignity. A word in time could have reconciled husband and wife; but neither one of them would speak the word. The hostility and tension between them continued to grow, until they were eating separately, and never seeing each other or addressing each other at all.

"About this time, a frigate being built for the Basque-Andalusian Company in Portsmouth was nearly ready—only the finishing touches remained. Menchada went to England to bring her back. I don't know whether or not you are aware that when a new ship is built, a book, or logbook, is made up and handed over by the builder to the first officer who commands the ship."

"Yes, I know about this log; everything pertaining to its construction and all the remarks about its characteristic peculiarities are noted down."

"Exactly. Well, when they handed over this log to Menchada and he read the name of the ship, he nearly had an attack."

"The devil! What was the name of the vessel?"

" 'Bella Vizcaína.' The beautiful Biscayan."

"Our ship?"

"The very same, the very same. And then someone thought they noticed that the siren carved as figurehead on the bow had the features of the lovely Hortensia!"

"Bah!"

"Fantasies of the imagination. Menchada grew more gloomy than ever. It was scarcely possible that Cepeda could have been the one to think of mortifying his partner by naming the ship in this deliberately underhanded fashion. The initial idea had surely come from her.

"The situation between husband and wife did not get any better, until one day, Menchada, playing with some pistols, solved the problem, no one knows whether accidentally or intentionally, by putting a bullet through his forehead and falling dead.

"Within the year, Hortensia celebrated her marriage to Don Matías Cepeda; they bought the house on Customs House Street and made it over.

"Eternal themes," Don Ciriaco concluded philosophically, "and eternal solutions, and these things have happened in the past, they happen in the present, and will happen in the future. I have told you the history of Hortensia so that you would know what kind of woman she is, and so that you won't unwittingly say something in front of her that would be embarrassing or untactful."

We both made our comments on the story of Hortensia, and soon we were doing honors to the supper, which was superb.

Don Ciriaco planned to weigh anchor the next day; I wanted to accompany him to the ship, but he would not hear of it.

"You go to San Fernando and study," he said. "It won't be long before you'll be the one to go and I'll be the one to stay. Goodbye, Shanti!"

"Goodbye."

We embraced, and then he got into his ship's tender and disappeared.

III. DOLORS OF VANITY

The following Sunday morning I walked through the streets of Cádiz on my way to Doña Hortensia's house. My heart was in my mouth, for I was afraid they would receive me coldly or even badly; but no: my countrywoman and her daughter Dolorcitas met me with the greatest demonstrations of friendliness. They were getting ready to go to mass, and I accompanied them to a nearby church. On the return trip we took a stroll through the Calle Ancha and the Plaza de Mina and then walked to their house.

The meeting with Don Matías occupied my mind. His stupid insinuation that I would be made a fool of in Cádiz made me feel uneasy. He was very suspicious and mistrustful, like all timorous men, and he was always on his guard, finding cause for offense on all sides.

Don Matías at length put in an appearance, and, sure enough, he received me coldly and even made a show of treating me as someone of no importance. "This insignificant youth does not exist as far as I am concerned," seemed to be what this gentleman wanted to make clear.

Though not in a too obvious manner, Don Matías was clearly my adversary. He pretended not to notice me because of my insignificance; but, beneath his air of indifference, I sensed his hostility. He had the advantage over me of speaking Castilian well, and he made use of this ability to humiliate me. It is a stupid and vile idea, very frequent in Spain, to believe that one demonstrates superiority by mocking some innocent and in-genuous person, especially through the use of phrases loaded

with double meaning, phrases which can only astound whoever does not understand their implication. This was the method
chosen by Don Matías to demonstrate his superiority.

For my part, whenever I fell into one of these stupid snares
laid by Don Matías, I would grow thoroughly confused, and
this would serve as the signal for the merchant to roar with
laughter. This reaction increased my confusion and anger, and
I would gaze about me with a look which included everyone
from the master of the house to his servants in the category of
enemies who were trying to humiliate me. It is absurd and
ridiculous that one should suffer in this way, when one is
young, as a consequence of someone's unimportant stupidities.

Don Matías and I were like types belonging to opposing races.
He must have sensed in me a lack of sufficient respect, and the
fact that I might allow myself to hold an opinion of any kind
drove him into a rage which was mixed with astonishment. All
this could only seem comic to me now. Señor Cepeda was unable
to reason, to think freely; he could not count on a sufficient
number of ideas to make comparisons and obtain his own individual judgements; the truth is that this is the dilemma of most
people. In order to make up for this lack of ideas, Don Matías
would take refuge in anecdotes. In his head, each rough primitive idea carried with it, as if screwed on, a whole series of tales
and jokes.

"That's not the way it is," he would say, for example, if I ventured any opinion whatever, "and I'll answer you with the
statement made by Periquito Sánchez to Don Juan Martínez
in Cádiz in the year 27. . ." And Don Matías would go on and
on, with the speed of a tortoise, until he had finished telling
some crushingly vulgar anecdote.

Being a man of little natural delicacy and of rudimentary culture he was scarcely, to say the least, a model of discretion; and
he often had outbursts of boorish wit which pleased him im-
mensely. Basically, he was surprised that he had come so far;
he made an effort to convince himself that his wealth, which was
the result of a fortunate marriage plus a little luck, and nothing
more, was really the work of his genius and perseverance.

Don Matías was the archetype of the good bourgeois, the good
middle-class burgher: he was brutal, a slave to routine, indelicate,
and, in his heart, immoral. All routine seemed to him holy, and
precedent was the best of all reasons. Don Matías also had his
peculiar manias; for example, he was always late for meals, so
that he might thus demonstrate that his many labors did not allow him to be punctual.

Don Matías made a habit of staying on in his office, wearing
a cap and a bathrobe, when he was not walking about his warehouse, between the aisles of sacks and boxes, giving out orders
or strolling with his hands behind his back. The chief clerk,
a gossipy chap from Jerez who knew Cepeda well, used to
say that his employer spent his time cutting up paper for the
toilet or sharpening pencils as slowly as possible so that he might
appear as a continually busy person in the eyes of his family. Even
in these habits he proved himself niggardly, for he gave a very
short point to the pencils and he cut the paper very small.
Miserly in everything, he was a man of ostentatious generosity
in regard to his house and the beautiful Hortensia. He had the
rich merchant's feeling that a wife is the best means of making
a display.

In appearance, Don Matías was a man of the utmost respectability, serious, and full of profound ideas; in all truth, he was a
poor fool, a grotesque example of presumption and vanity. He
treated Dolorcitas very curtly, not because she was his step-
daughter but simply because he considered this to be the proper
role and attitude for a man of affairs. This solemn and majestic
idiot thought that to be a husband and father in the English
fashion, which was his aim, it was necessary for him to act coldly
toward his wife and daughter.

The Anglomaniac tendency which has developed in some of
the cities of Andalusia is something that escapes my understanding. The English themselves, who are in general stiff and formal,
reap the advantages to be found from stiffness and formality;
but those Anglomaniacs of the Spanish South, with their mixture
of stiffness and Mediterranean effusion, strike me as simply
comic.

Dolorcitas, as was only natural, felt no great affection for her
stepfather. Don Matías had promised on several occasions to
take her to the theater, and then, doubtless to demonstrate his
authority, pretended as if he had forgotten the promises and
left the girl in tears.

Every Sunday, after midday dinner, Don Matías—in his frock
coat, his gloves, his top hat, and his boots, which always squeaked
—marched off to the Moderate Casino, and did not return until
nightfall. Doña Hortensia, Dolorcitas, and I would remain sitting around the table after the meal. And later, Dolorcitas and I
would play like two boys, running through the house, climbing
up to the flat roof, and gazing out to sea from the observatory.

Señora Presentación, an old woman full of good humor and
gesticulations whose every word I failed to understand, was the

one who usually came to announce to Dolorcitas that one of her friends had just arrived.

Whenever Dolorcitas was visited by one of her girl friends, the game was up for me: I no longer played, and instead they played with me. I can remember my conversations with Dolores and with a friend of hers by the name of María Jesús; the spectacle must have looked like a game between a bear and two little monkeys.

The girl friends would tell each other their affairs, both talking at the same time, chattering at a dizzy speed; I, on the other hand, proceeded in the manner of a barge loaded to the gunwales. I never have been able to speak Castilian with any rapidity, and at that time I spoke it even more haltingly. Besides, as a good Basque, I have always been somewhat disrespectful in my treatment of that respectable and honest lady called Grammar. The two girls would chat along, to the accompaniment of a hundred expressive gestures and monkeyshines. Though she was the daughter of Basques, Dolorcitas was as voluble and witty as a native of Cádiz.

After the arrival of María Jesús, who was usually the first to appear, there would be a stream of other friends, boys and girls of the same age. And then I would sink into complete muteness. What was the use of talking, if for each word of mine they uttered ten or twelve?

There is a saying that a new language is a new soul, and there is some truth in this. For I understood, whenever I listened to these youths, that I not only did not know Castilian, but that my soul was different from theirs. I felt myself to be some other kind of being, but I did not have the courage or the will to believe that my spirit, uncommunicative and more somber, was worth as much as theirs, all expansiveness, words, and grimaces. My humility made me think of myself as a savage among the civilized.

My timidity caused me to pass some horrible moments; a word, a gesture, any little thing, was enough to send the blood rushing to my face. Dolorcitas would smile at my confusion. She would see that I was suffering and she would be pleased: it was the natural cruelty of a woman.

Later, she was not content with the pleasure to be gotten from confusing me and also liked to make me jealous. I was enamored of her. Enamored? I do not really know if I was enamored, but I do know that I thought of Dolorcitas at all hours, with a mixture of anguish and wrath.

If she had merely spoken to one youth on one day and to an-

other on another day without paying any attention to me,
perhaps I would not have minded; but I felt her carrying on
her coquetries for my benefit, with the express intention of mortifying me, and this incited me. In general, love consists precisely
in this jealousy, especially among young people, who have no
spiritual development; it is an instinct closer to cruelty and hate
than to calm affection.

Fleeing sometimes from the coquetry and the humiliating
disdain of Dolorcitas, I would pretend to have some other engagement or work to do and would abruptly quit the house.
What consuming anger! What heavy weariness! What bitterness!

The sun shone in the deserted streets, the sky was pure blue,
the sea lovely and calm. What was I to do? The whole world
seemed pointless to me. Disgust with myself, the hostility of the
environment, the impossibility of making someone else in my
own image and to my liking: all this fell upon me as heavy as
lead.

More than once it happened that when Dolorcitas saw in me
a determination to walk out of her house and not return, she
treated me with renewed affection. I did not dare to reproach
her openly for her coquettishness, but I did tell her that I well
understood her lack of sympathy toward me, since I was rough
and uncouth; and she answered that she liked me that way.
She liked me that way so she could humiliate me.

Still, on Sunday afternoons we used to go to the mall at
Apodaca, Dolorcitas and some girl friend or other dressed ele-
gantly, and I in my sailor uniform.

We would gaze down over Cádiz Bay, usually intensely blue.
Far off, we could see Rota and Chipiona, their white houses
shining in the sun. Then, the low coast forming a series of reddish beaches as far as Puerto de Santa María, and in the background the mountains of Jerez and Grazalema, turning purple
toward nightfall, and running in a strange silhouetted line
along the horizon.

We would watch some frigate or brigantine entering the bay,
being warped in. As the afternoon wore on, we would head
toward home, walking alongside the city walls, and going
around a point which, if I remember rightly, was called San
Felipe. We walked along the top of the city wall behind the
parapet and saw the batteries of ancient cannons through the
crenels of the battlement. We would delay as long as possible in
walking home. It would be getting dark as we reached the Customs House.

On the white towers of the houses near the wall the sunlight still shone. We would give one last look out over the bay.

The sea, like a blue lake, was scarcely ruffled by the wind. The lights began to appear on the ships, and a line of street lamps outlined the port. The autumn sky, rose and blue without a cloud, would be darkening. The lights of San Fernando were reflected in the water, and the circular sphere of the Cádiz City Hall clock was illuminated and stood out against the pallid sky. Oftentimes from that spot on the wall we would hear the slow bells of the Angelus.

At nightfall I would take the stagecoach from a small plaza nearby and start out for San Fernando, my soul anguished and filled with a strange bitterness.

IV. THE TREE AND THE PINE

I have heard mention of a poem by a German poet—Heinrich Heine, I believe—in which the northern pine longs to be the tropical palm tree.

This symbol could serve to represent my spiritual situation in that far-off epoch when I studied at San Fernando. Today, strangely enough, I am not at all attracted toward the south, and neither am I enthused by palm trees, which are, indubitably, decorative, but which somehow have an artificial aspect.

At the time of which I speak, I was the pine aspiring to be a palm tree. I would have liked to talk fast and with abandon, have known how to tell jokes, and been a Don Juan. I even thought of abandoning the sea and becoming a merchant, or at least an employee.

I no longer thought of desert islands nor of Robinson Crusoe; my ideals had changed. I wanted to be an Andalusian flamenco, a gypsified Andalusian. My ideal was to go into one of those *tiendas de montañés,* part store and part tavern, to eat fried fish and drink white wine and watch a girl with a pale and expressive face, with purple circles under her eyes and skin the color of a brown lizard, dance the flamenco on a table top, to have the pleasure of clapping my palms the whole night long while a dock rat sang a song about his dead *maresita,* his little old mother, and about the *simenterio* where she was buried, to hear a flat-nosed ancient with locks of hair over his ears and his Andalusian hat tilted toward his nose caressing a guitar, to watch a chubby fellow in tight pants moving his buttocks and shaking his rump as he strutted and swaggered, and to join the chorus of the people yelling *Olé!* and *Ay tu mare!* and *Ezo é!* These were my aspirations.

Today, I cannot abide people who play with their vocabulary or their hips. It seems to me that a person who retrieves from words not their significance but their sound is very close to being an idiot, but at that time I did not see the phenomenon in this light. Each age has its own notions.

In those days I would have liked to have been as witty, sententious, and affected as all my acquaintances. I read the novels of Fernán Caballero, which were enjoying great fame; I did not like them at all, but I convinced myself that I should like them. I have read them since, and they have struck me as rather pretty, although of small importance. They gave me the impression of being like a well-decorated room, but a room so tiny and narrow that it is impossible to stretch out one's legs without knocking over something.

I have never understood the enthusiasm developed in Spain during the nineteenth century for trifles and things of no importance. In books, in the theater, in every kind of writing the most insipid, cold, and vapid pettiness and narrowness has been exalted as the unique virtue of man.

In that epoch I was too timid to think along these lines, not because I did not feel that way but because I did not have enough confidence in myself to assert my ideas with determination. I felt a continual dull rage, a frantic indignation, because of my inability to live like the others. I was like the loose wheel of a watch, unmeshed with any other wheel. The truth was that if civilization was what Don Matías Cepeda thought it was—possession of a cocoa and sugar warehouse and of a store of jokes and ready-made phrases—then I was not on the road to becoming civilized. Sometimes I had the urge to kick all these people, for they did me no good, to send Don Matías, his wife, his daughter, and all their girl friends and boy friends to the devil. I did not then understand that I was possessed of a vital exuberance, of a will to action; I did not see that I was dealing with people who were organically and morally emaciated and that I simply needed to do something, to utilize my energy, in short, to live.

I would stand on the city wall and look out over the bay of Cádiz flooded with light, at the somnolent sea, at the distant towns with their white houses, at the blue sierra of Jerez and Grazalema silhouetted against the sky, and contemplating all this splendid decoration I would ask myself: "And all this, what for? In order to live like a miserable rabbit and recite a series of stupid jokes?" It was in all truth very little.

Toward nightfall one Sunday in winter I decided, I do not know why, not to take the stagecoach to San Fernando but to stay on in Cádiz. The docks were enveloped in that Sunday sadness that pervades a sea port. I was not joyous; on the contrary, I felt aggressive and disposed to commit some barbarity.

I went into a tavern and asked for fried fish and white wine. I ate and drank abundantly. These Andalusian taverns sum up the character of the region: they are small, picturesque, and complicated.

I left the tavern and went on to a café on the Calle Ancha, where I had several drinks of liquor; when I walked away from the café I was ready for anything. It was night now, and my steps echoed in streets empty for the dinner hour.

It occurred to me that I had still not drunk enough to be as insolent and bold as I wanted to be, and I sat down at the side-walk table of a tavern in a street so crowded with taverns and barber shops that it seemed as if the people there must pass their lives between the plates of fried fish and the curling irons.

There was a drunken man at the next table, dressed in black, his hat on one side of his head and a red flower in his button-hole. He stood up from his chair and came toward me smiling broadly. I gave him a hard look and asked him angrily: "What's the matter with you? What do you want?"

He smiled stupidly.

"Sailor?" he asked me, using the English word and pointing at me with his finger.

"Yes, a sailor," I replied. "What about it?"

"I am sailor, also," he said. "You Spanish?"

"Yes, Spanish."

"I am Dutch. The two of us sailors . . . the two of us drunk. Good friends."

After saying this and shaking me by the hand, the Dutchman sat down at my table. We drank together. The Dutchman was captain of the corvette "Vertrowen." He was pug-nosed, red-faced, blond, with yellow mustaches which hung down thinly like those of a Chinaman; his black suit, which was of an almost formal cut, was conspicuous in that low tavern.

I constituted myself his defender, and thought that if anyone made fun of him they would have to answer to me and that I would have the right to commit any atrocity.

The two of us got up and started off. At that time in Cádiz, and probably the same thing is true now, there was the custom, especially on holidays, of strolling at night along a certain definite network of streets; these streets were Calle Ancha, Columela, Aranda, San Francisco, and perhaps one or two more. This nocturnal *paseo* was almost in the nature of a procession.

The captain of the "Vertrowen" and I set out along those streets; there was an odor of frying oil everywhere and the smoke of roasted chestnuts. The benches in the plazas were filled with people peacefully taking their ease; some workmen, dressed for Sunday, passed by in coaches, playing the guitar and singing.

The children of the night laughed at us as we passed. We invited some girls of equivocal air to have something with us in the taverns or cafés, but they ran away from us when they saw we were drunk.

Bored and weary, we stumbled into another tavern near Puerta del Mar. That night I was expending my great rage pointlessly.

As we entered the tavern I noticed a dark, evil-faced man who was staring at me in a provocative manner. He looked like a troublemaker. I was happy to have found him; my moment had come. I went up to him and demanded:

"What's the trouble with you? What are you looking at?"

"Me!" he exlaimed taken aback.

"Yes, you; you were staring at me with the face. . ."

"The face of hunger, *señorito*," he interrupted amiably. "In this whole day, there hasn't passed through my body so much as a half-portion of one meal."

His explanation made me both mad and profoundly sad. The man went on to tell me that he was without a job, and his family and children without food. I invited him to have something on me, but he said that if I was disposed to pay for something, he would prefer to take it home. I gave him two or three pesetas, and he ran off.

My boredom and my desperation were merging to form a melancholy cloud which enveloped my brain. The captain of the "Vertrowen" and I stood looking at each other without speaking. Suddenly we decided to leave. On the way out, the captain collided with a seaman who was coming in, and almost tumbled to the floor. The Dutchman not only was not outraged, but he offered apologies to the sailor, who in his turn begged a thousand pardons for his clumsiness.

I grew ashamed of my ferocious instincts. The fog of melancholy was advancing on my soul, and all my ideas were tinged with a sentimentalism that was altogether ridiculous.

The Dutchman and I continued on to the dock. My companion in drunkenness descended two flights of stairs along a narrow stairway and commenced to yell into the darkness until a white boat appeared from the black nowhere. I was sure that the Dutchman would fall into the water, with his formal suit and the flower in his buttonhole; but no, he held himself erect and jumped into the boat with agility.

Then he saluted me gravely, his hat in his hand, and with a very reverent manner.

"Good night," he said, in English.

"Buenas noches," I answered.

I was left alone. I was weary, sad, my head heavy. Not a trace of wrath was left in me. I did not know what to do, and I decided to return to San Fernando on foot.

V. NEW FATIGUES OF LOVE

Like all sentimental men who expect too much from women, I have had my moments of despising the fair sex. Don Ciriaco would often say to me, with that joyous exasperation which was characteristic of him:

"Shanti, you must always remember that of every one hundred women, ninety-nine are animals with vain and cruel instincts, and that the one woman left, who is a good person, almost a saint, will serve as a pasture for some petulant and cruel little man, a pasture where he can satisfy his bestiality and his cruelty. And thus we take vengeance, one upon the other, in the most inhuman and stupid manner."

In truth, nature is prodigal, unstinted, in the creation of egotistic men and of fickle and insensitive women. Perhaps it is natural for a man to be a little vulgar, and for a woman to be a little cruel. It may even be possible that goodness and generosity are anomalies, pure paradoxes.

I must admit that Dolorcitas was not the one exception among the hundred women in Don Ciriaco's statistics. She was among the remaining ninety-nine: she was capricious, cruel, purely instinctive, fickle. To satisfy a whim she would have sacrificed her father, her mother, the entire town, probably half of humanity.

Dolorcitas seemed to favor me, but at the same time everyone said that she was going to marry the son of the Marquis of Vernay, a gentleman of Jerez, who was not very rich but came of an aristocratic family.

I wrote to Dolorcitas and spoke to her on various occasions through the iron grille of her window. She denied that she was going to get married and assured me that they could not change her mind. Nevertheless, all the indications pointed to a wedding.

In every seaport, precisely because seaports are almost always made up of an adventurous, upstart, unstable population, there exists a bedeviled and perverse spirit of aristocracy. Whereas in old, archaic, traditional towns the individuals who feel they are the aristocracy base their claims on the prestige of class, with more or less reason, in modern cities it is no longer the class which is defended but the nuance, a mere shade. So that as a result, Bilbao or Buenos Aires, Manila or Barcelona have more prejudice of caste than do the ancient cities of Toledo, Burgos, or León. In Lúzaro, this phenomenon has occurred on a small scale ever since the town filled up with foreigners and with Spaniards returned from America.

The merchant, who in general comes from the most turbid and muddy, the most indistinct section of society, must always demonstrate, since he can not say that his grandfathers were at the conquest of Jerusalem, that his countinghouse possesses a sacred character, and that all his small devices and proceedings for successful robbery constitute a letters patent of nobility.

I was always annoyed and shocked to hear Don Matías speak of his "class." At the same time, alluding to Dolorcitas, he would say that his daughter would marry a man of his position, thus indicating to me in passing that I had best not set my sights too high.

For Señor Cepeda, as for all seaport merchants, there doubtless existed the double aristocracy of blood and of the countinghouse, of the prayer book and the ledger book, of the sword and the scale, of knight's armor and importer's apron. It was strange, but just as my grandmother upheld an aristocracy of the sea, Señor Cepeda upheld an aristocracy of the countinghouse.

In the commerce of sugar and cocoa, social elevation is in direct proportion to the quantity dispensed; on the other hand, in the commerce of drugs, it is in inverse proportion. If a man sells sugar and cinnamon in small quantities he is a vulgar shopkeeper; if he deals with these materials on a large scale he is a merchant prince. On the other hand, in the drug trade the opposite is true. If drugs are sold in large quantities the seller is a drug wholesaler; if sold on a small scale the seller is a pharmacist, a man of science.

The first time I clearly understood the pretensions to aristocracy which possessed the family of Dolorcitas was during the course of a conversation with an employee of Don Matías whom I called "the Admiral."

Often on Sundays, on arriving at the house of Doña Hortensia, I would find that no one was about, and I would go on into the warehouse. The employees all knew me. They worked the same hours whether it was a weekday or a holiday. It was still the good epoch for Cádiz, and cargoes were constantly being loaded and unloaded from carts drawn up in Customs House Street, which was lined along its length with warehouses and offices; carts came and went continually from Don Matías' place.

The warehouse was immense, with vaults where sacks, barrels, casks, and boxes were piled up. The office was at the entrance, surrounded by an enclosure, with lettered signs over the various windows. One part was devoted to business matters, the other to the dispatching of ships.

Before entering the storage caves, one passed through a hall in which a set of enormous scales hung from the ceiling. It was in this hall that one commonly saw, keeping an eye on the weights and on the passage to and fro of the bales and bundles, a man with the appearance of an important personage, though he was in truth no more than a kind of concierge or porter. Half seriously, and half in jest, he was known to everyone as Don Paco. For my part, I called him "Admiral" or "First Lord of the Admiralty."

This decorative person sported long white side-whiskers, a prominent belly, dark pants, and a white drill-cloth jacket. He spoke in a doctoral manner: geography, history, commerce, navigation—this extraordinary man has mastered all these disciplines.

Don Paco explained to me that Don Matías and Doña Hortensia were seeking an aristocratic husband for their daughter. They needed a title for the decoration of their family tree, and they had already spoken with the old Marquis of Vernay, and the marriage with his son had been arranged in principle. The "Admiral" knew that the girl favored me. I did not know as much.

I concluded my course at San Fernando and went to live in Cádiz; I was now to await the arrival of Don Ciriaco and embark with him on his next trip. I spoke to Dolores through the grille on various occasions. I told her not to marry, to wait my return.

"Yes; I will wait for you," she told me flatly.

I learned that I was not the only person to talk with Dolorcitas through the iron grillwork. A young midshipman often came at night to talk to her. I dreamed up some absurd projects to provoke him and issue a challenge; fortunately, however, these plans came to nothing, and in the middle of July I was surprised by the entrance into Cádiz Bay of the "Bella Vizcaína."

The fatal moment approached. I must embark. I said farewell to my sweetheart, who made me a thousand promises of faithfulness and vowed she would write, and then I went aboard the frigate, in the settled conviction that I was a doomed and unfortunate man. Don Ciriaco signed the bill of lading in triplicate attesting to the goods aboard his ship, and we hoisted the anchor.

As a means of relieving my sorrow, I recounted my amours to Don Ciriaco. The old captain listened to me with mocking amusement.

"When you get back, that girl will be already married," he said placidly. And he added: "All the better for you."

Don Ciriaco was a discerning man.

VI. GREATNESS AND MISERY

We set sail from Cádiz and began the long voyage across the Atlantic to the Cape of Good Hope, and then across the Indian Ocean to Sunda Strait and the Philippines.

For commercial reasons, instead of returning directly to Europe, we traversed the Straits of Saint Bernard and headed into the Pacific toward the Strait of Magellan. Before we reached the Palaus, we found two coral islands which did not appear on the maps, and we named one of them after Don Ciriaco, calling it Andonaegui Island, and the other, the Isle of Santiago Andía.

Two and a half years after setting out, we returned to Cádiz. I remember that I made my last readings amid great emotion. I would be lying if I said that I did not remember Dolorcitas, but I remembered her in a vague way, remotely.

I learned, while still aboard ship, that she had gotten married; but for all the effort I made to fall into despair, I was unable to do so.

We entered Cádiz Bay on a winter morning full of sunshine. I felt a great joy; there lay Chipiona and Cádiz with their houses white as calcined bones; there stood the castle of San Sebastián and La Caleta.

As we passed in front of the Navy Yard and I caught sight of the city wall, I recalled my walks there with Dolorcitas and my epoch as a student at San Fernando. The houses of Cádiz were before my eyes, those white houses without eaves, the cathedral with its two towers and its gilt cupola, the roofs with their minaret-like towers, and the white faces of the walls with their scattered small windows like the thick walls of Arab houses.

I had the greatest urge to walk on Spanish soil again, to stroll along the city walls, with their sentry boxes and bulwarks and cannons, and gaze on the whole lovely gulf of Cádiz.

The first visit, perforce, had to be a call on Don Matías. Doña Hortensia received me as if I had been her son. The captain praised me warmly to her. Doña Hortensia was splendid. She was a most attractive woman; she was like a Roman empress. Later on, when I saw the statue of Agrippina in the Capitoline Museum in Rome, I was reminded of her.

From what I was able to discern, she had grown to feel a total lack of respect for her husband. She considered herself totally emancipated. I was somewhat more worldly now than when I had been a student, and I could see that the beautiful Hortensia had turned her back on all moral punctilio, that she sought only to prosper and take her pleasure, to satisfy her senses and her vanity. Her fame in Cádiz had grown somewhat equivocal.

Don Ciriaco planned to retire and he wanted me to take over command of the frigate from him; but this arrangement did not suit Don Matías. The captain and I went on several occasions to see Hortensia to secure her intervention with her husband. She promised she would insist on it until he gave his consent.

"Friend Shanti, you handsome lads have all the advantages," said Don Ciriaco, in his bantering manner, "the women are always on your side. They help you, they protect you, they even think you know all about seamanship. I'd like to see old Captain Cook, bald and white-bearded, in her house. I'm sure that Hortensia would find that he was not very well versed in the sea."

I laughed at the picture he presented.

"Yes, yes, laugh," said the captain, "but be careful. This woman has evil intentions toward you. Now that you've gotten free of the daughter, don't fall into the hands of the mother."

"What can she do to me, Don Ciriaco?" I asked smiling.

"I've seen pretty boys smarter than you fall head over heels on their faces and act the fool because of a woman. So, keep an eye on the compass, matey, and take care with the wheel!"

"We'll lash it down, if you think it's necessary, Don Ciriaco."

"No, no; a good helmsman has no need of that precaution."

Don Ciriaco's warning had the effect of reducing the frequency

of my visits to Hortensia's house. My petition was making progress, in any case. Before the month was over, I was able to read
the following sign in Customs House Street: "BASQUE-
ANDALUSIAN COMPANY: The frigate BELLA VIZCAÍNA will
sail January 5 for the Canaries, Cape Verde, the Cape of Good
Hope, and Manila, under command of Captain Don Santiago
de Andía."

I planned to make full use of the days remaining to me in
Cádiz. I was beginning to enjoy myself there; I led a happy and
untroubled life. I strolled about at my leisure, and the town enchanted me, from its joyous plazas to its straight streets. I enjoyed
gazing at the white houses with their enormous miradors, the
churches, which were also white, and I liked to stroll along the
city walls at sunset.

One afternoon at dusk as I started to go into a restaurant the
old serving woman at Doña Hortensia's house whom we called
Señora Presentación hurried past me and wordlessly handed me
a letter. It was from Dolorcitas. She wanted to see me at ten
that night; she had to talk to me. She would wait for me in her
grilled window. She lived in Doubloon Street, near the Customs
House. All my composure fell apart at that moment.

I thought of two solutions: one, the more prudent, to go and
talk to Don Ciriaco and get his advice; the other, which appealed
to my vanity more, to write a note saying that I would keep the
appointment. I decided on the latter course.

Among the seamen aboard the "Bella Vizcaína" there was a
chap from Cádiz, whom we called Little Moor because he had
lived in Tangier and often wore a red fez on his head. The Little
Moor was a strong supporter of mine. Every ship is a world
apart, where sympathies and antipathies are quickly established;
the Little Moor, who was young and impressionable, had demonstrated his sympathy for me. This chap used to spend his time at
a tavern near Puerta del Mar. I went to look for him, found him
at once, and asked him to take my reply to Dolorcitas, and then
come back for me. We had supper together, and just before
ten o'clock we walked into Doubloon Street.

The Little Moor was happy to take part in an affair with a
little mystery to it.

"You keep watch," I told him. "If someone comes, let me
know."

"Don't worry, I'll take care of it," he answered.

At ten sharp, there was a sound behind the iron grille, a vague
light appeared, a bolt was softly drawn back, and the persian
blind swung open.

My heart was pounding in my chest as if it were a hammer being swung in the forge: I thought I would topple over. She appeared and extended her hand to me. I took it between my own. I was so overcome with emotion that I could not speak.

Then Dolores started talking in a rush, and told me she was very unfortunate and unhappy in her marriage. She had found out that her husband, the marquis, was her mother's lover, and she wanted to leave him and come to me, and go away from Cádiz.

I was completely astonished; I did not know what to do, or even what to say. The Little Moor put an end to my quandary by telling me that someone was coming. We stood back, and a man passed. Dolores and I talked again. She said she would wait for me on the next day, in a nearby house, which had a second entrance in another street which I could use to get in.

The persian blind swung shut, and I called the Little Moor; together we went back to my inn. That night I could not sleep. The truth was that I was not in love, for I was able to reason quite coldly with complete composure. I could see that I was gambling with my future. My relations with Dolores would soon be found out, whatever precautions we took, and Don Matías would put me into the street as soon as he discovered what was going on. A solution that persistently occurred to me was to board my ship and lock myself up, but this seemed a shameful way out.

The next morning, after a night of total insomnia, I determined to pursue the adventure to the end. I was sure that in my heart I was not in love with Dolores. I thought it likely that she was probably not even in love with me, that she was motivated by revenge, but it did not matter; I must go on to the end.

We saw each other that day. Dolores had changed a good deal in the two years since I had first known her. She was a woman, and a splendid, beautiful woman. I began to feel as if I were playing a part in a dream.

"Is it possible that real life is like this?" I wondered as I walked back to my inn later.

It was an extraordinary beginning to my life. After having circled the globe and breathed the voluptuous air of the Pacific islands, after having sailed through Atlantic hurricanes, schools of sharks in the China sea, and ice banks off the Cape of Good Hope, I now found myself in the hands of a young and beautiful woman, a marchioness, who said she loved me.

I felt myself old from the things I had seen, and young from an immature heart. My situation was truly extraordinary. I had not read any of Balzac's novels of the kind in which only duchesses and ambitious young men appear; if I had read them I would probably have found myself doubly interesting. My own conceit made me bold.

In the course of my new life I recall going openly on various occasions to visit Dolorcitas in her box at the theater. She was like a princess; and I wore my blue close-fitting dress coat with gold buttons, gray *collant* trousers, leggings, and black tie wound several times around. People pointed me out surreptitiously. If any one had told me that I was not a king of fate, a czar, an emperor, a youth pampered by fortune, I would have gazed upon him with Olympian disdain.

Opera was sometimes performed at the theater, and more than once, standing beside Dolores in the box, my eyes filled with tears as I listened to the tenor in *Lucia* singing, *"Tu che a Dio spiegasti l'ale."*

Petulance, sentimentality, vanity, sadness, all these qualities were merged in me, so that sometimes I thought of myself as a hero and other times as a prisoner of suffering. My sorrows were all related to Dolores. I would have liked to have identified myself with her, participated in her most intimate thoughts, penetrated her soul. Vain dream! There was always about her an air of reserve, a fear of having her soul uncovered.

"What more do you want of me?" she would say to me.

And the mere question, asked with a certain acrimony, was enough to make me feel downcast. What stupidity it is, I used to think at such moments, to consider woman an ideal creature! And what an error to look upon wealth and magnificence as synonyms of happiness!

The moment was approaching when the "Bella Vizcaína" must set sail. I went aboard the frigate to take charge of the preliminary operations of maneuvering the ship into the open sea, out beyond all the vessels in the bay. By the time I returned ashore in the launch, I was prey to the greatest uncertainty.

A development over which I had no control and which came as the culmination of a logic I had not bothered to trace put an end to my hesitations, and in a manner not exactly pleasant. One morning two gentlemen appeared in my hotel, on behalf of the Marquis of Vernay. They had come to challenge me to a duel, with pistols, in circumstances of the utmost gravity. Naturally, I accepted the challenge. I was completely convinced that nothing could happen to me. As seconds I named a former fellow student from San Fernando and an English naval officer who took his meals in my hotel while his vessel was anchored in Cádiz Bay.

As I say, I was possessed of an absolute confidence in myself, a stupid confidence in myself. It seemed impossible that the marquis could harm me in any way. I do not know how the absurd idea of my own invulnerability had entered my head so convincingly.

The duel was to be held at Puerto de Santa María, on the property of a friend of the marquis. The preparations were carried out with the utmost secrecy. The marquis and his seconds, with the boxes of pistols, repaired to the appointed spot in the earliest hours of the morning, and I with my seconds got aboard a small boat just after lunch.

The skipper of the launch took his seat in the stern. He was a type straight out of the theater: wearing side whiskers, a red sash around his middle, and an Andalusian hat on his head.

We laughed to ourselves at him, because he spoke in a very noticeable Andalusian accent, making all his *s* sounds into *z*.

"All right; lez go, the wind'z dying down."

We crossed the bay of Cádiz, disembarked, rode through the streets of Puerto de Santa María in a coach, and arrived at the property of the marquis' friend about two in the afternoon.

It was a beautiful winter day. The seconds paced off twenty paces with enormous strides. We were handed our pistols, fired, and, at the same time that I heard a report, I felt a blow which knocked me to the ground. I strove for breath, my mouth filled with blood, and I heard a rush of air entering the hole where the wound was.

A lung had been pierced. I spent some very bad days between life and death. Then I was in bed for a month, and at the end of this time I was able to get up, looking more like a mummy than a man.

From the moment he had learned what had happened, Don Ciriaco had been at my bedside, watching over me as if I were his son. Hortensia also came to see me. Dolores and her husband had gone to live in Madrid, apparently fully reconciled.

When I was at last in a condition to leave the house, Don Ciriaco took me to see a friend of his, the captain of the frigate "La Ciudad de Cádiz." Old Don Ciriaco, who had a real affection for me, wanted to arrange for his friend to take over command of the "Bella Vizcaína," while I took his friend's place in command of "La Ciudad de Cádiz."

The friend had no objection to this arrangement; Don Ciriaco went again to visit Doña Hortensia, and she apparently assured him instantly and without hesitation that she would see to it that we got what we wanted.

Sure enough, a few months later, once again my normal self, I was given command of a beautiful frigate. I was twenty-three years old.

VII. THE WHEREABOUTS OF JUAN DE AGUIRRE

I had not concerned myself any further with the fate of my uncle, Juan de Aguirre, who had captured my imagination in my childhood. But one day, while I was crossing Manila Bay in one of those canoes which are known as *guílalos* and are used to transport passengers, I fell into conversation with an old Basque sea captain who was in command of a brigantine; when I told him I was from Lúzaro, he asked me: "Do you know anything about Juan de Aguirre?"

"No, I don't. And I should, because he was a relative of mine."

"Juan de Aguirre y Lazcano?"

"The same. He was my uncle."

"What became of him?"

"He apparently died. I was at his funeral."

"How long ago was that?"

"Why, that must have been about twenty years ago."

"It couldn't have been. Juan de Aguirre was alive about fourteen or fifteen years ago; according to what I heard, he was in Iloilo."

"I don't believe it could have been he: I think that would be impossible."

"I didn't see him," replied the captain, "but I know people who talked to him."

"It could have been someone of the same name."

"The same name, from the same town, and who sailed as mate on the same ship? That would be a pretty rare coincidence."

"Yes, that's true. But if he had lived in Iloilo, he would have written his mother."

The old captain shrugged his shoulders, as if to say that this argument did not convince him, and then added with indifference: "It's been twenty years since I've written my wife, and she surely must think I'm dead."

I parted company with my countryman, who was obviously

not a very noteworthy example of marital tenderness, and later I recounted the story to my second mate. We carried out a long series of inquiries among Basque sea captains, mates, and boatswains. Several of them asserted that they had in fact heard speak of a Juan de Aguirre, ex-mariner and proprietor—about fifteen years previously—in Iloilo. On the other hand, the captain of the corvette "Mari Galante," a man named Francisco Iriberri whom we met south of Madagascar in the course of one of those calms common in the Indian Ocean, furnished some quite different information. Iriberri was a little old man, beardless, with a sickly air, blond hair, and a look of irritation in his eyes. Later, I learned that he was one of the most daring sea captains of his time.

Iriberri assured me that Juan de Aguirre had been for some time engaged, as Iriberri had been himself, in the trafficking of Negroes and Chinese—in fact, until his hooker had been captured by an English cruiser. Iriberri told me that the name of my uncle's hooker was the "Dragon," and that it belonged to a French-Dutch company, and he furnished such details that I was convinced his information was factual. According to him, unless my uncle had escaped or died, he was still in prison.

The conclusion to the tale remained unknown, but it was certain that my uncle had sailed as a slaver and been taken prisoner. From Iloilo he would have written his mother, and she would have had no reason to conceal the fact that he was alive. But if he were in prison, it was understandable that my proud grandmother would rather have announced that he was dead.

At the end of a very hard voyage, after seven months of battling storms and gales, we reached Cádiz. I had been five years at sea. I was twenty-eight. And I was tired. I picked up my mail at the post office, and in the first letter I read, my mother wrote that my grandmother had died. It would be best if I would go to Lúzaro to help in settling affairs.

I was so anxious to be on land that I turned down a friend's offer to take me in his ship to Bilbao, the port nearest my home, and I immediately took the stagecoach to Madrid.

I spent a week in the court city; on the first day, as I was walking near the Prado Museum, I saw Dolorcitas and her husband ride by in a coach. He, perhaps, did not recognize me, but she certainly knew me the moment she saw me, and she turned away with a gesture of disdain. It was a small and stupid thing, but her disdainful gesture made a deep impression on me.

I left Madrid more melancholy than when I arrived; I passed through Burgos, and Vitoria, and from there, in a series of relays, I arrived at Lúzaro.

My grandmother's estate was to be divided equally between my Aunt Ursula and my mother. Aguirreche was left to them both; but, inasmuch as my Aunt Ursula, seized by a mystic whimsey, had indicated a desire to retire to the convent of Santa Clara, and my mother did not wish to live alone in the old ancestral house, they decided to rent it out.

Driven by a desire to find out what had become of my Uncle Juan, I searched through all the closets and cabinets in the house and read all the papers and letters I found. I wanted to clear up the enigma of my uncle's life, after so many stories and rumors. In searching through the house I came across a daguerreotype made in Paris. I asked my mother if she knew the man shown there, and she answered that it was her brother Juan, but looking so strange that she could scarcely recognize him. She had never seen this daguerreotype before. In a package of yellow letters I found one signed "Juan." The letter acknowledged receipt of a rather large sum of money and mentioned sending a daguerreotype that had been made by a photographer in Paris. There could be no doubt that this letter was from my uncle. It had been written from a town in Brittany, and bore a date ten years after the time his funeral had been celebrated in Lúzaro. It seemed incontrovertible that Juan de Aguirre was alive when my family and I, as a boy, attended his funeral.

BOOK THREE

The Return Home

I. THE WOUND

In the mornings when I step out on my balcony I see the town beneath me, with its red tiles grown blackish, its square chimneys, and the smoke emerging from them in tenuous threads against the gray autumn sky. After the abundant rains, the houses are faded, the streets clear, the highway bare and its rocks washed clean. The blue of the sky seems freshly laundered when it appears between clouds: it is more diaphanous, purer.

In the garden of the convent nearby, two nuns wearing white headdress gaze up at me and talk to each other. What strange notions must these poor women have in their heads about a seaman; they who have scarcely ever stirred from behind the walls of their garden!

In front of me I see the ancestral homes that I have seen ever since childhood, houses that are sad, ancient, blackish. Among them stands Aguirreche, my grandmother's house, now converted into residences for fishermen and their families. These houses stand there solidly, rooted to the earth, their walls thick and black, and their roofs held in place by great stones. And they are always equally sad, equally severe, slumbering, wrapped in fog.

What a contrast to the disquiet of the sea and its thousand different routes! What immobile existences these nuns lead!

That house of yellow stone there, shaded by the projecting roof, recalls the face of an old villager, rough but pensive.

What quiet reigns in the town! The very mountain is not so static: at least it changes color in every season. The houses do not; thus they were two hundred years ago, and thus they are today.

All remains the same. Even my grandmother's parrot, inherited by my mother and now perched on the balcony of my house, continues screaming in his strident screech: "To port! To starboard!"

Yes, everything is the same; only I am different, only I have changed; I was a child, and I am a man; I was innocent and ingenuous, and I am disillusioned and sad. I have lived amidst events, and events have tricked me out of life and stolen it away.

Sometimes I gaze at myself in the mirror, and when I behold myself old and changed, I say to myself: "Ah, my poor man, your youth has vanished."

Many years have passed since I left my native town, and what have I accomplished? I have come and gone, moved from here to there, carried along by a sweep of events that have left my soul empty. Whenever I have sought a little warmth and shelter, I have encountered coldness, hardness, and selfishness.

At sea I lost the notion of time. Aboard ship the days are long, and yet the years, sum of the days, are short, and they fly by and are gone. Time has sped for me. The thought of the past, once youth has been left behind, is like a wound in the soul, a wound which flows continually and floods one with sadness. The entire route traversed seems like an Appian Way sown with tombs.

La Iñure has passed away: I will not hear her again telling superstitious tales; the candlewoman has died: I will not again make sacred wafers with her, as before; the watchtower guard, too, is dead: I will not see him again, at the end of the wharf, running up his signal pennants. Now, neither will Caracas fashion his boats, nor Yurrumendi talk of pirates, nor Josepe Tiñacu weave through the streets making *S* curves. They have all disappeared. I should not have left this place; I should not have come back.

A strange existence is mine, and that of other wanderers. During one long epoch, all is adventure, events; and then, in another, there is nothing but commentary on past events.

My first impression on returning to Lúzaro was one of astonishment at the insignificance of the wharfs, of the town, of the river. It all seemed to me so small, so deserted, so poor! I had imagined the entrance to the harbor as quite large, the river beautiful, the wharves wide, and when I saw them again I was astounded: they seemed mere toys.

"It isn't worth while living here," I said to myself when I returned.

And now—absurd change of mind!—I often say to myself: "It isn't worth while living elsewhere."

A month ago, I did not wish to think of remaining in Lúzaro; it seemed to me sheer madness to exchange the hours of seaborne indolence and shipboard calm for life in a sad little town, boresome and full of its own petty preoccupations. Now, the idea of returning to my ship, of plunging back into the continual commotion of sailing, alarms me. All of my life on shipboard is fading away; it all seems vague and lacking in reality. In the measure that I acquire character as a native here, my taste for the old and traditional increases; I spend hours on my balcony, watching the town, the fields, and the sea, and I find aspects of life in all three that I had never noticed before.

Every day I rise very early. I love to see, at dawn, the mist disappear up the slopes of Mount Izarra and watch how the town and the wharf emerge from the uncertain banks of fog; I am enchanted to hear the crowing of the cocks and the creaking of the cart wheels on the road.

When the weather is good, I set out in the morning and walk through the town. I like to look at the old family houses, looming and black, with their wide caissoned eaves. I walk down the narrow, steep, tortuous streets where the fishermen live. Some of these sloping streets have three or four flights of stairs; others are covered and are actually zigzag passageways. At dawn in fine weather, there is no one about in these narrow streets except a woman who runs from door to door knocking loudly to rouse the fishermen. The swallows sweep down at street level pursuing each other and screeching.

On rainy days I like Lúzaro even more. The monotonous sadness of gray weather no longer disturbs me. It has become a kind of pleasant memory of the days of my childhood. Accustomed to the violet-colored horizon of the tropics, to those skies alternately nebulous and brilliant in the region of the trade winds, I now feel myself caressed by the soft, gray rain clouds. The rain seems to fall on my soul as on parched land, refreshing me and making me joyous.

Often I sit on the enclosed balcony and watch the road becoming covered with puddles and the houses turning even darker with rain splotches.

At night, the sound of the rain, that song of water, is like a vague rumor, an accompaniment to thoughts, as it resounds on the tiles and windowpanes—a forgotten rhythm again remembered. Even from my bed I can hear the rain in the gutters of the loft and the metallic sound when it falls in the clay bowls. And the rain, and the wind, and the water all enchant me and sadden me.

That is the nature of the wound, that wound which goes on flowing and flooding my soul; a covered spring that spouts once more.

I do not know why it is that the past is flooded with a magical melancholy—it is hard to understand why it should be. One recalls clearly that one was not happy in those days, that one was possessed by restlessness and sorrows, and nevertheless, one has the impression that the sun then shone brighter and that the blue of the sky was purer and more splendid.

One would like the people and objects in our memories to be eternal; but our little existence represents nothing at all in the tumultuous flow of events. Here we had a friend; in that corner we were happy; but our happiness and our friendships are all of no higher concern.

As I think of all this, I feel a sudden horror, as if life were escaping from me in a single moment of faintness. The inanity of everything unnerves me—hope falters. I wish that my spirit were like the nightingale who sings in the black and starless night, or like the lark who flies over desolate fields, and not like the wounded bird who plummets to earth.

II. THE NATURAL FORMATION OF LÚZARO

If I had not returned to Lúzaro after I grew up, I would never have had a clear idea of what it is like. The memories of my childhood played me false; some things were magnified, others diminished, and between both extremes were great gaps. If I had attempted to describe my native town on the basis of my impressions as a child, my description would have resembled the original very slightly, or not at all.

Lúzaro is a pretty little town, though dark, like all the villages along the Bay of Biscay, but it is one of the less somber. A man from the north of Europe might get the impression that it was a town in Andalusia. Protected from the northwest winds and with a moderate climate in its environs, Lúzaro has lush vegetation. Everywhere, on the blackened housefronts, along the stone steps of some of the houses, on garden walls, grow heavy vines and tufts with red and blue flowers. The orchards and gardens are filled with great magnolia, orange, and lemon trees.

I find something of Cádiz in my town, a small, melancholy, black Cádiz, less mellow and much harder.

Lúzaro's outlet to the sea is quite narrow, and its sand beach is very shifting. The port facilities have been enlarged in my absence. Today, the jetty of *Cay luce* covers a good distance: it runs parallel to the houses of the fishermen, and ends in the breakwater. This breakwater is a handsome piece of work; extending in the form of an esplanade, it boasts, in the middle, a stone cross. The new watchtower is on one side, and the boys of the town play handball against the tower wall. From this point stretches the wonderful spectacle of the sea battering furiously up against the rocks.

As in all fishing villages, fishing craft are to be seen in the strangest and most unlikely places: on the slope of a street, blocking the way; beneath a tiled shed; in the loft of a house.

The Lúzaro inlet is small, but very picturesque. A single-arched bridge spans it, and across the bridge runs the road to Elguea. One of the shores of this inlet is rocky and agitated, the other is a blackish slough. On this marshland there has existed for many years now—centuries, some say—a shipyard installation. Previously, frigates and brigs used to be built there; nowadays only launches and an occasional small schooner of low tonnage are constructed.

The present owner of the shipyard is a man named Shempelar. The shipyard itself is not very complex; it consists merely of two black sheds built with the boards of dismantled ships and a ramp with a track in the middle of it. Usually, the work consists of caulking and repairing old ships. Whenever there is some new construction, Shempelar is in his element; he brings out his calipers and pair of compasses and sits there drawing the parts of the vessel without lifting his head. If he is asked how the work is progressing, Shempelar will answer that it is going badly, for he is a dilettante of pessimism and delights in it.

The master finishes drawing the parts and members, and then the ship's carpenters commence their work with hatchet and adz, cutting and drilling the boards and then binding the ribs. The skeleton of the vessel is gradually covered, the work proceeds apace: Shempelar, inwardly enthused with the work, walks around with a long face, quarreling with everyone. The ship-wrights nail heavy nails into the side of the ship with great hammer blows; the area around the work is littered with mallets, large drills, gouges, jacks to lift heavy weights. Various black cauldrons filled with tar, which Shempelar's small sons keep boiling by heaping shavings and pieces of old boards on the fire, stand to one side. The workers eventually each take some of the pitch and begin to caulk the ship, walking in the mud like ducks. When the vessel is finally floated, and everyone is saying what a fine boat it is, then it is a sight worth seeing to watch Shempelar making marvelous efforts to demonstrate to himself that he has reasons, serious reasons, grave reasons to be profoundly dissatisfied.

I often go to visit Shempelar, especially if he is in the course of some new construction, as he was recently, and we talk. Still, my most habitual promenade is not in the direction of the river, but rather toward the dock; I watch the fishing off *Cay luce* and the tuna boats and the coastal schooners coming in; I listen, with a smile, to the women quarreling in Basque with their children, for all these women of the sea deal with children almost exclusively by means of screeches, as if imitating the seagulls; and I exchange some gossip with the fishermen.

My mother has been anxious to help me reconquer my sense of being a son of Lúzaro by making a quantity of elaborate dishes and classical local desserts with her own hands.

"You used to like this . . ." she tells me.

"Really?"

"Yes. . ."

"Well, I still like it."

Satiated with local flavor, I have now begun to drop in on the conversational gathering at Zapiain's place, the shop belonging to the watchmaker and commercial traveler, and owner of the "Cachalote" until we sank it. The watch shop is the equivalent of an encyclopedic academy, an Athenian gymnasium. There everything human and divine is discussed; among the nondivine themes, one of the most debated questions has been the formation of Lúzaro.

Garmendia, the pharmacist, attributes the formation of Lúzaro almost exclusively to the action of the river, which slowly opened a passage, he says, pushing aside the softer earth, until it gained an outlet to the sea. According to Garmendia, Frayburu and the reefs thereabout, just as the sand banks at Legorreta, are no more than the remains of rocks acted upon by water; the strong nucleus resisted the corrosive action of air and water and remained as large and isolated rocks; the blander element was turned into sand.

Socoa, the old sea captain, attributes the narrow inlet at Lúzaro to the action of the Gulf Stream alone. The Gulf Stream, that immense river of hot water, as Major Rennell called it, which runs within the sea and obliquely traverses the Atlantic, on reaching the west coast of Spain sends off two streams: one runs along the Bay of Biscay and ascends the coast of France (there called the Rennell Current), and later rejoins the Gulf Stream; the other descends toward Africa and is called the Guinea Current.

The coastal current flows along the great curves in the coast and thence into the inlets and bays, bringing with it organic remains which are deposited on the beaches. As far as Captain Socoa was concerned, this current, and this current alone, had produced the inlet and beach at Lúzaro. Socoa's predilection for the Gulf Stream might be explained by the fact that he had voyaged repeatedly in the Gulf of Mexico, where he was impressed by the force of the current that takes its departure from this point and which acts later as the oven to warm the northwest coasts of Europe.

Another old seaman, also a regular at the watch shop meetings, asserted that the sand banks at Legorreta had been formed by the wind.

These three theoreticians disputed among themselves, each intent on proving that what he said, and nothing else, was the true explanation. Once they asked me my opinion.

"I believe the three of you are right in part," I said. "The river, as the pharmacist says, undoubtedly opened up a passage through the land, until it reached the sea and formed the breech; the coastal current came later and widened it, rounded it out, and formed the inlet; later, the northwest wind, which follows the Gulf Stream and is the nursery of all the storms in the Bay of Biscay, began piling up the sand toward Legorreta."

My reward for stating so dispassionate and sensible an opinion was to be called an opportunist and fence-straddler.

If Recalde's son had been an anthropologist at that time, he would have probably found that all these men had round heads and were for this reason absolutists and by nature violent.

III. CONVERSATIONS AT THE WATCHMAKER'S

My mother wanted me to take advantage of my liberty ashore to get married. She had picked out for me the daughter of a Lúzaro proprietor, a lady older than myself, ugly, skinny, and mystical. I, if the truth must be told, was not very enthusiastic about the matter. It is well known that we seamen are not models of amiability or sociability. The prospect of fasting and vigils every Friday, my destiny if I united myself with Barbarita —which was the name of my mother's candidate—did not make me smile. In general, the women of Lúzaro, despite all their sweetness, have a great predilection for doing as they wish. Since they are almost all of them the daughters or wives of seamen, their habitual living alone for long periods has endowed them with a decisiveness and energy and accustomed them not to obey anyone.

Nowadays this difficult situation is not so prevalent as before; not that the women have grown more humble, but simply because there are scarcely any deep-sea mariners left in Lúzaro, so that the women, willy-nilly, must put up with their respective husbands every day of the year.

The case of my friend Recalde, father of the present anthropologist, seemed to me symptomatic. They told me the story at the watchmaker's.

Recalde, my old comrade, the terrible Recalde, the most daring and bravest pilot in town, had married La Cashilda, daughter of the confectioner in the central plaza. She was a little doll with blue eyes, very proper and formal. All the sugar syrup, all the calabash sweetmeat of her father's store had had its influence on her.

Recalde was a despot: determined, bold, accustomed to giving orders as if he were always aboard ship, he could not abide anyone's contradicting him.

He got married; the honeymoon passed; La Cashilda had a child (the anthropologist); Recalde went off to sea for three years, and then he came back to his home for a spell.

The first day home he thought he would be polite: "How is everything? Anything new happen?" he asked his wife gently.

"Nothing. We're all well."

"Anybody die in town?"

"Yes; Don This One, Don That One. The wife of So-and-so has been sick."

Recalde listened to the news, and then he asked: "What time is supper here?"

"Eight o'clock."

"Well, we'll have to change that to seven."

La Cashilda made no reply.

Recalde was of the opinion that the way to put a house in good order was to bring it up to the standard of a ship.

The next day Recalde came home at seven o'clock and asked for his supper.

"The supper isn't ready," his wife told him.

"What do you mean, the supper isn't ready? Yesterday I ordered the supper to be ready at seven."

"Yes, but the girl can't make the supper until eight, because she has to be with the child."

"In that case, we get rid of the girl."

"The girl can't be gotten rid of."

"Why?"

"Because she was recommended to me by the sister of Don Benigno, the vicar, and she is a person of confidence."

"All right, then; but tomorrow, whether the girl makes the supper, or you make it, we eat at seven."

The next day, supper was ready at eight. Recalde broke two or three plates and banged the table, but he was unable to arrange the supper for seven o'clock. And when La Cashilda had convinced him that in her house things were done as she wanted them and that there was no sea captain or mate who could tell her what to do, she put the finishing touches to the argument by telling her husband: "Here we eat supper every night at eight, do you understand, little man? And if that isn't convenient with you, what you can do is leave. You can always go to sea again."

And La Cashilda, while she said all this, smiled at Recalde with her big blue eyes.

Recalde, the terrible Recalde, understood at last that he was not on board his ship, and he went back to sea. This case, this example of my own comrade subjected to the aggressive femininity of Lúzaro, did not impel me to get married, even if it were to the spiritual Barbarita.

As I said, I learned the details of this familial conflict between Recalde and La Cashilda in Zapiain's watch shop, which was the gathering place of the important people of the town. It was my uncle, old Irizar, who first took me there. The Lúzaro casino had not yet been founded—that institution which, after an initial period of snobbery and splendor, was reduced to being a somnolent and deadly reunion of adventurers back from America and of retired mariners.

At the watchmaker's I learned about everything going on in the town. Nearly all the regulars were Carlists and fanatics. I was not of the same ilk, but I enjoyed finding out about other people's lives, and the conversation was often amusing. My standing rule was not to discuss questions of politics or religion.

One of the regular attendants, who must certainly have been a liberal, even more than he let on in public, was the druggist Garmendia. It would not have been sensible for him to reveal himself completely, but nevertheless he obviously held no religious beliefs. Garmendia did not venture to declare himself frankly Voltairian, and his manner of procedure in conversation was to make his thought known by disconnected and chance phrases, apparently candid observations which always concealed an ambush.

His two most outraged opponents were a pair of inflexible Carlists from the interior of the province: one, administrator of a land title; the other, a rock and stone contractor. The adminis-

trator was called Argonz; the contractor, Echaide. Garmendia
would drive them wild with his observations, apparently harm-
less but double-edged.

The druggist would say, for instance, that he had met some
Protestant or Jew who had turned out to be a good person, and
he would add that it had always seemed strange to him, and
even sad, that someone who professed a false religion should be
better than many Catholics.

"What difference does it make if a man is good or bad if he
isn't Christian?" Echaide would demand fiercely.

"Well, now, it does matter."

"It does not matter, not at all," the other would reply. "Not a
bit. If he doesn't go to mass, he can't be saved."

Garmendia was continually exasperating them. Echaide and
Argonz were both of them very fond of hard cider, Basque
bitter wine, and all manner of local liquors.

"It's a shame," Garmendia told them once, "that the Basques,
despite their being so religious, are such drunkards."

"That's a lie!" exclaimed Echaide, turning red with indignation. "The Basque people are an honorable people, and those
that defame them are unworthy of belonging to them."

"Such people are swine," added Argonz, his eyes bulging from
their sockets.

"I don't doubt it," replied Garmendia. "I am as much a Basque
as anyone, but I regret that my countrymen are like the Irish,
who are also very religious, but who also like their liquor to
excess."

"And why shouldn't they like it?"

The two Carlist extremists understood that Garmendia was
their enemy, and one of them once said, threateningly:

"What's called for here is to take to the field, rifle in hand, and
every liberal we meet: Fire!"

"In the back, for ignominy," added the other, his face flushed
with rage.

The watchmaker was one of those men who agrees with everyone, and, with his jeweler's lens in his right eye, he would keep
nodding his head as a sign of agreement with everything that was
said by his fellow conversationalists; but as soon as the Carlist
extremists had gone, he murmured:

"They're barbarians. The Inquisition is a thing of the past. The
world advances."

In Zapiain's mouth this phrase meant only that he believed in
living quietly and with satisfaction, without wars or squabbles.

One or two months after my return to Lúzaro one of the

topics of conversation at the watchmaker's was the exploitation of the iron mines which had been discovered in Izarte, and the construction of a pier at one end of the Beach of Souls. These mines had been discovered and exploitation begun while I was at sea. The work was being directed by one Juan Machín, a native son of Lúzaro, who was remembered as a loafer about town.

When I was a boy, there had been a good deal of talk about minerals and veins of iron ore. Interest in the subject sprung from the activity of a man named Juan Beracochea, of whom people made fun because he went about with a manservant exploring the nearby mountains and said that the ground around Izarte was worth millions. Beracochea looked like a type of musketeer: aquiline nose, pointed black beard, wide-brimmed hat, and long hair. He always carried a heavy cane, whose handle was in the form of a hammer, and he would return from his excursions with his pockets full of stones.

Beracochea was known as a heretic; he used to say with pride that his father had been one of the first subscribers to the famous *Encyclopédie* of Diderot. When he died his house was found full of books. Berocochea's niece, who was his heir, called in Don Benigno, the vicar, so that he might examine the books, and he announced that they were so wicked that it would be best to burn them. Some people asked how the good priest had determined the wickedness of the books when he could read neither French nor English, which were the languages in which most of them were written. But a vicar scarcely needs to know languages to understand the poison inherent in the printed page. Beracochea owned a number of mining claims; but despite the proclaimed quality of the mineral deposits, he was unable to exploit them or even to sell them.

At this juncture, Juan Machín appeared on the scene, accompanied by some Englishmen; he came to an agreement with Beracochea's niece, an exploitation society was formed, and they soon began to make a profit. From being a vagabond with a bad name, Machín was transformed into a powerful figure; he gave employment, he befriended the fishermen, he was altogether a personage.

Juan Machín married a rich woman from Bilbao and bought an old family mansion in Izarte which he began to fix up to suit his tastes.

On several occasions I was invited to go and see the excavations and construction taking place in the nearby settlement; I was not very much interested in this type of thing, however, and perhaps would not have gone out there at all but for something my mother asked me to do for her. My grandmother had left us a country house in Izarte, on the dunes behind the Beach of Souls. The house was called "Bisusalde." Bisusalde belonged now to my mother. It was rented to an Englishman, and my mother did not know what kind of an arrangement my grandmother had made with him; since the beginning of a new year was approaching, she wanted to know what the agreement was, so that she could collect the rent.

And thus it was that one morning in November I started walking slowly to the Beach of Souls. I went across Mount Izarra, for I wanted to go along the cliff road I had traveled so often as a boy, and take a look into the cave of *Egan-suguia,* and recall the odors of the gorse and fern that I had left behind with my childhood.

IV. THE BEACH OF SOULS

Mount Izarra forms a small peninsula. On one side lies the inlet of Lúzaro, and on the other a beach running for several miles between Lighthouse Point and the slatey shelves around Elguea.

The Beach of Souls is solitary and deserted. It is bounded along its entire length by a ridge of dunes over a hundred feet high in places. Formed of sand and clay, they are thus white in places and yellow in others; at some points they form sharp peaks, and at other points they are in the shape of mounds cut through with gullies and crevices. A thread of water breaks through this barrier of dunes and runs along the foot of the cliffs. This small river is called Sorguiñ-Erreca (the Waterway of the Witches). In the combat between the sea and the land, the land of the coast is sometimes reduced by the sea so that a cliff is formed. Then again, the land will advance, and the sand is converted into a dune; the dune will defend itself from decomposition by means of its natural vegetation; it resists the action of the sea, consolidates itself, and makes itself fast. Over the dunes of the Beach of Souls the vegetation is growing thicker every day, and the meadows and farms of Izarte reach now almost to the border of the dunes and the edge of the sea.

Toward Izarra, on a small promontory, there is a diminutive lighthouse of little importance. Looking over toward Elguea, one has a view of the entire Spanish coast in that direction and part of the French coast as well.

The Beach of Souls is a focal point for the storms and north-west winds in the region. The sea on the Basque coast is one of the most violent and savage that exist. It is possessed by sudden choleric outbursts of unexpected proportions. It is perfidious and changeable, it boils and trembles, and it is always agitated and tumultuous.

Here, in the innermost part of the Gulf of Gascony, the Cantabrian Sea is very deep, the coast is rock, and the currents are strong.

In winter, the Beach of Souls is desolate; a whitish mist hangs over the sea; wisps of fog rise up the flanks of Mount Izarra; and the air and the water are everywhere confused. Not a single line stands out clearly; sky and water are the same substance—a chaos without form or color.

The silence of the sea is sensed: it is filled with the sharp whine of the wind, the shrieks of seagulls, the angry roar of the water, increasing as the waves sweep up on the beach and explode on the sand, and then diminishing to a soft *whish!* as they withdraw with the rumor of a protesting multitude.

Oftentimes the gray sky permits clear vision: a diffuse clarity seems to emanate not from the enveloped heavens but from the turbulent and whitish sea. The waves, the color of clay, sweep up on the beach, which is covered with a loose scrollwork of foam, and leave behind a silvery curve; and the sand seems to boil from contact with the surf.

The seagulls play above the waves, darting into the cavities between the crests, resting on the foam, approaching the beach to scan it with gray eyes which reflect the extinguished light of the sky, and uttering the wild cries that are like the sharp screeching of owls.

There are times, in the dead of winter, when the sky will light up, the clouds will vanish, and the blue will shine through in a marvelous manner. But the Beach of Souls never at any other time gives such an impression of serenity, of beauty, as it does in the fall of the year, when the equinoctial storms have passed.

It is well known that oceanic and terrestrial climatology are not the same: on land, the maximum cold and the maximum heat are in February and August; on the sea, in March and September. Along our Basque coasts, October is the real beginning of autumn; while the land begins to get cold, the sea continues warm.

During these days of calm, when the temperature is mild and equable, one can spend pleasant hours simply contemplating the sea. The great green waves pursue each other until their death in the sand. The sun forms whitecaps of light; at nightfall, the black fins of a porpoise are seen through the billows.

This spectacle of the waves, so soon advancing at a slow and stately pace as hurling themselves at a furious gallop, is of an inexplicable interest, despite all its monotony. The sea is a liquid heavy with salt, moved by the wind with a mechanical rhythm in its circulation, and yet it gives the impression of having the spiritual force of something infinite.

On the days when a south wind blows, the far-off promontories can be seen with diaphanous clarity, and the coast of France and Spain seem traced from a drawing. On such days the sand is not on fire, as it is in summer; the puddles left by the withdrawing tide are like mirrors, the green of the lichen on the rocks is greener, bubbles shoot up as the waves pass over the round holes made by the razor clams, the blackish seaweed forms into skeins like long leashes, and the bladder wrack and jellyfish shimmer in the sand.

At nightfall the twilight works its magic; the sun is enveloped in fantasy, appearing against a background of red clouds and lending the surface of the water rose reflections and even inundating it at times in a golden light so that it takes on the appearance of fused metal.

By March, when winter has passed, when the oven lit by the solar rays of summer is completely extinguished, the sea turns cold. Then comes the epoch of the great storms, of the agitated tides, and the sweeping ebb and flow.

Almost always before the coming of a storm, the sea throws up on the beach a quantity of jellyfish and starfish, algae and bits of wood, most of it torn from the abyss by the inner agitations of the ocean. After the storms and the heavy rains, the trickle of fresh water which flows down the gully beneath the dunes, the Sorguiñ-Erreca, swells and swells until sometimes it becomes a torrent.

V. FRAYBURU

And as a contrast to the regularly billowing surge on the beach is the fierce violence of the sea as it breaks over Lighthouse Point, over toward Izarra, on the reefs of Frayburu. There are few places where the meeting of sea and land produces such violence, such tumult and tragic overtones, as on the rocks at Izarra, dominated by that black island called Frayburu.

From the guardrail of the Lighthouse the spectacle is extraordinary. Below, at the very foot of the promontory, there is a chasm with a rock bottom, and at that point the water, almost immobile, is of a somber color; in the distance, the sea seems blue-green; up under the horizon, it has an emerald tone. When the wind ripples the water, it takes on the aspect of mica, and the sea is streaked with white lines that indicate the diverse depths.

Farther off, behind Izarra, the fishing boats, black in the distance, seem unmoving; a sailing vessel moves along the horizon and a seagull passes slowly, almost without moving its wings.

All this serenity, all this calm and placidity, is turned into violence near the coast, under the Izarra escarpment, with its slate-colored slabs, black and cleft, and its great rocks strewn about like marine monsters emerging from the water. The battle of land and sea is marked with the strongest accents along these reefs. The sea seems seized with desperation, green with ire, without ever a moment of respite, and it hurls itself against the rocks with all its force and fury in all its foaming rage. The black rocks advance out into the sea, defying the rush of the maddened waves; through the clefts and rents in the rocks—the visible marks of the agelong struggle—the water pours and leaps great distances in a fountain white and brilliant as a comet.

One is forced to wonder vaguely whether the sea is possessed of some mysterious design and purpose in its attempt to conquer these rocks, and whether it is driven to despair by its lengthy failure. Far-off the waves come on like herds of wild horses with silver manes, colliding and clashing as they come; they rush upon the rocks and trample them; but then, as if they lacked confidence in their right and dominion, they fall back with the clamor of a routed army, in sheets of brilliance, in sword-edges of water, in white spume.

Man is scarcely constituted to understand the transcendental nature of anything outside himself. And so he imposes his own designs upon things; he assumes the sun is made to give him light, and the stars to adorn his nighttime. We pour everything into the mold of our own spirit; outside this tiny mold, we are equipped with nothing with which to hold or comprehend the mysteries unfolding before our eyes. For this reason we assign a human intention to everything in the universe, from a drop of water to Sirius. Thus, we come to think of these waves cunningly climbing their objective, searching out the narrow, winding way, as a skillful guerrilla, who falls back in rapid flight after reaching the very top.

In the midst of the foamy water, black Frayburu is like a

visible representation of the pride and strength of the land out-facing the rages of the sea. On the days when the sea is running heavy, Frayburu disappears as if it had been swallowed in the foam, only to reappear periodically, black as the skin of a marine monster and trimmed with the silver scrollwork of the spray. Would not this mysterious and strange rock exalt the imagination of a Hamlet? Is it not perhaps the ruin of a castle? Or an enormous dolphin? A shark? Is it a Sphinx gazing out to sea, or the head of a sage?

The inhabitant of the seacoast, however, has not chosen to think of it as a dolphin, or a shark, or a ruin; he has decided that it is the head of a monk, and he has called it thus, in Basque "Frayburu."

The imagination builds fantastic images with rocks and clouds, that is, with the hardest and with the most impalpable of substances. In truth, all substances are smelted down in the force of the soul.

Mount Izarra gives grounds for fantasy to all errant and vaga-bond imaginations; on this high cliff, like a gigantic wall, slate-colored and shot through with veins of white, the niches seem to have been formed to hold religious images; the balconies, lined with green lichen, run along the heights. An undine might easily be expected to appear. And from time to time the red stains of algae adhering to the rock can be seen at the foot of the cliff, to lend a suggestion of some tragic happening.

But it is at nightfall that the entire coast, and Frayburu above all, reaches the culmination of its potent suggestiveness, the paroxysm of its mystery. At that hour the horizon extends itself under the reddish mist, the twilight blue sky begins to grow pale, and its rose tints turn to grays. The distant headlands, gilded by the last splendor of the sun, disappear into the mist, and Frayburu rises amid the solitude of its desolation more myste-rious and somber than ever, in its endless defiance of the dark sky and the deceitful sea that attempts to conquer it.

VI. BISUSALDE

So it was that on one autumn morning I reached the Beach of Souls before midday. A man was leading a cart along the sand, goading the pair of oxen along. There was a creaking sound from the cart axles, and the noise of the sand sinking and flicking under the hooves of the oxen.

I asked the oxherd for the quickest way to climb up to Bisu-salde, and he pointed out the road for me to follow. At the beginning, the way was less of a road than a stairs, formed by three or four flights of steps made with beams, and continuing in a zigzag up the grade. This footpath was known as the Dogs' Slope (*Chacur aldapa*).

Farther out than any of the other houses at Izarte and closer to the edge of the dunes lay my grandmother's country house. It was black, with a balcony running all along the side facing the sea. Bisusalde, the name of the house, means "close to the storms." In truth, the wind must howl and pound around there mercilessly.

I approached nearer the house. The facade looking toward the sea was completely black, the opposite side faced an abandoned garden with two withered cypresses and a small orchard which extended on into a meadow.

I entered the grounds and called. After waiting a short while, I was met by a man who came from working in the garden. He told me that the captain—which was the way he alluded to his master—was not at home, he had gone into Elguea with his daughter.

I remembered the old man before me as being the same man whom Recalde and I had met that far-off day when, after our expedition to the "Stella Maris," we had walked this way looking for whoever had the key to the launch tied up under Lighthouse Point.

I asked the old man when his master would return, and he said in the afternoon, around five o'clock.

And so I started walking toward the village, made up of fifteen or twenty houses grouped around a church, and stopped at a roadside inn where I thought I might get something to eat for lunch and incidentally make inquiries concerning the people who lived in Bisusalde.

The inn was one of the kind that are halfway between rustic and maritime; its doors and walls were painted green, there was a counter in the entranceway, and a small room off to one side containing a white pine table, a mirror draped with chiffon, and chairs.

The whole place was very clean from the action of the sand and from scrubbing. Next door to the inn, under a portico, there was a forge where at that moment a yellow ox was being shoed.

I called, and a woman appeared. When I asked if I could get something to eat, she told me to wait a moment. She came back

and agreed to fix something, and then we began to talk. I told
her who I was, and what I had come for, and she answered my
queries by giving me all the information I wanted concerning
our tenant.

The man at Bisusalde who was known as the captain was an
English seaman; he lived with his daughter, a girl fourteen or
fifteen years old, and a servant named Allen.

There was talk about the old man's having been a pirate, but
this tale, according to my present informant, was merely an
obvious example of rumor and gossip.

The Englishman gave lessons in his language, and every day
he would walk into Elguea, where he had various pupils. He had
been invited to set up in Lúzaro as well, but he had declined, for
he preferred to live in Izarte.

The life led by this little family was one of the utmost simplicity and poverty. Each morning the captain and his daughter
would walk barefoot along the deserted beach. There was a
small cave with a doorway in one of the dunes; there, on good
days, the girl would change into a bathing suit and then take a
plunge in the sea. She would swim until she was tired; when she
came back up on the beach, her father would be ready with a
white blanket to cover her. After the midday meal, the captain
would walk into Elguea; later he would return slowly along
the beach. Often he would stay among the rocks until nightfall.

The girl scarcely ever appeared in the town, the manservant
worked in the field, and on Sunday the three of them would go
to the lighthouse at the Beach of Souls, for they were on friendly
terms with the keeper and his family.

The woman at the inn added that at first it had been said that
Mary, the captain's daughter, was weak; but leading the kind of
life she did, always in the open air, she had begun to develop
into a very robust girl.

All this information led me to believe that these people were
rather strange and misanthropic.

After lunch and a brief rest at the inn, I set out along the edge
of the dunes. It must have been about half-past four when I
caught sight of the captain and his daughter, who were returning
home along the beach. He was walking very slowly; she was
running, throwing stones and yelling. The climb up the slope
was obviously hard on him, and he had to stop to rest several
times. He had the air of a sick and weary man; whenever he
stopped he would let his head drop until his chin rested on his
chest.

I walked up close to them, and could see that the girl was

very pretty; she was blond and deeply tanned. As she passed in front of me, she looked at me with the air of something completely wild. I waited until they entered the house, and a short time later I decided to call on them.

It had already gotten dark. The old manservant working in the garden motioned me in when I came up to the house. An oil lamp illuminated a small and modest room, containing a white-curtained wardrobe.

The captain was sitting beside a table, reading. The girl was preparing the supper without the aid of the manservant, who stood behind me scraping off the handle of his hoe.

When he caught sight of me, the captain stood up with an air of alarm. I begged him to be seated, and I immediately told him who I was and why I had come. The girl left the room.

"Then you're the grandson of Doña Celestina?" the captain asked.

"Yes, sir."

"Son of Clemencia?"

"That is my mother's name."

The man appeared to be taken aback. He seemed unable to tell me what rent he had paid my grandmother, and only murmured:

"Please tell your mother to let me know what I should pay yearly for this house, and if I can, I'll stay on."

I told him repeatedly that this was unnecessary, that he should continue paying whatever he had paid in the past; but I was unable to convince him.

From time to time, the blond daughter would look in at the door, and stare at me with an expression of fear and distrust in her deep blue eyes, as if she were afraid that I would hurt her father in some way.

I got up, annoyed by the suspicious air surrounding these people, and, taking my leave coldly of the three of them, started back to Lúzaro.

VII. THE MESSAGE

One afternoon in December, as I was returning from the watchmaker's at dusk, a boy stopped me in the street and handed me an envelope. Who could be writing me? I examined the envelope in the light of the street lamp. The handwriting was that of a woman. I studied the letter with the utmost curiosity. It read as follows:

To Captain Don Santiago de Andía:

My father, who is sick, kindly entreats you to come and see him as quickly as you can; if possible, this very night. He must speak to you of important matters. If you come tonight, a friend with a horse will be waiting for you at the edge of town, at Aspillaga's smithy.

Mary A. Sandow

Bisusalde, the Beach of Souls.

When I got home I showed the letter to my mother, who was as astonished as I. Because I was very curious, I was anxious to leave at once, but my mother insisted I first sit down and eat my supper. I ate hurriedly, and then, putting on a cloak, started out toward Aspillaga's smithy.

There I found Allen, the old gardener and manservant from Bisusalde. I asked him about the captain, but he answered me only in monosyllables. Since he seemed intent on not talking, I fell silent.

The horse started off at a rather uncomfortable trot; we rode along the misty highway, and within an hour were at the Beach of Souls.

The wind whistled and moaned in alarm; the sea roared on the beach, and the surge hissed ominously.

We approached the house. There was no need to call: the door was open, and the Englishman's daughter stood on the threshold in the company of a dark-haired girl, who was ungainly and barefooted.

The captain's daughter looked as if she had been crying.

"You've taken so long!"

"I couldn't come any sooner."

"We'll go at once and see my father."

We went around the corner of the house and climbed a stairway on one side to the top floor. The captain was sitting in an armchair in his room, wrapped in a threadbare blue cloak, his eyes closed.

At the sound of my approaching footsteps he stood up and muttered in a dim voice:

"Mary, bring a chair."

I drew up the chair myself. What could it be that this man wanted from me? What could there be between us?

The girl gave the old man some coffee to drink, and I was able meanwhile to study anew the father and daughter. He was an emaciated man, perhaps sixty years old; his white beard was trimmed to a point; his eyes were gray and strangely alive under long and blondish eyebrows; his nose was aquiline.

The girl was perhaps fifteen; slender, graceful, her cheeks

tanned by the sun; her eyes brilliant, but shaded; her hair, blond, or the color of fire; her expression frightened, wild.

The walls of the little room were covered with charts, and there was a barometer, a ship's clock, and a compass; it was obviously the room of a seaman.

Outside the wind was howling continuously, rattling the doors and windows.

The captain seemed to be revived by the coffee; he gazed at me attentively while he waited for his daughter to leave the room; when she had gone, he said to me quickly:

"I am Juan de Aguirre, the seaman, your mother's brother, the one that disappeared."

"You're Juan de Aguirre!"

"Yes."

"My uncle?"

"Precisely."

"Why didn't you tell me before?"

The old man looked at me with a certain astonishment. He apparently had not expected my question, nor my immediate acceptance of what he said. So that he replied: "I thought you and your mother would take me for an impostor. . . My legal status isn't very clear, I couldn't very easily prove my identity."

"What of that?"

"It would soon have been revealed where I'd come from, and your mother would have been unhappy. . . Your grandmother knew I was here."

"I, too, had an idea that you were alive."

"Yes?"

"Yes. A certain Iriberri, a ship's captain, told me of your wanderings."

"Iriberri, Francisco Iriberri, who commanded the 'Fénix,' a slaver. . . Yes, I remember him. . . Let's leave that, though, if you will. . . I've been an unfortunate man, but not a criminal; you can believe me. Irresponsible, imprudent, violent, if you will; but not bad. Now, before my mind grows cloudier, I want to ask you to do two things for me. First, I would like you to give this envelope to Juan Machín, the miner. Give it to him a year after my death, or before, if circumstances force you to leave Lúzaro. The other request is that you protect and help my daughter in whatever way you can, for she will be left all alone. Have you understood me?"

"Yes."

"Would you object to taking an oath that you will do what I ask?"

"I have no objection."

"Very well then. Will you swear to accept my daughter, Maria de Aguirre, as your relative, always, whatever people say, and that you will help her in any way you can?"

"Yes, I swear it."

"Do you swear that you will give this letter to Juan Machín within a year, or sooner if circumstances force you to leave Lúzaro?"

"I swear it."

"Oh, thank you, thank you! . . . It's not that I could doubt your simple promise, but this way I'm easier in my mind. Here, take the envelope. Keep it safe somewhere."

I put the envelope in an inner pocket of my coat.

"Is there something else I can do?" I asked.

"No, nothing more. What is your name, nephew?"

"Santiago."

"Ah, yes, Shanti. That was my father's name. Please tell my daughter to come in."

I called out the door, and the blond girl—my cousin!—appeared. Her hair was undone by the wind, her clothing wet from the rain; her eyes shone with such melancholy, with such an unsociable determination, that I was taken aback.

"Come here, Mary," said the old Captain. "Give this gentleman your hand. He is your first cousin. He will be your friend, and protect you when I am gone."

The girl broke into sobs when she heard this.

"Give him your hand," my uncle continued. "He has an open and frank face, and though I scarcely know him, I believe you can trust him completely."

"Yes, I am sure she can," I said.

The girl gazed at her father and then at me with profound bitterness. She stretched out her hand to me, and I took it briefly in mine; it was small but work-worn.

"Well," murmured the old man; "I don't want to keep you any longer, Shanti. Goodbye, then," and he stretched out his arms and hugged me weakly. I left the room and walked down to the ground floor.

"If I can do anything for you, let me know," I said to my cousin.

"There's nothing now. When I need help. . ."

"When you do, let me know without any hesitation."

"I will. Thank you very much!"

"Goodbye, Mary."

"Goodbye."

Allen was waiting for me at the gate. He held the horse while I mounted, and then said: "You don't need a guide, I expect?"

"No."

"The horse knows the way; you can leave him at Aspillaga's smithy."

"Very well."

The night had cleared rapidly. The moon, almost full, was enveloped in clouds, but its light vaguely illuminated the sea. The wind still howled furiously. Circles of phosphorescent foam shone upon the waves.

Just as Allen had said, the horse knew the way, and I had merely to hold him in, so that he would not break into a gallop. I reached the smithy very quickly, and from there I returned to my house on foot.

I did not know what to tell my mother; perhaps it would prove too emotionally unsettling to tell her that her brother lived a short distance away, and that he was on the point of death.

When I entered my room, my mother, still awake, called from her bed: "Did anything happen?"

"No, nothing."

"Did you get wet?"

"No."

"Was it important?"

"No. I'll tell you tomorrow."

I put the letter my uncle had given me for Machín in a locked drawer of my table; then I went to bed; but try as I might to sleep, I could not.

The next day I told my mother everything that had happened at Bisusalde the night before. I do not know whether she doubted the truth of what her presumed brother had said, or whether she thought he was trying to get some of the inheritance away from us, but the fact was that my mother was much less moved than I had expected, and I even got the impression that she thought I had done wrong in swearing to help my cousin.

Later on in life I have come to realize that mothers concentrate all their hopes and attention on their children's interests, and mistrust everything that might possibly affect them adversely.

I harbored no doubts in the matter: the evidence convinced me that the old man was Juan de Aguirre and that Mary was my cousin.

VIII. URBISTONDO AND FAMILY

For some time I went almost every day to the house by the beach. My uncle grew steadily worse. The doctor predicted the end within a brief period.

Several times I asked Mary if she had any plans for the future. She told me that she could give English lessons to some of the young men at Elguea and continue living there. But I told her this would be impossible.

"Why?"

"Because it simply can not be, child. How do you expect boys of your own age, or older, to show you any mercy? It can't be."

"But if I teach them English just as well as any other teacher?"

"It doesn't make any difference. No one would pay any attention; or rather, they would pay you too much attention."

She thought a moment.

"Supposing I set up as a dressmaker and make dresses for women?"

"But, do you know anything about that sort of thing?"

"No, but I could learn."

"Perhaps it would work."

I offered to pay for everything she would need to begin, though I was privately dubious of her success. That very day, she wrote off to Bayonne and Paris, requesting catalogs and fashion magazines.

My mother, who had felt a definite antipathy toward the girl from the moment I spoke to her of my cousin's existence, made inquiries and received bad reports. According to a woman in Izarte, Mary lived the life of a savage, running about the rocks, throwing stones, and had often been seen with the lighthouse-keeper's daughter, an equally wild young girl, fishing for squid.

I attempted to point out to my mother that Mary was not of the age in which she might be expected to act sedately, and that if she went with the lighthouse-keeper's daughter to fish for squid, it was probably not so much a whim as a necessity. My mother could not be convinced, and she let me understand that if the girl was left an orphan, she was not disposed to take her in.

"Even if it were proved that she is your niece?"

"If that can be proved, then we'll put her into some school."

A few days after this conversation, I found Mary at home with her friend, the lighthouse-keeper's daughter, the wild girl with whom she went fishing for squid behind Mount Izarra.

This girl's name was Genoveva; but everyone called her Quenoveva, and she had grown to believe that this was the correct pronunciation of her name.

Quenoveva I found instantly sympathetic. She was a robust girl, intrepid but shy, deeply tanned by the sun and the sea air, with eyebrows that almost met. That first day she was dressed in her best clothes, a light blue blouse, a blue skirt, red stockings, and white rope-soled sandals. She was thrown into confusion by the slightest thing. All in all, she seemed an excellent friend for Mary, for whom she obviously had a deep affection.

Mary told me they were planning to go to the lighthouse.

"If you like, I'll go along with you."

"Fine."

The three of us walked along the beach and were soon on the promontory leading to the lighthouse. I was astounded that Mary could speak Basque so well. She was like a village girl who has never left her native home. As we drew near the lighthouse, Quenoveva suddenly began to yell like a man, and ran toward the guardrail on the tower, where she had seen one of her little brothers leaning over.

Mary looked at me, doubtless to see what effect her friend's explosions made upon me.

The lighthouse and the keeper's house formed a single structure built into a recess of the rock. We descended to the house by means of a narrow stairway and entered along a corridor with doors on either side. A swarm of children, yelling and fighting, came toward us. The lighthouse-tender was a widower, and Quenoveva watched over her eight brothers and sisters as if they were a drove and she their drover, controlling them by yelling.

Quenoveva showed Mary and I into her father's office, the best room in the dwelling, and she closed the door so that the mass of progeny should not pile up around us.

"A *señorito,* a gentleman!" cried several of the tiny savages, bitten by curiosity.

Mary opened the door and brought back one of the youngest in her arms; when he found himself scooped up and imprisoned, and in the presence of a stranger to boot, he began to cry and kick with such fury that she was forced to put him down.

"The lighthouse-keeper is taking a long time," I said to Mary.

"It's because he's lame."

"Oh! He's lame?"

"Yes."

We waited on in the office. The walls were hung with a map of the world and the plan of the lighthouse on blue paper, both of them tacked up. The room also contained a chronometer and a barometer. On the table there was a half-finished boat model, which the keeper was apparently carving with a pen-knife.

Soon the sound of a wooden leg was heard approaching along the corridor, and the lighthouse-keeper came in. Juan Urbistondo was an extraordinary type, an old sea wolf.

He must have been close to sixty; his face was weatherbeaten, his expression warm, his nose red and shining amidst his wild beard, like a rose among foliage. We talked together for a long time, and I was genuinely astonished. He was a man of such an absurd faith in himself and his own strength that he felt capable of undertaking anything. He did not entertain the most minimal doubt, the slightest hesitancy that might have shaken his settled conviction. To this enormous self-confidence was added such simplicity and complete lack of malice that one was nonplussed. Only the sea can produce such types.

The lighthouse was of the latest model; some person of influence at Elguea had arranged for Urbistondo's appointment; and now Urbistondo was of the belief that the entire world depended on his light. He also thought it was something transcendental and a matter of the utmost complexity to light a petroleum lamp and fit the chimney.

Urbistondo would climb the winding stairs up the tower, convinced of his sacred office and of the transcendence of his mission. He was also convinced that there was a profound and hermetic science involved in the comprehension of the barometer and the thermometer. As for himself, he possessed a barometer more accurate than all others in the world: his leg. He explained to me how it had come to be amputated, when a cask had fallen on it, and I was not sure whether to be horrified or laugh when he told me that because the stump continued to show gangrene, the leg had to be cut two or three times, in round slices, as if it were a piece of hake.

The day after meeting him, I found out, at the watchmaker's, all about his life and his one great resentment.

For a long time Urbistondo had been skipper of a passenger ship running between Bilbao and Liverpool. The ship company owners had begun to replace all their old sailing vessels with the then new auxiliary steamships.

Urbistondo did not believe in steam. It seemed to him the

height of stupidity to waste coal when a ship could run along under sail, and whenever the wind was fair, in the thought that he was doing the company a favor, he would order the fires extinguished, the sails run up, and he would navigate as the Good Lord had meant man to do. The company recommended that he do them no favors; but the captain, with that admirable faculty for believing implicitly in his own mental faculties, paid no attention. He considered it his duty to do his best by everyone. Finally, the director of the company took him off his ship and put him to work in the warehouse, where the accident involving his leg took place.

The ex-captain had very little money with which to feed nine children, and the eldest two worked in town as apprentices. Urbistondo also fished from his tower, using equipment that had been given to him, and he sold his catch. Quenoveva fished, too; she and her brothers would go looking for squid in their boat.

The family was quite amusing and very warm. The old man showed us around his house, and then he took me up to his tower. There, he asked me confidentially about Mary's father; I said that he was not getting any better, and when I added that I was worried about what would become of Mary, the old man exclaimed: "Eh! See here, my friend. If Mary has to leave Bisusalde, let her come here. This house is open to her. I'll give her a room, and Quenoveva will take care of her."

"But, Urbistondo, you've got a lot of people to support."

"It's nothing, Shanti. There's nothing more to say. She can come here."

I thanked this strange man, so absurdly generous that though he had nine children to support on a tiny salary he was willing to burden himself down with still another person. In the face of his insistence, I agreed to do as he said; the lighthouse would actually be a good refuge for Mary, at least at first.

We took our leave of the lighthouse-keeper; I accompanied my cousin to her home, and then I went on to Lúzaro.

IX. ALLEN'S PRAYER BOOK

My uncle's illness was approaching its natural conclusion. And the day when I must return to sea would soon be at hand; my leave was nearly up, and I was receiving urgent messages from Cádiz. The idea of spending four or five years in a row at sea was beginning to seem like a hard fate. My mother was lament-

ing both the idea of my having to leave and the alternate possibility of my losing such a good placement.

I was somewhat at a loss as to what to do and to whom to
turn for advice; half in earnest, and half as a pleasant diversion,
I decided to go and visit Quenoveva. One morning I walked
to the Beach of Souls' lighthouse. As I came up on the platform, I spied one of the keeper's children and asked him: "Is
your sister in?"

"Who, Quenoveva?"

"Yes."

"She's down here."

I descended and found the girl, her hair loose, her legs bared,
wrapped in a tattered and rent skirt. She was washing. When
she saw me she got up slowly, deeply embarrassed; I tried to
put her at ease, and explained why I had come and what was
worrying me. I told her that my ship's run was such a long
one that I would have to be gone from Lúzaro for two or three
years and would be unable to see Mary. I did not like leaving
the girl alone, and I wanted the advice of her friend.

Quenoveva listened to me with the greatest attention, as if
she were afraid to lose a word. She thought it over, and announced that she believed I ought to abandon the Philippines
run, and attempt to find a berth on a ship plying between
Bilbao and Liverpool. Her father could write to the director of
the company for whom he had sailed before.

This advice seemed good to me, and I spoke to Urbistondo
about writing a letter for me. He was very happy at the opportunity of being able to use his influence.

I wrote to Cádiz, telling them that I was sick, and planned to
give up my position as frigate captain, and then I sat back and
awaited developments. My mother announced herself of the
opinion that to abandon the Cádiz-Philippines run in order to
sail to Liverpool was a lowering of category, but I was never one
to think much of categories.

One morning at the beginning of February Mary sent me an
urgent message, summoning me to Bisusalde. I dressed, borrowed
Aspillaga's horse, and I made my way to the house on the beach
at a trot. My uncle, Juan de Aguirre, was dead.

In the house I found Mary, the old manservant, Quenoveva,
and Urbistondo. I ascertained what was needed. A casket would
have to be ordered from Lúzaro. The burial could be carried out
the following day, in Izarte.

We sent off the servant to order the casket from the carpenter,
and Urbistondo and I remained in the house.

It was odd to see the doctor from Elguea sitting at a table in the house and making out the death certificate in the name of Tristán de Ugarte, seaman.

I was fascinated, but I said nothing. That night, Urbistondo, Allen, and I sat in wake over the body, and the next morning we buried my uncle in the small cemetery of the settlement.

The day after, Mary was installed at the lighthouse; Allen went to live at the inn at Izarte.

A few days later, Allen presented himself at my house with an extraordinary request. He was carrying a prayer book in his hand.

"Your uncle and I," he began with the air of imparting a mystery, "knew where there is a treasure buried."

"Heavens!" I managed to exclaim.

"Yes. It's on the coast of Africa, and the directions are in this book."

"In a prayer book?"

"Yes."

"And what is it you want me to do?"

"First, read what's in the book; then, if you like, we can join forces."

"As far as reading is concerned, I don't mind at all. Though I don't understand why you don't read it yourself."

"The directions are written in Basque, and I don't understand the meaning very well."

"Well then, let's see it."

I opened the prayer book, which was in English, and saw that on one page a number of letters had been circled with a pencil.

"The marked letters have to be put together," said the old man.

I took a piece of paper, put the letters together in a sensible spacing, and finally I had a sequence of words in Basque which, literally rendered, meant: "Fifteen miles from the coast, on the river Nun, North 7 degrees West. Old castle. Line of sight from the eye of the elephant between two rocks towards the sharp boulder half a mile away near the river. In the shadow of four in the afternoon of the 27th day of September."

I handed the translation to Allen, and he asked me: "Do you want to come with me?"

"Where to?"

"To Africa, for the hidden treasure."

"I can't, my friend, I don't have the means. . ."

I did not want to tell him that this tale of a treasure struck me as a piece of absurd fantasy.

"So that you would be willing to grant me your rights?"

"Absolutely."

"That's very good of you."

Allen took his leave of me, and a few days later he vanished from the town.

X. THE SERPENT'S CAVE

The following week my cousin told me she wanted to move into Lúzaro.

Once again I urged my mother to take in the orphan, but she flatly refused. She did not even believe the girl was her niece and intimated that she was probably the daughter of some adventurer, God knows who.

I went to see Cashilda, Recalde's wife, and arranged to pay her for Mary's room and board, providing the girl gave no trouble.

Urbistondo had received a letter from Bilbao accepting my petition. I would have a ship to command.

I went to bring Mary back to Lúzaro and present her at Recalde's. It was the day of Christmas Eve. I had brought with me a little jewelry box lined with satin, containing a gold ring set with pearls for Quenoveva, which had cost me eight *duros,* and a package with some toys for Urbistondo's children.

Quenoveva turned pale and then red with pleasure when I gave her the ring. In regard to the toys, Urbistondo was of the opinion that for the first day it would be enough for the children merely to see the toys, otherwise they would break them at once.

I took my leave of Urbistondo and his family, and Mary and I started out toward Lúzaro via Mount Izarra. She walked along at the same pace I did, with the agility of a country-woman; her glances seemed alternately to express fear, boldness, and anger. The day was gray, the sea covered with mist; the wind whistled among the trees, shaking the red leaves still remaining on the beach trees and the black cones on the pines. Large raindrops fell noisily on the dry leaves that lay in the protection of every rise in the land.

Mary was sulking.

"What's the matter with you?" I asked.

"Nothing."

"Yes, there's something wrong. Are you mad at me?"

"Yes."

"Why?"

"You didn't bring me a ring!" she said with a pained expression.

"That doesn't matter. I'll buy you a prettier one."

"No, no. I want one the same as Quenoveva."

"Well, one like Quenoveva's then."

"Besides," she added, her voice tearful, "your mother doesn't want me. . . She says I'm a bad girl . . . that I go around throwing stones. Your mother doesn't want me . . . and you don't either. My father is the only one who wanted me, and I'm going to go with him."

And the girl, in a moment of sudden and uncontrolled despondency, approached the edge of the cliff, with the apparent intention of hurling herself into the sea. I took her by an arm and drew her back.

"Mary!" I yelled, and shook her. "You'll regret this foolishness."

The girl now began to sob with immense bitterness. I let her cry for a time, and then I stretched out my hand to her:

"Come, Mary, it's beginning to rain."

She placed her tiny, rough hand into mine, and we began to climb the Izarra. We scaled up the side as fast we could, scurrying to avoid the wet. It was raining harder all the time; soon we were nearly in front of the cave of *Egan-suguia*.

"Let's stop in there," Mary said; after her tears, she felt better and was smiling and seemed in good humor despite the downpour.

"In there, my dear Mary," I said to her, "lives a great winged serpent, with the claws of a vulture and the face of a woman, called *Egan-suguia*."

"And what does she do?"

"She poisons the air with her breath, and eats little children."

"Who has ever seen her?"

"I don't think anyone has."

"And are you afraid of her?"

"Not I."

"Then let's go into her house."

"Let's go."

We went into the cave. It was not, as it had been in my time, filled with weeds, but was completely cleared; at the back of the cave there was a straw paillasse, probably made by some shepherd.

"Where are you, *Egan-suguia?*" Mary called. "Come here, we

want to talk to you and thank you for the loan of your house. . .
She doesn't come!"

"She must be out on an errand," I answered. "Maybe she's lost
in the woods, or is in Lúzaro looking for an umbrella."

"Poor thing! In a cave like this she must be very cold! I don't
think this *Egan-suguia* can be as bad as people say. If she ate
children, there would be some bones lying around, and there
aren't any."

"She has a strong stomach, and she swallows the children
whole. . . Mary, what should we do? Do you want me to go
to Lúzaro and bring back a raincape?"

"No. Sit down here. The rain will pass."

"What shall we do meanwhile?"

"We can talk."

We sat down together on the floor of the cave.

Mary wanted to know where I was intending to take her. I
explained about Recalde's wife and how she lived. She next
asked about what I was intending to do. I told her about my
plans for returning to sea, about my earnings, when I would return.

We were very serious for quite a while. After a spell it began
to let up, and we left the cave.

"Thank you, *Egan-suguia!* Thank you very much," Mary
called as we left. "It's not true that you eat children. You're
very good, and lend your house to people crossing the mountain.
Goodbye!"

We finally reached Lúzaro and I took Mary to Recalde's house.
She had grown quiet and content. She was planning to begin
work soon. For my part, I was deeply disquieted. I understood
that I was enamored. Mary was merely a child; I was much
older. And I would have to be gone a good deal of the time. It
was a bad beginning for love.

BOOK FOUR

A Dutch Hooker called the "Dragon"

I. THE CAPTAIN OF THE "DAMA ZURI"

From service on the ships running between Bilbao and Liverpool I went on to work for a company with transatlantic ships plying between Bordeaux and Buenos Aires. The short periods I had in port I spent in traveling to Lúzaro to see Mary and my mother.

Mary had adjusted to a sedentary life, and was working for herself as a dressmaker. We wrote each other with every ship's mail: I addressed her as "My beloved Mary," and she addressed me as "My beloved Shanti." I had never clearly told her that I loved her, or that I wanted to make her my wife. "The *Egansuguia* will watch out for us," I would say in jest.

My mother knew that the doctor at Elguea had made out a death certificate for her presumed brother in the name of Tristán de Ugarte, and she chose to believe that any relationship claimed by the Bisusalde sea captain was fraudulent. Still, inasmuch as Mary's activity at La Cashilda's house was all laudable, my mother was beginning to feel a certain sympathy.

My days at sea had become painful to me. My thoughts were in Lúzaro.

I would stay in my cabin whenever I was not on duty. And the days seemed endless. I began to hate the blue skies of the tropics.

On the return trips, when at night we could no longer see the Southern Cross over our heads but instead began to make out Polaris and the two Ursas, I would begin to feel better.

As we approached Europe, passing ships that saluted us and hearing the foghorns off the coasts, I was filled with a sense of joy. Whenever I had the opportunity, I would take a boat at Bordeaux, even if it meant spending only a single day at Lúzaro. Otherwise, I would remain aboard ship, writing long letters to Mary.

The mystery of my uncle's two names was suddenly cleared up for me at Bordeaux. An old retired mariner who kept a nautical shop there, and who had sailed with my Uncle Juan, furnished me with new information regarding Mary's father.

I was making preparations for an early sailing one morning when I received a visit aboard from the Basque captain of the schooner "Dama Zuri," who brought with him a letter of introduction from my friend Recalde. The "Dama Zuri" was a three-masted schooner, white as a seagull and haughty as a swan.

The captain was anxious to buy some equipment for his ship, and he had been told that he could find the best and cheapest in Bordeaux; he had also heard that the seamen of Bayonne and the Basque coast of France dealt largely with a Basque merchant here.

I accompanied my countryman in search of this merchant; we asked at a rigging shop on the river bank and were directed to a place on the Burgundy quay, almost in the center of town.

The shop was a kind of cave, below street level, reached by a set of stairs leading from the sidewalk. The low, wide show window contained ship's lanterns surrounded by thick, gilded wires, chronometers, log lines, sextants, telescopes, and numerous other instruments; in addition, there were coils of rope, lead lines, hemp rigging, anchors, metal cables, iron rings, white and black rain gear, and an infinity of canvas nautical supplies manufactured at Angers and Bordeaux, numberless types of fishing gear, and English canned goods. The shop was pleasantly redolent of tar. A name, half-erased, was written in black letters on the glass window: Fermín Itchaso.

The captain of the "Dama Zuri" and I entered the shop. A young man came up to meet us, and I addressed him, but it was apparent that he did not speak Basque. My countryman did not know French and wanted to speak directly to the owner. The young man told us to wait a moment, until his father returned.

We did not have to wait long. The father was an old man, bent slightly forward at the waist, with white hair and a pipe in his mouth. He was dressed in black, was smooth-shaven, and wore the large beret of the Gascons; his side whiskers were short, of the type the French call rabbit-feet, and on each of his wrists blue tattoos showed beyond the cuffs of his sleeves. He had a long nose, small eyes, eyebrows thin as a painter's brush stroke, and a fixed sardonic smile.

His son told him what the captain of the "Dama Zuri" wanted; when he introduced us as Basques, the old man raised his arms in enthusiasm.

"From what town?" he asked us in Basque.

"From Lúzaro."

"Spanish?"

"Yes."

"I'm a French Basque. Our land is very good, eh? I don't mean to say that the Gironde is bad, no. It's rich, but the Basque country is something else again."

Then, fixing his eyes on me, he asked: "What town did you say you were from?"

"From Lúzaro."

"Lúzaro," exclaimed the old man. "I knew someone from Lúzaro. Ah, yes, now I remember," he added, putting his hand smartly to his forehead. "The mate of the "Dragon" . . . Tristán, Tristán de Ugarte."

Tristán de Ugarte was the name in which the Elguea doctor had made out the death certificate for my uncle; and the "Dragon" was the name of the ship on which Juan de Aguirre had sailed as mate, according to the tale told me by Francisco Iriberri.

"Then you knew Tristán de Ugarte?" I said.

"Yes. Did you know him?"

"I should think so! He was a relative of mine."

"Is that true? . . . Yes, there's a resemblance, your voice . . . or in something, I'm not sure what . . . And what became of him?"

"He died a few months ago."

"In Spain?"

"Yes."

"Who was he living with?"

"With his daughter; and a servant, tall, red-faced. . ."

"A Scotsman?"

"Yes."

"Allen. I remember him."

"How did you happen to know my relative?"

"Do you plan to stay in this port very long, sir?" asked the old man.

"Tomorrow morning we leave for Buenos Aires," I said.

"Well then, if you haven't anything more important to do, come by here this afternoon at five. I'll tell you what I know of Ugarte."

"Good enough. I'll be here at five o'clock."

"In that case, let's get on with our business," the shopkeeper said to the captain of the "Dama Zuri."

I took my leave of the captain and of Itchaso, and went back to my ship. At five I made the return trip to the Burgundy quay, and walked once more into the ship supply shop.

Old Itchaso was waiting for me, and the moment I arrived he led me into a small room with a window overlooking the quay.

The mixed and variegated masts of frigates, brigantines, and schooners stood out against the sky. The room contained a bookcase, with various volumes standing out prominently, among them the *Dictionnaire Philosophique* by Voltaire.

"This book is a particular friend," the old man announced, following the direction of my gaze.

"You aren't religious?"

"No. I don't believe in superstitions."

Itchaso had brought out a bottle of Bordeaux wine, an old vintage, the bottle still covered with dust and cobwebs. He poured two glasses and then raised his own:

"To the Basque country, sir."

"To Spain."

"To France."

We touched glasses, drank, and the old man began the following narrative.

II. ITCHASO'S NARRATIVE

I'm from Guethary, a small town close to the Spanish border, a town you may know. I spent my early youth there. You also know that we Basques have never felt any great enthusiasm for armies or navies. I was no exception; quite the opposite; the idea of a forced draft made me mad. A brother of mine had been killed in Algeria, and the other was serving on a cruiser; it was impossible to work our family land, and my father advised me to emigrate to America.

When I was sixteen I made a trip to Newfoundland as a cabin boy; it was a bitter experience. The Basques who went to the cod fisheries used to gather at Saint-Malo; we would lease our ships, and sail to Saint-Pierre and Miquelon. But the people who leased out the ships furnished us ancient schooners, some of them not even seaworthy, full of holes stopped up with oakum. On the trip I made, several ships went down—about fifty men being lost.

There was no future for me in my own country; I didn't have any money, and there was the damned military draft. I made up my mind to go to Brest or Saint-Malo, and from there to England, where I hoped to get a ship to America.

You probably know Brest. It has a magnificent roadstead. The day after I arrived, I made a tour of the city and walked around the docks, looking at the headlands of Finistère and Kelerun and the mouth of the river Penfeld, and at the harbor full of frigates, barks, steamships, and the fifty-oared shallops rowed by galley prisoners. I was getting tired of wandering about without any special purpose or goal when a sailor with a friendly appearance fell into conversation with me.

In that era the port of Brest used to be closed down at nightfall by an iron chain that stretched from one side of the harbor to the other; at the sound of the dawn cannon, the chain was lowered and the harbor opened again.

The port was being closed just as I started conversing with the seaman. I didn't know anybody, and I was happy to strike up acquaintance with anyone who could set me straight. I told my new friend I didn't have a berth on any ship, but that I wanted to go to America, and I showed him my papers and certificates clearing me of criminal activity.

The man said to me: "Don't worry. This is a big world. If you know how to work you can always live. Let's go have a drink."

I tagged along, and he led the way to a seaman's hotel, on Rue Souris, a narrow, dark, corrupt street. We went down some stairs and found ourselves in a bar, and there we ate and drank. I drank too much. I can remember stretching out on a table later to sleep; when I looked around to see where I was, I found myself, as if by magic, aboard a big ship which was already under sail and leaving Brest Harbor. We were passing Devil's Fortress when the noise of a cannon boomed out. It was the signal for the opening of the harbor.

I was aboard a slaver. I was told that I had signed up the night before in the tavern. I couldn't remember a thing. A little later, learning how others had been taken aboard, I came to realize how it was done: some were made drunk, others were given dope, then each was led to the ship and helped aboard, under the eyes of the police guards, as if they were simply drunken comrades.

Aboard ship I was given a rosy view of things. I was told I could become rich. As far as I was concerned, I figured there was nothing I could do, and that I might as well just keep going on.

There are only two paths to follow, whether on land or on sea: as long as you're going along the twisted path, there's no use trying to do anything good; you just go ahead, careening along, loosing your sails, until all the masts are down. Then the only thing left is to change ways . . . if it's still possible; anything else is pointless.

The vessel on which I had shipped without meaning to was modern for the times: a freighter with tremendous holds, a real

Dutch hooker. It displaced probably six or seven hundred tons, and was about one hundred and eighty or one hundred and ninety feet long, and more than thirty feet wide.

For a ship intended to carry freight it was rather heavy; and its lines were round, the prow being almost the same as the stern. Except for the forecastle, and some cabins aft, all the rest of the space was hold. Like most of the ships of the time, it had no bridge; its rigging was similar to that of a corvette or large bark. Leaving Brest, it was in ballast, and some two feet of copper were showing above the water.

The name of the ship was the "Dragon," which was something of a clue to its nature.

The "Dragon" was the property of a French-Dutch company engaged in the commerce of Negroes; its principal shareholders were in Amsterdam, Saint-Malo, and Nantes. The company's only name was a set of initials: V.d. H.Z. et Cie.

Compared to ships of today, that ship was laughable. It was wide and wooden; there was a kind of beak above the prow, and the bowsprit, raised high above the forecastle in the old fashion, was equipped with a net to catch seamen if they fell while walking aloft. Over the flare of the cutwater a Chinese dragon, white with gilt decorations, was fixed. The poop section was very well arranged; between the captain's cabin and the mate's there was a second small dragon, carved in wood, with "The Dragon" inscribed beneath it.

The ship was nothing like those old Dutch lighters that used to be seen huddled in the ports in my time. She was black, with a white band round her, and gun ports were painted along her sides to give her the air of a man-of-war.

She was a hooker, a coquettish and elegant hooker, that reminded you of a Dutch dame, white-bodied and plump and dressed in black, who ambled gracefully about the sea. The "Dragon" was a fine ship, a safe ship in which one could place one's confidence, with beautiful rigging and numerous triangular sails. It was one of those vessels the French call *ardent*.

Considering the epoch, the ship boasted veritable refinements: she was clean and comely; the crew's quarters in the forecastle were quite ample; the holds were airy, and there were two large iron water tanks, one forward and one aft.

The "Dragon" had authorization, so they said, to carry cannon, and she had three six-inch pieces on the poop deck, and two over the forecastle.

In the space between the center mast and the after mast we carried a large boat (a whaleboat); above it hung a smaller boat.

The crew was made up of a large nucleus of Dutchmen and Portuguese, and a smaller group of English and Frenchmen. Altogether we were about forty men.

The seamen slept in their forecastle bunks, but when it was too hot, they slung their hammocks on deck.

I wasn't slated to form part of the regular crew; instead I was led to a large common cabin in the poop, shown my hammock and a zinc chest, and told that my duties would be explained to me later. I quickly adjusted myself to my new surroundings.

As I said before, there are only two paths, whether on land or on sea: the straight and the crooked. While a man is proceeding along the crooked path there is no use in his consulting a compass or sextant: you just go on from reef to reef, until you founder.

There was nobody on that ship to give me any good advice or tell me the opposite, and so I thought that life aboard a slaver might be a pretty business; and all the time I was heading down the path to ruin.

III. CAPTAIN ZALDUMBIDE

To be a Basque aboard that ship was a great advantage. The captain was one himself, and so was his camarilla or trusted guard, with whom he always talked in Basque.

It was not at all rare, but rather quite usual, for the outfitters of corsairs or slavers to choose captains from the most distant ports; thus, those from Saint-Malo would select a captain from Bordeaux; those from here, a skipper from Le Havre or Honfleur. At the time when Nantes was one of the most active slaving centers of Europe, there were pilots and skippers there from all parts of the world.

Captain Zaldumbide was tall, stooped, withered. We called him the Old Man, using the English words, or in Basque, *Gure Zarra,* Our Old Man. Zaldumbide scarcely spoke; he habitually looked out of the corner of his eye or squinted, and his eyes were red and not very pleasant; he wore a fringe of whiskers, already turned white, under his chin from ear to ear, and his hair was long. He dressed in a threadbare black frock coat, wore a cap on his head, and when it was cold donned a pilgrim's cloak.

Zaldumbide drank little, or not at all. He was very religious. He would never sit down to eat without saying the benedicite. In his cabin he kept a Peruvian Virgin, with two sprays of blessed rosemary underneath the figure. He would pray before this image, using a rosary with heavy beads.

I often wondered if our captain was insane, for he passed many nights without sleeping, pacing the room and crying, calling on the Virgin. Perhaps his crimes kept him awake.

Before being a slaver, the Old Man had managed to sink several insured ships of which he was skipper, even risking his own life to do so, according to the stories. This series of shipwrecks earned him a good fortune and a bad name. And after that, he went into the "ebony" commerce.

Zaldumbide ruled the crew with a strict hand, and nobody got out of control. He insisted that Sundays be celebrated in a proper manner, and on this day he would dress up in a blue frock coat, which he called his new one, and he would make a tour of the ship. He would inspect the forecastle, walk about in all directions, poking into everything and scolding because he did not find things clean enough, and at the end of his tour of inspection he would go aft to the poop deck and there lean against one of the cannon, to lose himself in his own thoughts.

If any of the Basques blasphemed on Sunday or other holy days in the way the other crew members did, Zaldumbide was savage with us.

As a mariner he was very skillful, although in a routine way. He knew very little theory, but he had a great deal of experience and practice behind him. Navigational operations were not verified by the sextant. Zaldumbide made his estimate by calculating the location of the ship, the direction that should be followed in accordance with the indications of the nautical needle, and the distances measured by the log line. He would set down the figures daily in the logbook. I would often help him to play out the log line and to measure. He had an old-fashioned log line; in general, everything used by the captain was old: the barometer, the chronometers, the sea charts. He had a sandglass in his cabin—he preferred it, because of its silence and accuracy. Zaldumbide hated everything new. Like all old-fashioned men he believed that man evolved from good to evil; we, the believers in progress, believe the opposite: that man is evolving from evil to good.

In times of trouble, Zaldumbide was a great seaman and a man of ferocious bravery. He knew, merely by the way the wind hit him in the face, what had to be done. When he climbed up to the poop deck—followed by Old Sam, the bosun, who seconded the captain's orders with blasts of his whistle—Zaldumbide was clearly a man who knew how to command; he was exacting in his orders, and his rough sailor's voice, formed by shouting over the storms at sea, seemed made to dominate men and the elements.

As you know yourself, sir, a man who commands a sailing ship for any length of time comes to look on his craft as something alive; the Old Man thought this, and he talked more to his ship than to the men on it; he looked on his vessel as if it were a woman, his wife or his mistress.

The only diversion Zaldumbide allowed himself was to play with Mari-Zancos, a little monkey a Spanish captain had given him.

Zaldumbide was avaricious as are few men. In his cabin he had two or three brass chests which, according to general report, were filled with valuables.

The captain was a French Basque, and as a Basque he selected me to form part of his personal service and guard.

"On this ship," he told me the first day, "the man that does his duty lives well. Now then, the man that doesn't had better pray for his soul."

At first, I scarcely stirred about the ship. I never went forward to the bow. My domain was from the poop deck to the poop mast. The captain's cabin and the first mate's were under the deck, and were equipped with barred portholes; our general cabin was in front of them, and over us all, on the poop quarter-deck, there was an upper chamber, divided by a bulkhead and forming two cabins; one of these cabins was occupied by the navigator, Franz Nissen, a Dane who never spoke, and the other by the medical officer, Doctor Cornelius.

Franz Nissen was a very serious man; he steered a straight course with the greatest precision; he noticed the water only when the waves were of a size to cause trouble.

The compass was in front of the poop deck, in sight of the helmsman. The binnacle was a large one, with glass case and two copper lanterns to illuminate the compass face at night. On those old wooden ships there was no need for the corrections that are necessary today on iron ships, with their Thompson compasses and their Flinders bars.

The cabin belonging to Nissen, the helmsman, had a small porthole, from which he could see the compass, and a trap door which led to the captain's quarters. In case of mutiny or any trouble, the upper chamber on the poop quarterdeck and the three cabins—the captain's, the mate's, and ours—could be closed off; these cabins, moreover, were equipped with armor plate.

Under the captain's cabin was located the powder magazine

and arsenal; beneath the mate's room was the bread pantry; and beneath our cabin, which was called the Basques' cabin, the storeroom.

As I said before, the Basque camarilla apart, the crew was made up of Englishmen, Frenchmen, Dutchmen, Portuguese, and one Spaniard, a couple of Chinamen, a Malay, and a Negro.

We Basques formed the poop-deck guard. We scarcely ever ventured toward the prow beyond the large hatchway. From the whaleboat to the bowsprit the bosun and the cook kept things in order. We stood four-hour watches, divided into a port and a starboard watch; Tommy, the cabin boy, signaled the changes of watch by sounding the ship's bell.

The captain obviously placed very little trust in his men, for he had taken elaborate precautions. To reach his cabin it was necessary to go through our cabin, where his trusted guard slept, and then to follow along a zigzag passageway, lined with iron sheeting and fitted with small round peepholes from which we could fire in case of attack.

The ventilation openings in our cabin were protected with iron bars, and the doors and portholes lined with metal. A table fastened to the floor in the middle of our cabin could be dismantled and fitted into the wall as a buttress.

Our lamps were put out at eight o'clock by regulation. By that hour our hammocks were slung every night, and they were taken down at dawn. The rest of the crew and the bosun were quartered in the prow, in the forecastle, but in the torrid zones near the Equator they slept on deck.

We Basques, following the captain's instructions, ate separately, and Zaldumbide saw that we got cold cuts and sweets to keep us happy.

Every day we got some strong coffee, prepared by Arraitz, one of the Basques, and a ration of rum. Our material life was good —we ate well, and we had tobacco. In bad weather, we would shut ourselves up in our cabin to talk and play cards.

The captain was a barbarian, like all slaving captains. Whoever fell down in his duty was flogged like a dog. Zaldumbide had a long rope's end with which he would administer a "small dose." That was what he called flogging a man until he was unconscious. By and large, Zaldumbide was quicker to punish bad will than he was to punish laziness.

When Zaldumbide was in a gay mood and felt like a little sport, he did the whipping himself. When he didn't feel like it, the Negro Demosthenes, who was also the executioner and hangman, did the work. To punish theft, Zaldumbide used stocks and chains.

Basically, the captain was more of an egotist and skinflint than a cruel man. His only real interest was piling up money. He must have made a lot. The skippers of slavers did not make out cargo manifestoes for their shiploads nor for rendering their accounts. I imagine that Zaldumbide must have kept more than half the profits of each voyage.

All through the trip, when he was not doing his work, his favorite occupation was praying. And then, he liked to play with the objects in his brass coffers, while Mari-Zancos the monkey kept him company.

His system for making a little additional money was to cheat the sailors out of their earnings by not paying regular wages.

"In the end you'll have more money," he told them.

But later, after the passage of a sufficient period of time, he would muddle all the records and confuse the accounts, and he would always come out ahead.

His favorite phrases were taken from the English pirates: "No prey, no pay," and "No peace beyond the line."

To give you some idea of Zaldumbide's barbarity, I'll cite you two examples. One day, as we passed near Cape Verde, we sank a fishing boat; a few hours later, we found a Portuguese sailor, dressed only in pants and shirt, in a recess on deck.

"What will we do with this man?" asked the bosun.

"Tie him up," answered the captain.

He was tied up, despite his shouts and protests.

"And now?"

"Now throw him overboard."

And so he was thrown over the side.

On another occasion we arrived in Barbados with a load of "ebony wood." We were flying our signals offshore when suddenly a boat appeared carrying two individuals belonging to the local police. The captain received them very amiably, and meanwhile he ordered the Negro Demosthenes and the Malayan Chim to surprise and kill them. They hurled themselves on the two policemen like dogs, and a few moments later the pair were on their way to the bottom of the sea, after being slashed up. We set sail on the instant, and the next day unloaded our cargo of "ebony" with perfect ease.

IV. OTHER DISTINGUISHED MEMBERS OF
THE CREW OF THE "DRAGON"

The ship's crew was made up of individuals who were fugitives or outlaws, and it was only natural that there should be some very exotic types aboard. The Negro Demosthenes, whom I just mentioned, was gigantic, tattooed, and as strong as a winch. Chim, the other's friend, was a dayak from Borneo, one of those Malayans who are as violent as they are cruel.

Chim had been, according to himself, captain of one of those pirate craft called *paraos* in Borneo; captured and on the point of being hanged, he had made his escape.

Chim wore a shell comb in his hair, which was as long as a woman's. Even in the severest cold, he usually went around bare to the waist. The Negro Demosthenes was a man who had been made cruel, but he was not a bad man by nature; Chim, on the other hand, was bloodthirsty and perverse, and his greatest pleasure lay in making other men suffer.

The Basque guard was made up of five men: Tristán de Ugarte, mate, who was from Elguea; Albizu, from Pasajes; Burni, from Ondárroa; Arraitz, from Fuenterrabía, and myself. Our work consisted of cleaning and taking care of the ship from the large hatchway aft to the poop, attending to the cabins, polishing the cannons, and administering the stores from the storeroom. We cut the bacon and pork ration for the day, doled out the coal supply to the cook, the oil for cooking and for the lamps, the bread, the water, and all the other provisions and supplies.

We five Basques knew each other as well as brothers. Each man had his vice. Burni was gluttonous and brutal. Albizu thought only of personal elegance and women, and as soon as he reached port he spent all his money on them. He was the only one of us who had the morals proper to a slaver or a pirate, in short, he only cared about enjoying himself. But still, he wasn't a real tough, the real pirate was Ugarte. The rest of us were amateurs. Arraitz was a gambler; he was always inventing projects while he stared vaguely at the smoke coming from his pipe; he would have gambled his eyelids away, and when he couldn't gamble at cards, he simply laid bets; but he was unlucky, and also very superstitious. He wore a portion of scapularies and little medals around his neck, and he was innocent enough to believe that these little pieces of cloth and tin would preserve him from harm.

Burni we called "Sad Guts" because he was always complaining about some ailment or other which affected his stomach when he was hungry or didn't eat enough.

The lady's man Albizu was very husky, but also very nervous, thin, dry, and tall; his fingers were like iron. The captain was afraid of him, and never let him do anything delicate, for fear he would break something.

Zaldumbide did not want us to be friendly with the sailors. And so we five Basques were hated among the crew. We had a white poodle, which we all fed, and the crew had a dog of their own. Even the two dogs hated each other. The crew itself was divided into two general groups: the Dutch and the Portuguese.

It was impossible to know which were the worst: one group was made up of blond ruffians, the others were dark-haired thugs. The most innocent of the lot had a murder or two on his conscience. They were always quarreling at mess; and every so often a dead man would turn up. We would throw him over the side and go on.

The chief of the Dutch gang was the cook, Ryp Timmermans. His body was one continuous tattoo, a series of replicas of the ships he had served on.

Ryp the Cook possessed a stomach that was a specialty all of his own: he could just as easily drink pure alcohol as petroleum, turpentine, or ink; and then he could bend coins with his teeth, or eat glass. Anything he sank his teeth into was doomed.

Ryp's sidekick was a Chinaman named Bernard the Chinaman; he was a light-haired oriental who liked to hunt down all the rats aboard and eat them.

The leader of the Portuguese band was a half-breed Indian, sniveling and dirty, who acted also as general interpreter; his name was Silva Coelho.

The bosun, Old Sam, was often unable to keep these men under control, and he would ask for the captain's help. We Basques would come on the run to establish order. On the other hand, if the two gangs got together and turned on us, we would have to retreat to the poop, and sometimes even lock ourselves in our cabin section, close off the hatchway, break out the rifles, and prepare a defense.

In such conditions we sailed along by the grace of God and in the hands of the Devil; the crew, drunk, would pay no attention to the bosun's blasts on his whistle, and we ran the danger at any time of running into another ship or into any reef that lay in our way. Zaldumbide's policy, whenever he could not control the situation, was to ignore it.

Old Sam was a deserter from the British navy, and an intelligent and practical man. He was about fifty years old, always wore a heavy pea jacket and a fur cap, and hung his silver whistle from a black silk thread in the buttonhole of his jacket.

Franz Nissen, the navigator and helmsman, was always at the wheel. He was an old ex-convict who spoke with no one and never mixed in anything. He had enough with his own memories. He and Old Sam were the only two the captain paid regularly and correctly. Nissen got us out of many a scrape.

The Basque guard, indifferent to all the turmoil and habituated to our privileged position, would shut ourselves up to play cards and gamble our earnings. We would carry on endless discussions about the most stupid subjects; for instance, we would argue as to which of our home towns was the biggest and best, and we would go so far as to count up the houses in each town.

The English clock we had in the cabin would mark off the hours of our interminable talking by striking loud, sharp notes.

Thanks to the fact that the Dutch and Portuguese hated each other, we were able to dominate them to some extent. Of the five Basques in the guard, four of us were decent enough fellows; but Ugarte was the exception. He was bad, vicious, damned.

Captain Zaldumbide knew him well, and, since he himself was the one and only authority aboard ship and there was no question of any other rank, he told us more than once in Basque, within hearing of Ugarte: "This fellow is a dog. When you're with the other men show him the respect due a mate; but if he bothers you when you're alone back here, I authorize you to give him a thrashing."

We heeded his advice, and one fine day Arraitz warmed his ribs for him so that he wouldn't forget it for a season.

We were the soberest part of the crew, and a quiet Irish lad named Patrick Allen soon joined us out of natural friendship. He was a good boy, very big, with blue eyes and red hair; an excellent fellow, but too melancholy for comfort. He had a fine voice, but he was always playing sad pieces on his accordion. I don't know how he ever extracted such melancholy sounds from the instrument. The happiest noise he produced was when his accordion failed to produce a certain note, and instead had a slight attack of asthma. Just from listening to Allen you would feel wretched and out of luck, and it seemed as if loneliness, the wind, the sea, and fog all rolled over you and bore you down.

The Spaniard, Don José, was a sympathetic figure, and he sided with the Dutch. He was generous, noble in gesture and attitude, and a man of his word; he had only one defect: he was a thief. He claimed that there was nothing comparable to the thrill of stealing. He had never stolen anything because of its value, but always from enjoyment of the act itself. According to him, he had received a good Christian upbringing and education; he said he was the son of a canon in the cathedral of Toledo.

Don José had worked at his trade in nearly all parts of Spain and the Spanish Indies; then, finding his fatherland and its possessions too small for his further glory, he had moved on to other countries until, finding himself wanted by the authorities, he had been forced to ship aboard the slaver, much to his profound disgust and the outrage of his humanitarian instincts.

Don José considered his masterpiece to be a robbery he had carried out in a certain city in South America, where he had stripped the church of a monstrance, several chalices, and various crowns. Having perpetrated this beautiful subtraction, as he called it, with marvelous agility, Don José had called on the judge, reported the theft, given a series of false clues, and left town without anyone lifting a finger against him.

When he was asked if, as a religious man, he did not feel terrible remorse at this type of crime, he said he did not, because he had committed it with certain mental reservations and, moreover, had felt and still felt a noble impulse to change his ways.

Another curious pair were the medical officer, Ewaldus Hollenkind, whom we called Doctor Cornelius, and little Tommy, the cabin boy.

Doctor Cornelius was a corpulent man, bent over, sad-faced, and disagreeable. He had yellowish, sparse whiskers, had a look of continual suspicion, and was the color of lard. He was said to be a Jew. He always wore an old bathrobe and a fur cap. Master Ewaldus had a cabin full of books in all languages, and he could sometimes be heard talking to himself in Latin. But he did not understand Basque, and he would often ask us the meaning of such and such a word; but since we did not like him, we told him any lie that came into our head at the moment.

If Doctor Cornelius was not a witch doctor, he was not very far from it. And he cynically calculated exactly the amount of air the Negroes would need to stay alive in the hold. He also studied the sea, and it was rumored that he was writing a book about the different depth areas.

Some crew members said that Cornelius was so clever that he

had succeeded in changing Indians into Negroes for quick sale; but others said that he had merely tinted their skins with a mixture of pitch, tallow, and nux vomica.

Doctor Cornelius must have employed a unique system of espionage, for he knew everything that went on aboard ship; how, I don't know. He was like one of those fat spiders which remain hidden in their hole but come pouncing out to devour their prey the moment they feel any part of the web move.

Cornelius was a practitioner of homeopathy, a method he called the system of *l'homme du coq.* I did not understand this phrase at first, until he told me himself one day that homeopathy had been invented by a certain Dr. Hahnemann, whose name in German meant Cock Man.

To a sick man he would always quote a Latinism, which, if I remember right, went *simila similibus curantur,* though I'm not sure what that means; but the fact is that whenever a sailor would complain to the captain about a beating he had been given, Cornelius would advise giving him another to counteract it; and if a man complained about a shortage in his pay, Cornelius would recommend suspending his wage. This was his system of the Cock Man.

Every man aboard hated this buzzard of ill omen. His only friend was a black cat, Belzebuth, which he carried around with him on his shoulder everywhere he went.

Just as Doctor Cornelius was the black beast of our ship—the *gettator,* as the Italians say; or a Jonah, as the English say— Tommy, the cabin boy, was our mascot. This boy had been found aboard the "Dragon" one day as the ship coasted along Saint Helena. Where was he from? Where had he gotten aboard? Nobody questioned him very long. He said his name was Tom, and since he was only a child, we all called him Tommy. The sailors tried to get him to clean their boots, but he refused; then they tried to thrash him, and he ran off like a squirrel and hid, and the next day, he threw something with a good aim and gave one of his persecutors a swollen eye, and the day after that he dumped a kettle of boiling water at the feet of another tormentor.

Tommy established his position among us in very short order. He wouldn't work, and he treated the crew with profound contempt. He was an example of the power of self-confidence, even among wild men. Tommy laughed at us all; he even sounded the ship's bell in a contemptuous manner, making it sound crazy and ridiculous.

Since Tommy didn't do anything, all the menial work aboard

fell to the lot of two poor boys, one Portuguese and the other Breton, whom the crew treated scurvily and beat all the time.

Zaldumbide himself looked on Tommy with a certain sympathy. The lad was a clown, a real imp. He had won his independence, and beyond sounding the bell to signal the change of watch, which he did in the most impertinent manner, he didn't work at all. He spent his time teaching our dog and the monkey Mari-Zancos useless tricks.

He also used to do juggling tricks with the Negro Demosthenes and Chim the Malayan. Chim and Tommy also did their own version of William Tell. Chim was an expert knife-thrower, and Tommy would stand in front of the galley door with an apple on his head; Chim would throw a knife and stick the apple to the wooden bulkhead. Once the apple was in place, Tommy would pull out the knife and eat the target, while the seamen roared approval of the performance.

When he got into a bad humor, the little imp would climb to the top of one of the masts and stay up there until the fit passed, when he would come down, gayer than ever.

Another important personality aboard ship was Poll, the English parrot. Old Sam and a friend of his had stolen the bird one night from the British consulate in some Brazilian town. Instead of screaming "Bonjour, Jaquot!" or "Lorito real!" as it would, had it been a French or Spanish parrot, Poll screeched: "Scratch Poll! Scratch Poor Polly!" And it would stick its neck out between the bars of its cage so that it could be scratched.

Belzebuth, Doctor Cornelius' black cat, had a terrible hatred of Poll, and two or three times was on the point of killing the bird.

Tommy, too, would entertain himself by driving the parrot wild. He would blow smoke in its face, and he would taunt it by putting a stick of wood between the bottom bars of the cage, pretending it was his finger, until Poll, who was very vicious, would take a swipe at it and give it a strong bite with its beak; as soon as the bird discovered that it didn't have a finger in its beak, it would draw back in a rage, while the cabin boy laughed loud and long at his success.

With this strange troop aboard, we left Amsterdam behind in May, passed the latitude of the Canaries in June, and soon were among the Cape Verde Islands. Here we made a watering stop, and then crossed over to the African coast. During the voyage we often passed ships going to India, frigates and brigantines; but in that epoch, maritime cordiality was not very great. Everyone was afraid of running into pirate ships, and the slavers, which were numerous off that coast, fled from a meeting with any other ship for fear it would turn out to be an English cruiser.

We reached the coast of Angola, where the agents of all nations, especially North and South Americans and Portuguese, were active. These agents were in contact with all the petty kings and chiefs of tribes and would deal directly with them. In exchange for slaves they would barter rifles, powder, iron instruments, and bracelets made of glass and brass.

We took aboard some two hundred or two hundred and fifty Negroes, men, women and children, and sailing before the southeast trade winds our course led almost straight to Brazil. There we sold our entire lot of cargo. The merchant who bought from us retailed his purchase. The men were worth from two thousand pesetas to five thousand; the children, one hundred and twenty-five pesetas before baptism and two hundred and fifty after; the women were sold at conventional prices.

Zaldumbide did not spare rifles or powder to get a good lot of Negroes. Nobody could give him a venerable old man for a youth, even though his skin was rubbed with dye, nor a man with a hernia for a well-organized individual.

He and Doctor Cornelius would examine the Negroes' teeth, observe their muscles and their movement, and carefully note whether their bellies were swollen or not.

"When I sell a Negro, a good Negro, for five thousand pesetas, he's worth it," Zaldumbide would say, and then add, "Business ethics above all."

The captain did not like feminine merchandise, probably for reasons of morality.

Zaldumbide was not in favor of ill-treating or even beating the blacks, not from sympathy for them, but merely so as not to ruin the goods.

The skippers of other slavers dealt with their Negroes on the basis of the *fouet,* the whip. The whippings were merely a light prologue, in any case, to the treatment they would receive at the hands of the scoundrelly Americans. One must admit, to the honor of *la belle France,* that French slavers left everyone else behind in the art of flaying Negroes, for it was the French word for the scourge that passed into the colonial vocabulary and established itself as the definitive term, and everywhere that Negroes were to be found, the French *fouet* was gloriously present too.

Of course, we should remember that in exchange for losing a few hunks of their flesh the Negroes gained the right to Christian baptism, and so they came out ahead after all.

Zaldumbide was the St. Francis of Assisi to the Negroes. First of all, he didn't put them all into one chamber, but rather into four large cabins divided by bulkheads, he provided straw paillasses for them, and had them brought out on deck to be aired and washed.

"The merchandise is delicate," he used to say.

The captain was not one of those who felt that in order to do his duty as a slaver it was necessary to abuse the human cattle. In fact, he would rather have killed a sailor than a Negro. When he was condemned for this attitude, he would reply: "There's no comparison between a sailor and a Negro. A sailor isn't worth anything; I can replace him anywhere. But a Negro might cost me as much as five thousand pesetas."

The sharks didn't have much to do with us; other slavers, who piled up their Negroes like wood in the hold, were always dumping one of them over the side, where they made a meal for the sharks; but we ran no such mess service for the fishes; there were even voyages on which we didn't lose a single Negro.

Zaldumbide was a diplomat. When he went ashore to visit King Badgu, or Marshall Bungtap, he would urge them to whip the slaves they wanted to sell him. The chiefs were happy to do as he asked. That left Zaldumbide to emerge in a good light later, by contrast. As soon as the Negroes were aboard ship, Zaldumbide would address them, for he knew some Bantu and some Mandinga, and would tell them, in that horrible Negro gabble, that he was taking them to a country where all they would have to do would be to sit in the sun and eat string beans and bacon. The Negroes were delighted to hear this. And Zaldumbide did not feed them on shipboard the way the other slavers did, with millet and palm oil, but gave them smoked fish, beans, and honey. He fed them better than he did the crew. As a result there was never trouble with them. On the contrary, when a Negro got out of the prison compound in which he had been kept on land, and found himself aboard ship with a certain liberty of movement and without being always in danger of a whipping, he would naturally look upon the captain as a benefactor. The old fraud Zaldumbide would smile sweetly; at such times he considered himself the St. John of God to the Negroes. He was a picturesque old scoundrel, was Zaldumbide. And he would have made a good organizer and administrator.

On other slavers, it was customary to make the Negroes dance to the drums, and when they didn't feel like it, they were urged on and made to strut with a whip. This wasn't the case on our ship. Zaldumbide, instead, had Tommy dance for *them*. Fifty

Negroes at a time were led out, formed into a circle, and Tommy would begin by putting the monkey Mari-Zancos, all dressed in red, through his paces; and then he would jump our poodle through a hoop. When Tommy himself finally appeared with a high hat which came down around his ears, and his nose painted red, walking so that his legs bent in; when he imitated the captain and Doctor Cornelius, then the Negroes would begin to laugh, showing their teeth and letting their jaws hang open to such a point that Tommy would go around deliberately pushing them shut with his hands. Then the bass drum—a cask with a skin stretched across the top which was played with bare hand slaps, like a tom-tom—was brought out, and the Negroes would begin to dance. For his part, Tommy would perform all the jigs known to the United Kingdom. And thus the Negro, an innocent creature by nature, would have an amusing time of it and feel no reason to riot.

We would stay in Brazil for a season. The captain would let us have some money, which we would spend deliriously, until we didn't have a penny left, and then we would begin to show up, one by one, aboard the "Dragon."

It was impossible to make as many expeditions as we would have liked; in the first place, there were not always Negroes available to transport, and secondly, we had to take numerous precautions in cleaning the ship, inside and out. If the hold was neglected, for instance, it stank so that we found life impossible aboard ship.

We were forced to keep cleaning continually. We worked on the outside every week, and when we reached some harbor known to the captain by experience, the first thing we did was to scrape the bottom to get rid of barnacles, algae, and seaweed of all sorts; in tropical seas particularly, these growths accumulate at such a rate that the bottoms of ships are like jungles. When we were pressed for time, or did not feel entirely safe, we would run slowly up over a sand bank, at high tide, and when the water flowed away with the ebb, we would scrub what we could reach of the bottom with strong brooms.

Sometimes we would find that even after a long voyage the ship's bottom was as clean as when we had left, and that the copper of the keel and adjacent areas was like gold; at other times, we would soon find it completely covered with marine growth, and would have to set to work cleaning it.

If we had time enough, we would look for some secluded, deserted place, where there was a good anchorage. There we

would lower the whaleboat and the small boat, lash them together with planks, so that they formed a raft, and then we put
the cannons aboard as ballast. Next, we would attach a pulley to
the raft, tie a line to the first crosspiece of the large mast, and at
the same time drop an anchor at the prow and another at the
stern.

We would then begin to haul on the lines tied to the large mast
and the two anchors by taking turns around the windlasses until
we succeeded in forcing the ship to turn over on its side and uncover its keel.

First we caulked the openings on one side, so the water would
not flow in. We would erect some scaffolding, and scrape all the
exposed area; afterwards we would turn over the other side of
the ship, expose that part, and repeat the operation.

All these precautions to keep the ship clean were little enough
to ensure our making a quick escape, in case of pursuit.

V. THE TWO TRISTÁNS

I had been sailing aboard the "Dragon" for several years, and
often I began to think of the possibility of abandoning this kind
of a life.

The crew was always changing. We Basques remained together
for a long time until on one of the voyages, Ugarte, the mate,
suddenly left us; he was replaced by a man bearing exactly the
same name.

On ships such as ours, names meant nothing; no one put any
trust in another man's name, nor asked for his papers. Each man
called himself by whatever name he chose; I myself changed my
name; in case it should come to a hanging, I did not want my
father's name dragged to public disgrace.

The new Tristán came aboard in Batavia, where we had gone
to disembark some Negroes. This new mate was not a thug, like
his namesake, who had been an invidious and impossible man
aboard ship; he did seem, though, rather sad and somber of
spirit. He had been sailing with honorable companies all along,
but his wife had just died, and he was desperate to forget, and
had decided to live a fast and chancey life as the best way of for-
getting his sorrows.

The new Tristán calculated the errors in dead reckoning by
use of the sextant; he would take the altitude of the sun, and then

figure out the latitude. Zaldumbide, who was a keen judge of men, treated him with respect, and mate and captain stood watch on equal terms.

This Tristán, or whatever his name was, didn't give us any luck; from the time he came aboard the "Dragon" we never again made a fortunate voyage. From Sunda Strait we went to Mozambique, and dropped anchor near Quelimane, in an inlet known to the captain.

The new mate was interested in seeing how we embarked the Negroes. We used to hang the regulation red and green lights, and as we came in toward shore we would place a large white lantern on the foremast.

A lookout sat on the bowsprit and he would call back as soon as a red lantern flashed from shore.

At that instant, Doctor Cornelius, Zaldumbide, and the interpreter would row ashore in the ship's boat. The agent would be waiting for them at the trading post.

The "Dragon" entered the river slowly, using only the triangular sails of the jib and a little canvas on the foremast.

As we entered the river we prepared the four anchors. Meanwhile, I was taking soundings. I would fill the hole of the heavy ball with tallow, whirl it around in the air, and fling it as far as possible. Very soon I would call off to the mate the fathoms beneath us.

"What kind of a bottom is it?" he asked.

I would bring up the sounder to see if it was sand, mud, or if there were traces of coral or shell.

When the depth lessened, the bosun would climb to the forecastle deck and stand there ready to hammer the anchor chain loose, as soon as the order to drop anchor was given.

"Bottom!" yelled the mate.

Old Sam gave a whack at the iron piece that held the bow anchor in place, and a moment later the other three were let go, and the ship was firmly secured in place.

The new Tristán and I watched the embarkation of the Negroes shortly after; it was the first load we had taken aboard since the mate joined the ship. Apparently, however, the sources of the ebony supply had dried up in this part of Africa, for the agents were able to send us only twenty or thirty Negroes, in chains. And what a lot they were! Old men, scabby and scurvy, ulcerated, covered with sores. They made a horrible spectacle.

Doctor Cornelius took charge of them in an attempt to make them presentable. We set our course for the Cape of Good Hope, and, after a few days of rough weather, fighting the current around Cape Agulhas, we passed into the Atlantic; after a further series of the usual hardships, we reached Angola and dropped anchor in the Bay of the Elephants, our port of refuge.

Of the twenty or thirty Negroes we had taken aboard at Mozambique more than half had served as feed for the sharks.

We waited in the Bay of the Elephants for a considerable period. We had been told that one of the petty kings thereabouts was organizing a *razzia,* a raid which would net hundreds of slaves.

After waiting for almost a month, we were able to embark only fifteen or twenty Negro men, a like number of women, and a handful of children. A miserable bag. The captain was desperate, and the crew was furious, rebellious. The only indifferent man around was the new mate, who was not interested, in any case, in the money to be made.

With this light cargo in our hold we sailed north before the trade winds; on more than one occasion we were forced to throw another of our Negroes over the side as a present for the sharks. As we passed close in to Ascension Island, we were on the point of falling into the hands of an English cruiser, our mortal enemy.

The voyages of the "Dragon" were taking on a new aspect. According to some of the crew, Doctor Cornelius had bewitched the ship.

We reached Brazil, dropped off the carrion we were carrying, and ran back to Africa. We found the markets empty. There were neither Mandingas, nor Congolese, nor Oulofs, nor Bantus, nor Lucumees to be bought anywhere. There could be no doubt but that the commerce of Negroes was undergoing a crisis. The captain was soon ordered to Batavia, to wait new orders there.

Zaldumbide railed and cursed. The voyage to Batavia would be terribly long, and there would be no money to be made at the end of it. We took four months to reach Sunda Strait, we passed through it, and reached Batavia.

In those days—I don't know if it is still true—people died in those seas like flies. We lost several crew members at the outset.

The captain and Doctor Cornelius conferred with the representatives of the shipping company, and one night we were told that we were sailing for China. We were to load China coolies near the Portuguese colony of Macao and take them to America. Silva, the Portuguese, was to handle the negotiations.

We sailed into China waters, and found ourselves in bestial heat. We all had to go around almost nude. As we approached land, we could see a green marshy coast, and at some distance away, the mouth of a river. The captain, Doctor Cornelius, and Silva Coelho went ashore. We soon learned that we were to carry three hundred Chinamen to America, plus fifty barrels of opium, which at that time was worth a fortune. Four or five pounds sterling were paid for every pound of opium.

The captain was anxious to make good his losses no matter what he had to do. He immediately set to work calculating the amount of water necessary for the voyage. But, as you know, calculations of this sort for ships that depend on sail are almost useless.

The Pacific took a long time to cross, the voyage would be a long one; there were too many of us on the ship, and the water would be our downfall.

One night the embarkation of the Chinamen began. They approached our ship in canoes equipped with two mat sails, canoes they call *tancals*. They kept on coming up the Jacob's ladder, passing along the gangway, and disappearing through the hatchway to the hold.

Our whaleboat came and went on various trips. Three hundred Chinamen went aboard that one night.

"When do we move?" asked Ugarte.

"At once: as soon as there's a little wind," answered the captain.

The mate took charge of the departure. The ship's boat put out to make ready to weigh anchor, and shortly afterwards the windlass began to whirr as it began its work; the sails were hoisted, and at the first whiff of fresh air, we started to move.

As we passed near Cape Engaño, at the tip of Luzon, we were met by a junk; on board was our old mate, the original Ugarte. He had been living in the Philippines, but was tired of it and was anxious to go to America. He had learned of our passage and had arranged to be picked up.

The first Tristán de Ugarte was a changed man; his face was slashed by a fresh scar, still red, which ran from the corner of an eyebrow down to the opposite side of his mouth, cutting across his upper lip. Our old mate had taken to drinking brandy as if it were water.

There must have existed some previous reason for enmity between the two Tristáns, because the scar-faced one, as we now described and distinguished our old mate, seemed to hunt for the occasion to insult and mortify his substitute.

VI. THE MUTINY

The crossing of the Pacific, as you know, is a voyage of deadly monotony. In general, the winds in the far south are steady enough and sailing is fairly simple; but we had first to travel hundreds of miles to reach the trade winds.

We started out in March, and it took us an endless amount of time to get out of the China Sea and cross the line.

We had been sailing for a month, waiting in the equatorial calm for the southeast monsoon, when the captain was forced to cut down on our ration of water. Then, luckily, we were able to make a watering stop soon after at the island of St. Augustine, and start out again.

The mate urged the captain to set some of the Chinamen ashore, for a shortage of water might overtake us a second time; in any case, we didn't know what the crossing of the Pacific might hold in store for us. But Zaldumbide was thinking only of making good his previous losses, and he replied:

"If the Chinamen begin to bother us, we'll throw them overboard."

"Zaldumbide had no sentimental attachment to the Celestials, and it was his fixed axiom that if we got into tight straits it would be easier to put the Chinamen into the water than to put water into the Chinamen.

Three weeks later we were becalmed between the Equator and the Tropic of Capricorn. We were some fifty miles from Society Island. The heat was frightful. The sky was burning, without a cloud, like a red cupola. Not a breath of wind was stirring; the deflated sails hung down the masts. The sea was like molten glass, reflecting a light so bright and cruel that it blinded us all.

On deck, the tar melted; our feet stuck to the boards; the steaming heat was impossible to bear. Skin and throats were parched. Some of the sailors passed out in corners, others seemed to lose their minds, and the sun continued to bite into their flesh where they lay.

In the hold, meanwhile, the Chinamen were smothering, and they had begun to yell for water. The captain sent word that there was no water, and then he ordered us to go and disassemble the hand pumps on the water tanks. As we carried out this task, we understood that the crew was on the point of getting out of hand. However, we were able to immobilize the pumps and bring them back without being attacked. The seamen then poured aft to see the captain, furious as madmen, their eyes bloodshot and wild. The captain repeated that there was no water, and that they would have to make the half-ration do them. Finally, he went and sat down by the whaleboat and engaged Doctor Cornelius in conversation.

It was dusk, and we Basques came out on deck to try and get some air in the midst of that furnace. The sea was still burning and giving off a glare like an incandescent metal. We were gazing about in despair, when Arraitz came running up to tell us that the Chinaman Bernard had opened the hatch to the hold containing the coolies, and that they were rioting. The captain and the doctor were still talking, the two of them seated on canvas chairs in the lee of the whaleboat, and they could not see the seamen and the coolies as they circled around the other side of the boat.

We warned them with a shout. Zaldumbide grabbed up the whip he kept on deck, and dashed among the sailors, beating his way aft with strokes of the lash. We came forward to meet him, thinking he would gain the upper hand; but as he got in front of the galley, where some buckets littered the way, one of the sailors threw his knife, and did so with such skill that he stuck Zaldumbide through the throat.

The captain fell into the middle of the tumult. A moment later, the entire crew hurled themselves against us like dogs; it was only due to the lucky fact that the mate had left open the door to the top chamber on the poop that we were able to save ourselves.

We Basques and the helmsmen were the only ones safe inside. Doctor Cornelius had been trapped; no doubt they were taking care of him at that very moment. Tristán, the scar-faced one, had apparently joined forces with the mutineers.

The seamen and the Chinamen did not take any further notice of us for a while. They were busy putting back the hand pumps and drinking water until they were full.

Once the first moment of panic was over, we made ready to defend ourselves. As I explained before, the upper chamber on the poop contained a trap door which led to the captain's cabin. We descended down it now, and then closed and secured the door to our common cabin, where we Basques slept. This cut us off from the rest of the ship. At the mate's orders we lit the lantern in the magazine, and climbed down into the storeroom containing the weapons, and there we each took a rifle and armed ourselves with plenty of cartridges.

This done, we returned back up under the poop deck, both because it was cooler there and because from there we could see something of what occurred on the deck below. We were apprehensive and excited enough so that we no longer felt any thirst.

We spent the first hours of the night on the alert. There were bottles of beer in the captain's cabin; it was a drink he had liked. We Basques all drank some beer, and the mate gave some to Franz Nissen, the helmsman. Nissen, indifferent to everything, stood at the wheel, a small hand compass in front of him.

About midnight there were two smart knocks at the door.

"Who goes there?" yelled the mate.

"Me," replied Silva, the Portuguese.

"What do you want?"

"We've killed the captain. You'd better give up. Nothing will happen to you."

"It's you who'd better give up," answered Tristán.

Just then, someone stuck the barrel of a pistol in through an opening in the door and fired blindly in on us. I doused the light and we were plunged into darkness.

"If you give up now, we won't do anything to you," the Portuguese repeated once more.

"You're drunk," answered the mate. "We'll talk tomorrow."

"All right, boys, let's break down the door!" the Portuguese yelled. "Bring a sledge."

"I'm warning you," Tristán shouted, "we're all armed in here. We've got the powder magazine, and there are three tons of powder in it. We haven't attacked you yet because we don't want to be held responsible for a massacre. But don't forget that we could blow up the ship if we wanted to."

This threat had its effect. Silva ordered one of his men to investigate to see if we were secured all around, and if the door to our common cabin was fast; when the man returned to say that it was, Silva muttered, "These pigs are ready for anything."

All the rest of the night we could hear, by listening at the peephole of our door, the singing and shouting of the sailors and the gabble of the Chinamen.

We took turns standing guard, though nobody could actually sleep.

The light of dawn finally began to filter in. The heat under the deck was already hideous. When there was a little more light, we opened the door cautiously, hoping at least to get some ventilation. There was no one standing guard outside.

We couldn't hear a sound, and finally Arraitz and I ventured out slowly to see what was going on. The mate did not want us to get into a pitched battle, because even assuming we would have won out, being armed as we were, the cost of our victory would have been too high.

Arraitz and I continued to advance cautiously. Everybody was asleep, and the ship was sailing along alone. Nissen was still at the wheel.

The absolute silence surprised us and aroused our curiosity. Later we learned that the cook had filled some barrels with an equal amount of water and rum, and that the sailors and Chinamen had kept on drinking until they were all drunk.

Since no one seemed to have us under observation or to be concerned with us in any way, we thought we might be able to secure a store of water. Tristán agreed. We found a demijohn in our cabin, and took it along in hopes of filling it.

It was our plan that Albizu and I work the pump; Arraitz and Burni would escort us, armed with rifles, and the mate and Nissen would stand at the door, ready to shout a warning to us if they saw anything we did not.

We started out slowly. We tried the pump on the poop cistern, not expecting there would be any water left, and found none. We would have to make our way to the pump near the forecastle. The four of us moved forward cautiously, looking around in every direction. We found the decks littered with Chinamen. In the midship gangway, there were a number of sailors stretched out drunk. We carefully passed around the side of the galley.

We finally reached the other pump, set it in motion, and brought up some ten or a dozen liters of water. Since we had made the trip without mishap, we made it a second time, and then a third, and filled all the bottles and containers we could find. The forecastle cistern was pretty low by the time we had pumped out all the water we wanted.

On one of our trips, Burni, brandishing his rifle to point, cried out:

"Look! Look over there!"

We were taken aback at the sight. In the pale light of dawn, Zaldumbide's body, strung up to a crosspiece, was swaying to and fro with the motions of the ship.

We told the mate about it, and Nissen, standing beside him, said in his laconic manner, "The keys, the keys."

"That's right," added the mate. "We should search him, and see if he still has his key ring on him."

None of the other Basques wanted to touch Zaldumbide, but I climbed up a rope until I was under the corpse. Suddenly a shudder of panic went through me, as something heavy fell on my back. It was the monkey Mari-Zancos, who had been hunched up and probably sleeping on the dead man's shoulders. I found the keys, and was bringing them down, when the voice of Tommy rang out from the top of one of the masts:

"Hello there! Good morning below. The captain seems to be in an uncomfortable position. . . Ha, ha! . . . Old Doc Cornelius is hanging around on the other side. He's pretty frisky on the end of his string."

We invited Tommy to come down and join us, but he refused, saying that he was having too good a time out in the open to shut himself up in some hole.

The mate ordered us to secure the door leading to the poop deck and follow him. We descended to our common cabin, opened it, and then followed along the ladder.

"Close the hatch," said the mate. "When those people wake up they'll loot the pantry first thing. They won't leave anything behind. We'll have to make use of this opportunity."

We gathered up and carried back to our cabin enough provisions for two weeks: a barrel of rum and one of wine, sausage, dried meat, hardtack; next we went to the bread pantry, and practically emptied it.

Arraitz, who was on guard, soon warned us that the men on deck were beginning to stir.

"Let's get back," said the mate.

"Should we lock up the pantry?" I asked.

"What for? If we lock it, they'll only break in the door."

"Then I'll leave it open."

"Yes, leave it open, and leave the hatch open too. But let's get back inside now."

From the upper cabin we were able to watch the confused situation on deck. The Chinamen had begun to set up an unholy din.

Nissen remembered that Doctor Cornelius had kept a small still in his cabin. We had a surplus of alcohol in our possession, and it would be handy to distill sea water if we needed it. We set up the still, and got it to work. The water problem was solved.

The Portuguese Silva appeared again, with a demand that we surrender. He was anxious to get at Zaldumbide's coffers. The mate answered that we could easily defeat them in a pitched battle, and that we did not attack simply because we did not care to butcher the men. He went on to say that if the crew would put us ashore at some reasonable place, we would quit the ship and leave Zaldumbide's chests behind.

Silva went away, and a little later Ryp the cook came to make a similar demand on us: he also wanted to get at Zaldumbide's coffers. When he learned that his Portuguese rival had already been there to ask for the same thing, he was furious, and he swore he would take care of Silva in his own way.

On the night of the second day, the weather began to change: we could hear the rain falling outside, and soon the ship began to pitch and roll.

The rain murmured outside on deck, and then it began to lash the entire ship. It was a tropical rain, a heavy downpour. The mate managed to hail a sailor, and ordered him to tell the bosun to come aft; when the bosun appeared, the mate told him what should be done to take advantage of the rain and fill the cistern with fresh water.

A workable relationship thus began to be established between ourselves and those on the outside, but we still could not be very certain of anything.

Since the chamber under the poop was very small and closed in, the mate had us use all four cabins in our possession for sleeping purposes. I, for instance, slept in the dead Zaldumbide's bunk.

The rain soon ceased, but the wind and high sea continued, and we were getting buffeted about. Every so often, the water would pour in tons over the deck, and since it could not be drained off rapidly enough, it formed into a permanent wave which slushed to the left and the right and into the cabins.

What could those animals in the forecastle be doing? we wondered. If it were left to them, they would succeed in sinking the ship.

We urged the mate to let us go out and put an end to the mutiny with force, but he held us back saying: "No, no. Let them realize that we're needed. If they don't see that, they would simply mutiny again later."

On the fifth day we were astonished to hear the noise of scuffling and turmoil on deck; we could hear the sound of furious shouting, angry voices. At dusk, I was on watch when I heard knocking at the door.

"Who goes?" I cried out.

"It's Allen. I'm with Sam Cooper and Tommy; we want to talk to the mate."

"Wait a moment."

I woke Tristán, who jumped out of his hammock and directed me to open at once. From what Old Sam told us we learned that the Portuguese and the Dutch, their old hatred flaring up, had set upon each other with clubs and knives on the open deck.

After a battle in which various antagonists had been left dead where they fell, the Dutchmen, more numerous, had driven their enemy into the forecastle, where they were now locked in.

The moment for regaining possession of the ship had come.

"And the Chinamen?" asked Tristán.

"The Chinamen have discovered the opium barrels, and they're lying in the corners, intoxicated, like dead men," answered the bosun.

Tristán had three more rifles brought out for the three Englishmen who had come to report to us, Old Sam, Allen, and the cabin boy; and shortly afterwards, by the light of a lantern held by Tommy, the nine of us set out to regain control of the ship. We found the deck between the aft quarterdeck and the forecastle littered with Celestials, fallen almost on top of each other. The galley funnel was giving off sparks that disappeared up toward the sails. We thought we would find the cook, the leader of the Dutch faction, among his pots, and so he was. He did not attempt any resistance; on the contrary, he was glad to give up, and promised he would see to it that his followers followed suit.

And he was as good as his word. As soon as he had gathered his men, we started for the forecastle, where the Portuguese had fortified themselves. Tristán called Silva Coelho and told him that we outnumbered them decisively, and that we were well armed; he added that we did not plan to attack them; it was up to them to make a choice. The Portuguese chose to surrender.

Tristán de Ugarte, captain in effect, ordered that all the Chinamen be carried back down into the hold. The dead who lay around the deck were thrown overboard, and the rotting bodies of Zaldumbide and Doctor Cornelius were cut down.

Cornelius had a pipe stuck in his mouth, and his belly had swollen. The bodies of the two officers were thrown over the side as well, to feed the fishes. The hatches were battened again, and the sailors were ordered to set to work cleaning up everything.

Once the Dutch and Portuguese found themselves side by side again, they began to quarrel. In order to settle the matter once and for all, each of the two gangs decided to pick one of their own number to fight it out.

Chim, the Malay, was on the side of the Dutch; the Negro Demosthenes, on the other hand, had joined forces with the Portuguese. It would have been logical to pit these two, former friends, against each other. But it worked out differently. A coin was tossed, heads or tails, and Chim was chosen to fight Silva Coelho.

Tristán could only let well enough alone, and he withdrew to his cabin. I stayed on to watch the contest. The dawn was about to break; heavy, scudding clouds could be seen above us, a sign of wind to come.

The two challengers were strong, cunning men, and they both could manage a knife with the best of them. Each one was given a coat to wrap around his left arm by way of shield.

It was a terrible battle; the two enemies leaped at each other, grappled, and bit. Silva Coelho had Chim fast by the hair several times, and he did his best to stab him deeply. But the Malay always succeeded in getting under Silva's guard and would ferociously bite his arm until the Portuguese was forced to let go. Finally, as a conclusion to one of these maneuvers, when one of them broke away from the other, and although I, for one, saw no blow exchanged, Silva began to fall backwards to the deck, a slow scream coming from his throat as he clutched at his stomach. There was a wide gash in his middle, and he was bleeding heavily.

"Now you have 'im! Kill 'im off!" someone shouted.

The Malay hung over the wounded man like a jackal, and sank his knife in his chest with such force that the steel point stuck in the deck.

As if at a signal, the Negro Demosthenes and another man picked up the body and hurled it over the side.

"Bravo, Chim!" yelled Tommy, tumbling over twice and making a splendid somersault, followed all the while by Mari-Zancos, who had taken to Tommy as his new protector.

The day kept coming on. The new captain appointed Nissen to be mate-helmsman, ordering him to stay at the wheel until a substitute could be found for him there.

The new captain and the mate sat down to decide what measures should be taken in view of the changed circumstances. The ship was heaped with garbage, covered with marks of blood and struggle, dirty on the outside. It barely made any headway; masses of green vegetation were to be seen floating in the sea around the "Dragon's" hull.

The captain ordered that we man the whaleboat and the smaller ship's boat and cut the vegetation that was wrapped around the ship; after a few hours' work we were able to accomplish our task, and the ship gained speed.

The next day we swabbed the deck. All bottles, barrels, and containers on the ship were put under lock and key, and the captain ordered the cook not to take out any liquor without his express permission.

VII. ACROSS THE PACIFIC

Though our plans called for us to sail down the Pacific until we reached parallel 50 to 55 South, it was finally decided to head for Tahiti, and put half the Chinamen ashore on some small island in that vicinity.

The question of water no longer worried us; for several days following the re-establishing of order on the ship, it rained heavily and we were able to fill the cisterns.

By the time the weather had cleared, we were off Tahiti. We approached inshore, coasted past narrow bays and luxuriant vegetation, and finally anchored off a small inlet.

The captain went down to the hold and addressed the Chinamen. He told them that the ship was overcrowded, and that we were in danger of running short of water again once we were at sea; he explained that we were in front of a very fertile island and that it would be in the interests of all if half of them went ashore here. He suggested they choose among themselves the people who would stay and those who would go on to America. The Chinamen answered through their spokesman that where one went they all went. They decided, then, that they would all go ashore.

They came out of the hold in groups of thirty, with their small bundles in their hands, and climbed down to the whaleboat; we set out toward shore, and as soon as the depth of the water was only a fathom or so, we would order them over the side; they screamed like sea gulls when they saw they had to jump into the rough water, but we told them to form into a human chain and thus secure their passage up to the beach.

Free at last of Chinamen, we set to work cleaning out the hold, which had become a pesthole.

We headed south, in search of the Straits of Magellan and Cape Horn, sailing before the monsoon across the immense desert of the Pacific. We encountered some whaling ships, hailed them and talked, and checked our position with them.

One day we sighted a ship which seemed to be drifting aimlessly. Desperate signals were made to us from the vessel, and when we came alongside we were asked for quinine. We searched Doctor Cornelius' medical chest, but found none. All we could offer them was some tea. When we took it to them, we found ourselves aboard a pestiferous ship. The crew, all down with the black vomit, were in a pitiful state: they were ragged and dirty, regular yellow skeletons, with rags tied around their heads.

It was not long before the black vomit broke out aboard the "Dragon"; one of the Dutch sailors, Stass by name, delirious with fever, suddenly got up from his sick bed, sang a heart-rending song, and then dived over the side to be seen no more. The mate had everybody who was uncontaminated come aft and sleep in the poop, and the forecastle was converted into a sick bay. Then nobody wanted to go near the forward part of the ship, and we had to cast lots to see who would take food and water to the sick; the man chosen would take the food on the end of a pole, hastily deposit it near the door, and then sprint back. In the midst of all this, Don José, the Spaniard, indignantly announced that we were all of us inhuman and that Christ had commanded us to care for the sick and console the unhappy. We laughed at him and said: "Go on, you go and do it."

To our immense surprise Don José walked forward to the fore-castle and began to take care of the sick.

The scar-faced Tristán came to see the captain and proposed that ship's logs be falsified, the name of the vessel changed, and that we take possession of it. The captain told him that if he ever repeated this proposal he would be put in irons.

The scar-faced Tristán seemed to accept this decision, yet actually he not only did not give up his idea but he began to incite the crew to another mutiny. This was a hard task for him, because most of the men were still convalescing. But a pact was drawn up by the bosun's mate, the cook, and the scar-faced Tristán in which they swore to seize the ship and declare themselves pirates. They planned to arrest the captain one night as he slept in his cabin, and then unfurl the black flag of piracy.

We were kept informed on the progress of the plot, and were convinced of its ineffectiveness. At dusk one day, when the conspirators were beginning to raise a fuss, we arrested the leaders and seized the document they had foolishly drawn up as articles of association; we also found a length of black cloth in their possession. We put in irons all those who had signed the document of association, whether by signature or with a cross.

The angelic Don José, who had joined the party of the pirates, suddenly died on us of the black plague. He was a perfect saint. He died confessing that he was a great sinner and lamenting the fact that there was no Catholic priest on hand to absolve him.

We Basques managed to stay clear of the black vomit, and also of scurvy, which was just then beginning to show its symptoms aboard ship.

We sailed on, in the direction of the South American continent, and at length reached Desolation Island.

There were no longer any traces of the black vomit left on board.

The captain did not think it wise to attempt a passage through the Straits of Magellan, and he decided to double Cape Horn, running a good distance out from land.

Merely to look at the map of that area makes one lose heart: Desolation Island, Port Hunger, Desperation Bay. . . Whenever we approached land, we could see only bare rocks and ice banks. The cold was ferocious, and it was hard to find a corner out of the wind. We spent days of anguish, frozen to the bone, and at one point almost ran into an iceberg which bore down upon us: we had taken it to be a boat under full sail at first, as we stared through the mist.

We reached the Falkland Islands and there rested, anchoring in Solitude Bay. Then we headed north, crossing the calms of Capricorn, crowding on sail to take advantage of the southeast trade-winds and the Brazilian currents.

This crossing was running along smoothly, when at dusk one day, off St. Vincent, an English cruiser appeared and signaled us to heave to, and by way of warning discharged a broadside that fell short.

The captain went into consultation with the mate and the bosun. The wind was strong enough to allow us to make a dash for it; and there was fog all around. After debating the question, the captain ordered the ship brought around into the wind, and we lay to. We were all furious, including the Basques. To hand ourselves over to the English seemed sheer folly; they would string us up with very little excuse; we knew their methods; whenever they captured a slaver, their practice was to hang the captain and sell the Negroes on their own; if the ship was suspected of piracy, they simply confiscated it and everything on board. It was their way of working for the good of humanity, and lining their own pockets at the same time.

It would be logical of them to accuse us of slaving and piracy. The death of the captain and the doctor, which would be hard to explain, would be enough to condemn us. To hand ourselves over to them seemed a piece of madness.

Nevertheless, despite the fact that we all bitterly and silently condemned the move, the ship was brought around until she lay to. The warship thereupon put out one of its boats and headed for us. The fog was sweeping along the waves, and was growing thicker by the moment. The crew was standing by expectantly.

What was the captain planning to do? Suddenly the bosun's whistle was heard; the orders were changed; twelve men swung aloft and moved quickly to crowd on all available sail; every inch of sailcloth was spread to catch the most wind; the grommets whirred, the yards bent with the pressure; jibs, flying jibs, every piece of canvas was put to use. The sails slapped furiously against the masts and yards, and one or two tore. The "Dragon," astonished, gave a great jump and lurched forward, sinking its bow into the water; then it hung on the wind and dashed forward precipitously.

"Hurrah! Hurrah!" yelled the sailors.

"Keep your mouths shut," thundered the captain.

The warship reacted to our maneuver and began to fire upon us; some of their shot passed through the sails, tearing big holes in the canvas. The scar-faced Tristán ran up to urge that we reply to their fire with our cannon, but the captain ignored him.

We sailed all that night, and the next morning we broke out new canvas from the storeroom and replaced the torn sails. As luck would have it, the wind soon died down, and we moved at a snail's pace. We were careful to keep navigating outside the usual ship routes.

All of a sudden, just as the dusk was falling, the English cruiser hove into sight again.

"Just what I was afraid of," muttered the captain. "These incidents always have a second part."

The warship was making better headway at that moment than we were, and it gained on us at a rather fast clip. We crowded on sail again and threw our cannon into the sea to lighten our load. When our pursuer had us within range of his guns, he ran up the English flag; then, without further preamble, the warship discharged a broadside against us; a regular rain of wood splinters and rigging of all kinds showered down upon us.

One of the sails split in two, and fell in a heap; a block hit a sailor and he fell dead on the deck. At the second broadside the mainmast was shattered, as if it had been a clay pipe, and another sailor was killed.

We ran up the Dutch flag, but in vain. The English cruiser did not let up its attack.

Our captain kept up a stream of orders from the poop. We threw the mainmast overboard, and continued ahead. Meanwhile, he ordered the whaleboat lowered; we hauled on the lines, and then lowered it on the side away from the Englishmen. The wheel of the "Dragon" was lashed.

The scar-faced Tristán asked permission to scuttle the ship. Though the captain did not reply, the scar-faced Tristán and Old Sam climbed down into the hold with some tools and immediately started pounding on the bottom. The captain, meanwhile, was transferring his charts and instruments from his cabin to the whaleboat, and the rest of us were scurrying about, gathering whatever money we had in our sea chests. Ryp was going through Zaldumbide's cabin, and while the captain was busy elsewhere, he appeared with two friends, who helped him carry the dead man's three brass coffers to the ship's side, where they were carefully lowered to the whaleboat and concealed under some other supplies. Following the captain's orders, some men were hurrying to put rifles and ammunition aboard the whaleboat while another group brought down tins of hardtack, food, and useful odds and ends of all sorts.

The whaleboat was already equipped with a barrel of water and a lantern to allow compass readings at night. We were tied to the ship and proceeding along at her side, sheltered from the fire of the English. Old Sam and the scar-faced Tristán at last appeared from the hold and climbed down aboard. The captain finally cut the lines holding us to the "Dragon" and we moved out, springing ahead under the force of our oars.

The "Dragon" maintained its course, but it began to settle slowly. The English shifted their fire, and some of their shot fell close to us. The cruiser apparently feared some trick, for they approached the sinking "Dragon" very slowly and carefully.

Suddenly the abandoned ship shuddered to a halt and began to vibrate in place. The "Dragon" resembled a dying animal. The bow began to go down, until it disappeared beneath the waves, and the poop rose high in the air.

Then the poop gradually sank into the sea, leaving behind whirlpools and clashing waves.

Majestically, the sails began to disappear, and soon there was no trace left of the "Dragon."

As soon as night had fairly fallen we hoisted the sail on the whaleboat and headed north. The captain was anxious to get further away from the regular sea lanes and make for the Canaries. When he discovered that Zaldumbide's chests had been hidden aboard the whaleboat, he was furious and wanted to throw them into the sea; but, seeing that we all protested, he decided to make for the African coast nearby first of all, and there bury the chests in a safe place, before going ashore in the Canaries. We all agreed that this move would be the most pru-

dent, since to appear in the Canaries with chests full of gold—
although in all truth we were not really sure what Zaldumbide's
coffers contained—would not be very wise.

The next day, in midafternoon, we sighted the coast of Africa;
it was low, sandy, and glittered in the sun; an isolated hill stood
out at intervals.

According to the captain's reckoning, we were somewhere near
the Spanish colony of Rio de Oro; as we came closer, we could
make out an occasional Arab hut. We decided against landing
on this coast, though we were already very hungry. We sailed
further along, and passed between the Canaries and the African
coast. At length, we made a halt at the mouth of a river on the
African shore. There was a scattering of what appeared to be
olive trees along the banks of the river; this tree, actually the
argan, bears a fruit very similar to the olive, though it is perfectly
round and yellower.

Before ascending the river, we halted before a fortress in ruins.
In this area, at the edge of the Atlas Mountains, there is a chain
of these powerful old forts. No one knows who built them or
against what enemy they were put up. The fortress in front of us
was made of hand-hewn stone and boasted arched towers.

As soon as we stepped ashore we hurried to open Zaldumbide's
coffers. The first one was a great disappointment. Inside it were
nothing but cheap trinkets, of the kind used in bargaining with
the petty kings of Africa for slaves. We had a hard time opening
the other two chests, but they proved to be full of gold pieces and
jewelry.

We all of us had our eyes on the contents, and were ready to
fill our pockets. But the captain convinced us that we were not
yet free of the British cruiser, which might still be lurking around
in the area looking for us, and we agreed that the best course was
to bury the chests and come back later.

The captain picked out a conical rock as the best indicator to
mark our burial site, and we dug a hole there and buried the
chests.

Soon after we finished this operation, a band made up of half
a dozen Moors suddenly appeared; they were filthy-looking,
ragged, but armed with ancient rifles. They had thought to surprise us, but when they were upon us they found that we were
better armed and more numerous than they had apparently
thought. They therefore pretended to be very friendly.

We made them a proposal, offering to exchange a rifle for two
lambs, and they accepted. While they went for the lambs, the
captain said that it would be wisest if we waited for them near

the whaleboat, for it was impossible ever to trust an Arab; they
were all treacherous. On our return to the whaleboat, we stopped
to strip the argan trees of their olive-like fruit. Then we waited
beside the whaleboat for the Moors, and posted one of our number as a sentry on the top of a knoll. We were still waiting, when
of a sudden there was volley of thunderous rifle fire, and the sentry and four men around me fell to the ground. Among them
was Burni. I moved to his side, but he was already dead. A
horde of Arabs was advancing on us at a run, hiding behind
trees and rocks as they came.

We got aboard the whaleboat and started rowing like madmen
out into the river. The Moors were now all out in the open; a
handful of the advance element even had the crazy courage to
run into the water, and two of them had gone so far as to try
to get aboard the whaleboat. Arraitz gave one of them such a
clout on the head with the butt of his rifle that the fellow's brains
could be seen flying through the air. The other one retreated. The
Moors on shore continued firing on us, but their fire was no
longer effective; they didn't hit any more of our number, but we
had the satisfaction of seeing at least a dozen of the vermin
rolling down the shore.

We headed away from that spot with the intention of making
a landfall on the island of Lanzarote.

Two days later we were caught up in a storm from the southwest; though the wind was strong, we could manage it, and we
hoped to make the Canaries soon. In the light of the lantern the
captain kept his eye on the chart and the compass.

When wave after wave and shower after shower had washed
over us, wetting us to the bone, we sighted Lanzarote. The island
looked like a low cloud on the horizon. We approached it full
of hope, when the devil of a cutter appeared from nowhere and
fired a gun at us. It was the signal for us to come around, and it
was impossible to resist. The captain ordered a white cloth tied
to an oar, and he waved it in token of surrender.

Our hope was that the cutter had no connection with the British cruiser that had pursued us, and that it knew nothing about
us, but this hope was soon shattered when we saw the cruiser
itself come into view a little later.

The captain's composure never left him. As the two vessels
bore down on us slowly, he instructed us in what we could admit
and what we should conceal for the common good of us all. He
also told us what each of us could claim as his personal defense.

The business with the Chinamen had been an affair carried
out solely by Captain Zaldumbide, the doctor, and the Portuguese

Silva Coelho; these three had been killed by the Chinamen, who had felt themselves deceived. As for the ship's cargoes and commerce, no one knew anything. If the ship had engaged in slaving or the like, it had been before the present crew signed on.

The captain showed what kind of a man he was: calm and dignified. The British ship took us aboard, and there we were all interrogated. All of us told more or less the same story, with the same details, making every effort to avoid implicating ourselves.

I found myself speaking up for the captain, and said he was a man fallen into difficulties and misfortune, but basically an honorable and just man, such as few are.

His composure saved the captain; probably our statements also helped. The Englishman, who is quite a dog, does not usually need much of an excuse to string up a captain suspected of piracy. It's not for nothing that the English themselves have practiced piracy for hundreds of years.

The scar-faced Tristán proved difficult to handle and was punished on several occasions. The rest of us, the crew, were not treated too badly, and merely had to carry out the hard work assigned us aboard ship.

We finally arrived in Plymouth harbor. We were all on deck, helping in the work of bringing the "Argonaut"—such was the vessel's name—into port, when a French ship passed alongside. When no one seemed to be watching me, I went over the side, and luckily was able to get a hold on the French vessel's anchor chain.

I finally reached Dunkerque, and there I shipped on a one-hundred-fifty-ton schooner, going to Iceland for the cod fishing. I spent a season in the Lofoten Islands, and then by chance we came to Bordeaux to get our sails mended, and here I stayed. I set up a ship chandler's shop, married, and my business has continued to prosper.

What happened to the others, I don't know. I took the straight road, and since then everything has worked out well for me. And that's all there is to my story.

The old man stopped, and looked at me with quiet gray eyes.

"Who do you think was the real Tristán de Ugarte of the two men by that name?" I asked him. "The one with the scar or the other?"

"The one with the scar, without any doubt. The other man apparently did not want his real name known."

I said goodbye to Itchaso, and returned to my ship.

There was no doubt left in my mind but that my uncle Juan

de Aguirre had sailed aboard the "Dragon." The only part I did not understand was why Ugarte had apparently at one point let him use his name.

To check on the truth of what the old man in Bordeaux had said, I asked one of the lawyers for the company that owned my ship to make inquiries in London to see if, among the records of ship seizures for some thirty years back, there was any information relative to the whaleboat of a ship named the "Dragon."

He was not long in finding what I wanted to know. I was sent a copy of a record, which certified that the whaleboat of a bark called the "Dragon," suspected of piracy, had been captured off the Canary Islands; a list of the crew was appended, and among the names were those of Juan de Aguirre and Tristán de Ugarte.

It was obvious that there was a close tie between these two persons. But, what was it? It was impossible to guess.

BOOK FIVE

Juan Machín, Miner

I. BAD NEWS

All the little activity I engaged in and all the concerns that helped me forget my one big preoccupation at home were of no avail the day I arrived in Bordeaux and found, among other letters, one from Genoveva, the daughter of Urbistondo.

Genoveva wrote to tell me that Juan Machín, the powerful mining entrepreneur at Lúzaro, was courting Mary. So far she had not replied to him in kind, but he pursued her with ever-increasing ardor and interest. The fishermen's quarter resounded with the reports of this courtship.

The receipt of the letter made me decide to go to Lúzaro. I had been planning to get together enough money to ask my cousin to marry me, but now I would wait no longer; we would get married at once, if Mary was willing, of course. We could spend a short season in Lúzaro, and then we would move to Bordeaux, set up house, and I would go to sea from that port.

My mind made up, I addressed a letter to the Company head, and looked around the harbor to see if I could find a ship going to the Spanish coast. I found one going to Bayonne, and took passage.

I remember the weather's being hideous, hot and horrible August days; one's eyes smarted from the heat, whether one looked at the burning sand, the yellow dunes back of the beach, the ponds surrounded with pine groves, or out at the hissing sea.

On board the ship going to Bayonne there was a Basque who had taken passage on my ship at Buenos Aires and crossed with us to Bordeaux. He had not ventured to speak to me all during the trip from America to Europe. He was apparently a very timid man. Now, on the trip to Bayonne, he approached me and we talked. He had spent twenty-five years on the pampas, until he had grown rich. He had no family, and he did not know what to do, nor where to establish his home. He was a man still in full vigor, strong, heavy, with fine features and gray hair.

I felt sorry for him, and his preoccupations made me forget my own. He was a regular Hamlet, I thought, a rustic Hamlet, one of those men who produce in me the saddest and most desolate feelings of sympathy.

This *indiano* Hamlet recalled to my mind a Basque song of a
rather grotesque epicureanism:

Muduan ez da guizonic
Nic aña malura dubenic
Enamoratzia lotzatzenau

Ardo eratia moscortzenau
Pipa fumatzia choratzenau
Ay zer concolatucotenau!

(There is no man in the world with worse luck than I. It shames
me to make love; to drink wine makes me dizzy; to smoke a
pipe makes me sick. Ah! What is there to console me?)

This country Hamlet and I reached Bayonne. I had the good
fortune to find a coastwise *patache,* called the "Rafaelito," that
was sailing for Lúzaro at dawn. I carried my trunks aboard the
ship, and lay down on a coil of rope, impatiently waiting for the
vessel to get under way. I had hopes that there would be a good
wind, for even in the darkness white foam could be seen dancing
on the water.

We were in the open long before dawn. There was no breeze,
and the sea had grown calm; overhead the stars shone very
brightly.

The shadows of the seamen came and went across my sleeping
place, and I could hear the sound of their bare feet on the deck.

The clock on the Bayonne cathedral sounded three o'clock, and
the skipper gave the order to set out. There were six men in the
crew: four sailors, a helmsman, and a cabin boy.

We were carried along by the current of the Adour and crossed
the Boucau; at dawn we went over the bar, propelled by our
oars.

Once over, the seamen put up their oars, the pulleys on the two
sails began to hum, the grommets sang along the lines, and a
dark form rose in the air over me. There was not a trace of wind.
The night was calm and humid. In the distance the red light of
Cape Higuer flashed intermittently.

All of a sudden, the sails flapped and then expanded like a
whip cracking. The ship inclined to one side and commenced to
fly along the water. The skipper took his place at the tiller and
the sailors sat in the gunwales. The sea opened before the ship
and whispered sweetly. Behind us we left a white wake, shining
in the light of the dawn.

Soon the sun rose above the waves, where it had been shining
and shimmering, and climbed into the clear sky, and the mist dis-

appeared. The sails were tinted red by the early sun and they continued to swell in the wind. From time to time the skipper ordered his men to haul in on the sails. In the bow, the cabin boy was singing a Basque song, a melody at once gay and melancholy, monotonous and full of variation.

We passed in front of Biarritz and its rocks and then advanced along the line of white dunes forming the French Basque coast until we were off the slatey promontory of Socoa. We saw Larrun outlined against the sky and farther on the mountains of Spain.

The wind was still increasing. The "Rafaelito" flew along like a gull. The coast, free of all fog, could be seen clearly, its dark cliffs standing out distinctly.

Responding to an order from the skipper, the four sailors commenced hammering a block in place under the mainsail so as to make it tip to windward.

These coastal *pataches,* like some fishing boats, are so elementary in construction that they have to tilt their masts into the wind whenever it is a bit strong. These vessels are only made to sail by the skill of the seamen and any sudden hurricane is capable of tipping them over.

Just before midday, the wind shifted. We were leaving behind us the French coast, with its low rolling hills, its purple sand dunes, and its slate slabs eaten by the sea.

We passed Hendaye and Fuenterrabía, sleeping in the sun on the banks of the Bidasoa. We were off Jaizquibel at the dinner hour. The cabin boy brought out a casserole of potatoes and cod fish, and we all sat down fraternally to eat.

We coasted the shores of Guipuzcoa, and the wind began to grow weaker and weaker, until we were moving very slowly.

As the afternoon began, the heat was suffocating. The sun rained down fire; the sea was devoid of any but the smallest undulation, with no more motion than that of a sleeping monster; the drowsy water reflected the land on that lazy afternoon. I gazed over the scene without any thought, with only a vague sense of sadness.

From time to time the cabin boy recommenced his song. In the distance we could see the different towns, blue like the sea, a Prussian blue along the coast. The rocks under the escarpments appeared bordered by a black line left against the coast by the retreating tide. The sand banks shone in the sun.

Before reaching Orio the wind failed completely, the sails hung down, wrinkled in large creases, as if utterly dead in the becalmed afternoon.

One of the seamen and the cabin boy put out fishing lines, the rest of the crew sat around discussing the divisions between the various confraternities of fishermen at Lúzaro.

Hours went by as we remained immobile in the same spot. The languor and indifference of the afternoon put an end to all my impatience.

It must have been around five-thirty when the sea began to show some motion, raising itself into undulations and white rounded waves that gathered size and body. The cabin boy climbed like a squirrel up the mainmast to fix a pulley.

Once again the wind came up, and we began to move. We passed in front of the high cliffs of Orio, the sand beaches at Zarauz, and then left behind the mountain of San Antón, which was outlined above the sea like a gray whale.

The sun dropped toward the horizon and the sea, making the waves look as if they were of melted metal. The heavens ran with brightly colored clouds: fire dragons disporting at the mouth of the furnace.

The sun was finally obscured by long scarlet clouds and dark cumulus in the form of fish. There were moments when the sky opened and a pencil of rays shot over the water in red and purple shades, while the hollows of the waves, in shadow, remained a strong blue-green.

Off Zumaya the sea suddenly was tinted through, the sun disappeared, and the dark rained down. Not long after, a new light illumined the scene when an enormous yellow moon ascended over the clouds and fantastically outlined the black escarpments of the coast and shone with sudden brilliance on the whitecaps in the water.

"We're going to have rain," said the skipper, pointing to the reddish halo that circled the moon.

The wind, which had leaped to another quarter, blew stronger as the night advanced, and we sailed along at a good clip. The waves trembled and grew impatient, were maddened and aggressive, and seemed like live beings in the light of the moon. The vessel danced along through the darkened passages in the water, the moonlight reflected in the scrollwork of spray, regular patterns alternating with broken design.

Along the sides of the ship the water murmured evenly—interrupted now and again by a sudden sea knock—in a mysterious, monotonous whisper. The spray, phosphorescent upon the black hump of the waves, suggested luminous tritons pursuing us in play.

We passed the Beach of Souls. By the light of the moon we

could see Bisusalde and the houses of Izarte close by the cliff.

Frayburu appeared in its infinite desolation. We rounded Izarra, and began to run in through the two points of land.

The lights of the harbor were reflected in the sea. A window here and there in the town showed some light. We advanced slowly along the narrow lanes formed by the fishing boats drawn up in rows along the silent wharf.

The *patache* moved carefully; I helped the sailors at the work of getting her in. I was very impatient now.

"I'll send a man down to pick up my gear. "I'm in a hurry now," I said.

"All right," answered the skipper. "Goodbye."

I jumped on to one of the moored boats, and then went from one to another until I reached the stairs on the wharf. It was deserted along its length. I was prey to a vast anguish. As I passed Zelayeta's shop, I ran into his son, my friend; I took him by the arm and asked him what was said in town about Mary and Machín. His answer calmed me. It was true that Machín courted the girl, but she had not responded to his advances.

"You can rest easy," Zelayeta told me.

A little less perturbed, I went home to my mother's house.

II. PLEASANT DAYS

At dawn of the next day I rose very early. It was already warm. I brought a chair out to the balcony, and sat down; leaning on the handrail, I gazed out over the town and at the house where Mary was staying.

The sun rose, dissipating the mist; the old bell tower, the houses, the harbor, the point of the breakwater began to emerge clearly before my eyes.

I do not know why the morning hours have a depressing influence on me, or why my illusions all seem dead in the morning. Everything that seems easy and attainable the night before, in the morning appears fraught with difficulties.

It was still too early to go and visit Mary. But I was terribly impatient; I left the house and started out along the highway, and there I met the old doctor of the town. He was an early riser and always began his rounds at dawn. I greeted him warmly, and fell into step beside him; as we walked along I asked him if he knew Mary, and when he said he did, I asked what the general opinion was in regard to Machín's courtship.

"Nothing bad. You needn't worry over it. I don't believe he is making love to Mary. He is quite formal, I think, and treats her with correctness."

"Nevertheless . . ." I began.

For, despite the doctor's assurance, I was not satisfied, and, following the natural tendency to pile up difficulties for oneself, I asked him for information relative to Machín.

"Machín is a man of iron will," the doctor replied. "You must know him."

"No. I don't think I've ever seen him."

"But you must have heard talk about him."

"Very little."

"Well, Machín was born on one of your grandmother's properties. I think he went to sea for a while, but if he did, the sea obviously didn't appeal to him as a career. I used to say about him, in the period when we loafed about town, that he was a Lord Byron of the taverns. Eventually Juan Machín went to Bilbao, and there he mixed with the trashy fellows of low quality who hang around the Miravilla quarter. But then, suddenly, the ne'er-do-well turned out to be a man of enterprise; he appeared in Lúzaro, took over the mines from Beracochea, and began to exploit them. At the end of four or five years he was earning money at a fabulous rate. When he was nearly forty, he married an upper-class miss with money; but now it seems he's fed up with her priggishness. The fishermen are down on him because he runs after all the prettiest girls in town. As far as your English girl is concerned, though, I don't think he's made any headway at all with her. But if you find that he's pressing her too closely, let me know; I'll call him, and tell him something that would make quite a difference in the matter."

The doctor was about to enter a house on the side of the road, and I took my leave of him and turned back toward town. I was finding it hard to think clearly. I waited a bit longer, and then called on Mary. The reception I got from her quieted all my fears at last and drove away my vague discontent. When I left Recalde's house I was deliriously happy.

As soon as I walked in the door of my mother's house I told her I was going to get married to Mary. My mother made no reply. The next day, however, she said that Mary was a good girl, but that I could have made a better match. I pointed out to her that it was not a question of making a good match, but of securing happiness.

I wrote to Bordeaux, saying that I would be delayed longer than I had planned.

I waited for Mary at the end of her work every day, and we would go strolling, by ourselves or in the company of Recalde's Cashilda. We would sit at the end of the breakwater and watch the sea swirl among the the rocks. Some friends told me that Machín was having me watched.

"Be careful," I was told. "Machín is a bad lot."

The implied threat struck me as ridiculous. It was true that whenever we crossed paths by accident—an occurrence that began to happen just after my conversation with the doctor—Machín gazed at me sullenly; but that was all there was to it. He scarcely ever came into Lúzaro, in any case; he owned a splendid low-cut racing schooner, made in England, and he spent a good deal of time sailing.

My first Sunday in Lúzaro was one of the happiest days of my life. I was with Mary the whole day and evening.

After lunch, when I went to Recalde's house to fetch Mary, I met Genoveva. I asked about her father, the great Urbistondo, and about all the children. Though she blushed and protested, I threw my arms around Genoveva and embraced her warmly. Mary was a little annoyed at my overflowing effusion, but she quickly forgot it.

"What's the matter with Quenoveva?" I asked Mary later. "She seems somewhat pale and sad."

"The fact is that she's in love."

"Really?"

"Yes."

"With whom?"

"A young sailor—you don't know him—called Agapito. He doesn't pay much attention to her."

"No? What an idiot! What more can the imbecile want?"

I found it completely absurd that a simple sailor should disdain a girl like Genoveva; but there was no use expostulating with Mary about it.

A few days later it was the day of the Exaltation of the Holy Cross, and there was to be a pilgrimage to a mountain top near Lúzaro. Mary and I went, along with Recalde's wife and son and Genoveva with all the children from the lighthouse. We took along a large basket, which Genoveva insisted on carrying up the mountain on top of her head, without help from anyone.

We walked along the Elguea road. I had never before noticed how beautiful it was. On one side were the woods, filled with oaks, blackberry bushes, ferns, every kind of wild plant and flower. On the other side, down below us, was the sea.

This Sunday was a day of absolute calm and repose; the

weather was splendid and the air was filled with a wonderful odor; all the people were streaming out into the country, and the villagers, as they climbed the sides of the slopes, going in and out of the bushes, seemed like figures in a Christmas crèche, something humble and pastoral.

We went along talking and laughing. And yet I was absorbed in my own sense of happiness, delighting in the beauty of the day, in the silence that was now and then interrupted by the sound of the sea, and in the perfume of the autumn earth.

We reached the mountain top where the gathering was being held and entered the hermitage. Inside the candles shone brightly, the votive offerings glittered, the customary ship hanging from the roof rocked back and forth under full sail.

In the open-air enclosure of the hermitage, bounded by a low whitewashed wall, groups of young girls had set up stands. We had to buy a string of white doughnuts and give one to each of Quenoveva's brood and to La Cashilda's boy.

We went later to spread our lunch among the ferns. Down below us, Lúzaro looked like a toy village. There was not a single fishing boat moving over the sea. After lunch, all the pilgrims gathered in the hermitage enclosure.

"Eh, Shanti, you've got to dance!" some fishermen called out, while several of their number clapped me on the back.

"Sure, sure; we'll all dance."

When the music began I was the first to take my partner out.

After the band had performed a while, the tabor player began. Genoveva was gazing sadly at Agapito out of the corner of her eye. I went over to him, and giving him a push, said:

"Come on. Don't be a jackass. Ask her to dance."

He made up his mind to do as suggested. This Agapito was one of those petulant little men who think they are handsome, and who, as a result of the hopeless gullibility of women (or so it seems to the rest of us men) can feel wings sprouting on their angelic backs. Agapito danced ex cathedra. I decided, then, to dance the fandango to the music of the tabor. But as I did not know the steps properly, I only made the people watching me laugh heartily.

"Bravo, Shanti! Bravo!" yelled the old fishermen, as they approached and formed ranks to see me better, their hands shoved into the pockets of their trousers.

"I'm dancing like a real sea wolf," I said to Mary.

She could not stop laughing. Between the two of us we demoralized the other dancers. She stood there laughing, while I leaped up and down heavily, with the grace of a polar bear jumping around the ice. Meanwhile, Quenoveva and Agapito, both of them ludicrously serious for different reasons, tried to dance. We were an insult to the venerable traditions of the region.

Among these traditions, religion and dancing are the two most important. And Voltaire was therefore quite right when he said that the Basques were a small nation that danced on the crests of the Pyrenees.

After we had gotten our fill of leaping and jumping we began the return trip, accompanied all the way by the uproar of the children and the singing of the youths.

At dusk, we were back in Lúzaro once more, dancing in the plaza.

After each set of dances, during which I covered myself with glory, to the delight of Mary, we took a stroll along the mall. At ten o'clock, after a vigorous afternoon given over to exercise and an uninterrupted series of habaneras and jotas, executed (as we say in the village) sometimes by the band and then again by a group of tabor players, there was a fireworks display featuring an exploding castle, much to the delight of the small folk and the fishermen.

Quenoveva deposited her collection of children with a relative, La Cashilda left her son—the future anthropologist—at home, and the rest of us, including Quenoveva and Agapito, went for a last stroll to the breakwater. All this is the classic custom of Lúzaro.

When they reach the cross on the breakwater, the men customarily put out a hand and touch it, while the women put their lips to it.

On the way there, Cashilda explained a detail of the ceremony that I did not know about. If the girls want a seagoing sweetheart, she told me, they kiss the side of the cross toward the sea; if they want a land man, they kiss the land side. There are naturally girls who are amphibious.

We reached the breakwater, and Mary and Quenoveva kissed the cross on the sea side.

On the way home, behind Cashilda's back, I tried to kiss Mary in return for the kiss she had given the cross, but she escaped me with a laugh.

III. A NIGHT IN FRAYBURU

Though I saw Mary every afternoon, I also found myself standing in front of her house every night. There seemed to be no point of satiety. She remained near the window, knowing always that I was there, and at length would close her shutters for the night.

I liked to be alone, thereafter, to savor my happiness. Instead of going home or to the casino, I would walk out to the breakwater, and there sit against the railing, with my legs hanging down, and look out to sea, while the water swirled in furious whirlpools in the light of the moon or under the bright stars.

One night towards the end of September, I stayed later than usual. I was all alone on the breakwater. The sea, unusually rough, sent up clouds of spray.

I heard the clock on the church strike eleven, and I got up to go home. Stretched along the esplanade of the breakwater were two enormous fishing nets, spread out to dry; so as to avoid stepping on them and causing any damage, I skirted around the edge of the sea wall. I was walking steadily along when suddenly two forms hurled themselves upon me, grappled briefly, and before I could cry out stopped my mouth with a cloth and bound my hands behind me; a moment later they bound my feet as well.

I thought they meant to throw me into the water, and I kept thinking of Mary in what I supposed were my last moments.

But instead, the two men, moving swiftly, dragged me down the wharf ramp and pushed me into the bow of a ship tied up close in. Aft of where I was thrown stood a man enveloped in a sou'wester, so that his face was hidden. Nevertheless, I recognized him. The man was Machín. It was his schooner I was aboard.

Why had I been brought here? He obviously planned something more complicated than murder.

Leaving me bound and gagged to lie where I was, my two assailants each took an oar and, now pushing against the sea wall and now rowing, they worked the vessel out into the open. Once there, they hoisted the sails in the darkness.

The jib unfurled with a crack that sounded as if it would break; then the other sails unfurled, and the vessel tipped violently; I braced myself to prevent being thrown into the sea. We began to move at a rapid clip.

Over my head the sail was alive with the wind, the mast hoops clattered, and the sea sped by beneath the sharp bow, seeming to whisper something as it went. From time to time we would ship a wave, and I would be soaked to the bone.

The night was very black, the wind whistled furiously; the dark masses of clouds opened now and again to reveal a patch of light where the stars shone.

I pushed against the deck for a time and at length succeeded in slipping the gag off my mouth; I was able to breathe deeply now, and took several large breaths. I began to think coldly: What could these men be planning? If they had wanted to get rid of me, they would already have thrown me into the sea.

We crossed the bar in a series of violent rolls. We would climb, one after another, the mountains of water, and then descend into the abyss each time.

All I could see was the spray on the waves, which gleamed in the dark because of their phosphorescence.

An hour later we were off Frayburu. I don't know how Machín succeeded in bringing his ship alongside the rocks in the midst of that darkness and the great sea swells. He proved that he was a daring and skillful seaman.

He succeeded in running the bow of the ship lightly aground on the Frayburu sandbank.

"Take ahold of him," he said to his two men, "and take him up to the rocks." And to me he said: "You can think for a while up there. You might come to realize that girl is not for you. I'll leave you here this time, and you can figure things out; let your thoughts mature a bit. That's all for today. If you need another outing, I'll take you out to the fishes."

I gazed back at him without answering. What was the use of protesting, if a protest was of no avail?

The sailors jumped into the water and hauled me out of the vessel from the outside. After much effort, they succeeded in carrying me up to a small ledge on the side of the rock and leaving me among some brambles.

The two climbed back down and I could hear them splashing out to the ship and climbing aboard.

"Goodnight," called Machín mockingly.

I immediately began trying to cut my bounds by rubbing against a jagged piece of rock.

The night was so black that I could not see where I was, and I felt that if I rolled or made any sharp movement I would fall over the ledge and down against the rocks below. The waves roared desperately in the dark, very close to my ear.

After a great deal of work, and badly skinning one hand I was able to get it loose and then undo the rest of my bindings. Finally I was able to sit up on the ledge. I was already numb, and was terrified at the thought of falling off my perch.

For a while I did not dare stand up and find the manner of getting off the ledge. The wind swirled around me in violent gusts, with a noise as if all the Furies were assailing me. I spent a hideous night without moving from the shelf. There was no place to go in any case. I was numb with the cold and my own fears. I almost dozed, and felt as if I was slipping off. I quickly realized it was an illusion; but the consequent fright was greater than my faculties of analysis, and I clung to the rock ledge until my hands showed traces of blood and I heard myself screaming like a maniac.

As soon as the light of dawn began to appear I felt easier, and I once again breathed freely. The light spread across the water, which meanwhile had grown calmer.

The horizon grew red, and then the morning came on rapidly. Pink clouds filled the sky, and the red disk of the sun came up from the bottom of the sea.

Out from among the brambles and bushes of Frayburu, where I hung in the air, swarms of giant birds and seagulls came flocking.

The sea was flooded with light. The breeze made the cornfields of Izarte tremble gently. Overhead, an occasional swallow would fly by, alone and seemingly terrified, and lose itself in the infinity of space.

I was trying to decide what to do. I thought the best course would be simply to wait until a fishing boat passed close in. As a last resort, I could wait until low tide and walk along the rocks for a way, then swim to the cavern at Izarra and perhaps try to climb up somewhere and make my way out as Recalde and I had done as children. But it would be a hazardous trip, especially when trying to climb the face of the dark cavern.

It would be far best to wait. My mother would have already made known the fact that I was missing. When the poor woman saw the day getting later, with no trace of her son, she would be certain to become wild with anxiety.

The fishing boats were beginning to put out. From time to time I would yell, but the distance was much too great. It would also be impossible for them to see me against the rocks. At length I thought of the method used by the watch tower lookout when he wanted to communicate with fishermen who were very far out: smoke. I had matches in my pocket, and, though there was no straw available, there were plenty of dry weeds around me.

I did not want to waste my matches lighting weeds that might still be moist, and so I searched around for the driest parts of plants and growths, and then spread them out to dry in the sun in the protection of a hollowed rock.

Finally I attempted to light my pile of dried brush, but without paper I could not. I went through my pockets again, and found some letters from Mary that I had been saving. I would have to give them up; I lit one and then another, and by the fourth one I had a good column of smoke rising over the rock.

What a strange sight it must have been from afar to see a smoke plume rising from the solitary rock in the water.

I wondered if my plan would boomerang, and if those that saw the smoke might not think it the work of the devil and avoid the rock more than ever. Without doubt, a flame on the apex of that rock must have had the appearance of something magical, or sacred and religious.

When the oven on the rock began to burn, everything went up, green weeds as well as dry, so that I had soon left the place without a trace of vegetation.

One hour went by, and then another. It was suddenly midday. I searched the sea anxiously for sign of an approaching ship. No one came. Depressed and discouraged, I lay down, and in a moment of weakness and nervous exhaustion, I fell asleep in the hot sun. I was awakened by a voice and the sound of oars. A fishing boat had come to save me. In it were Agapito, Geno-veva's boyfriend, and some other sailors. Seeing me stretched out on the ground, they had thought me dead.

Back in Lúzaro, some boys had told of seeing an astounding and frightening sight: fire on Frayburu.

Mary had gotten word of this story, and, already alarmed at my absence from home, had insisted that Agapito put out in a boat to see if I might be the one causing the smoke.

I held back the name of my kidnapper, but everyone knew who was involved. The lads in the boat helped me wash up, for I was covered with scratches and cuts from the brambles and rocks.

Mary and my mother were waiting at the dock when we got back. The two of them embraced me and wept at the same time.

"Now you two embrace each other," I told them.

My mother hugged Mary to her and kissed her several times.

The judge interrogated me, and I told him I had no idea of who could have attacked me.

IV. STRATAGEMS OF WAR

A state of war, then, existed between Machín and myself. With his influence and his money he was in a position to do me a good deal of harm; on my side, I could count on the defensive support of all the fishermen and seagoing men of Lúzaro.

It would not be easy for my enemy to catch me as unprepared as he had the first time. I was surrounded by people who constituted themselves a spontaneous and watchful guard.

My mother was now anxious for me to marry as soon as possible. But it was necessary to apply for a special church dispensation, since Mary and I were first cousins; Mary's baptismal certificate listed her as the legitimate daughter of Juan de Aguirre y Lazcano.

One day, on returning home, I found a package had been left for me. It was a medium-sized bundle, well wrapped and covered with circles of sealing wax.

"What is it?" my mother asked.

"I don't know."

"Did you order anything?"

"Nothing."

"Were you expecting anything?"

"Nothing at all."

Meanwhile I undid the package, took off the paper, and brought to view a metal box with a handle attachment, to which was tied a key on the end of a string.

I was untying the key and getting ready to insert it in the lock when my mother said:

"Don't open it. I don't know why, but I don't think you should open it."

It was true enough that there was something suspicious about the package. It weighed some eight or nine pounds. I stopped opening it, and started looking over the wrapping paper to see if I could find some clue as to its origin or nature. There was nothing by way of indication. I called the maid, who was a new girl.

"Was this package handed to you directly?" I asked her.

"Yes."

"Who brought it?"

"A man."

"I assumed that. But what sort of man? Was it a local person, someone from hereabouts?"

"No. At least, I didn't know him."

"When did the package come?"

"A little after the stagecoach."

"And what did the man who brought it say?"

"Nothing. He asked for you, left the package, and then went away."

"Did you see him later on the highway?"

"No."

"Did the stagecoach go by right away?"

"Yes; it wasn't much later."

"So that he could have left on the stagecoach?"

"Yes; he might very well have."

The next morning, I looked up Samson, the coach driver, and asked him if he remembered the looks of a man who had been carrying a package on the stagecoach the day before. But Samson said he recalled only a man with a basket and a woman with a sack among those carrying bundles.

I had very little faith in Samson, for he was a deceitful fellow, and I felt there was no use in pressing him further. But I told Garmendia, the pharmacist, about the incident, and he told me: "Bring the package to the pharmacy, and we'll see what's inside."

That night I brought it over to him.

"If there's anything dangerous here, it's undoubtedly in opening the lock by means of this key. Let's try another way in."

Garmendia sent over to the watchmaker's for a metal drill, and as soon as it was brought to us, we set to work drilling into one of the sides of the container. It was very hard to drill and it took us some time to make a hole. This done, we stuck a needle in and a thin trickle of some fine black dust began to flow out.

"What can this be?" I asked. "It looks like powder."

"That's what it is," answered Garmendia. "It was no friend who sent you this. If you had opened the container as you were supposed to, you would probably have been blown up."

We drilled another hole into the metal, and then we submerged the case in water so that the powder would soak; at the end of two days, when we were sure the powder was well soaked, we brought up the case and opened it. Inside we found a most ingenious mechanism: a system of pistol barrels laid out in a fan shape, which would have been fired after the key was inserted in the lock and as the lid was opened. Garmendia commented that the device resembled one used some years previously in a box sent General Eguía, who had lost his hands on opening the container.

I did not report this incident either to the authorities. But I did take steps to see that La Cashilda should turn over to me anything that might come to her house addressed to Mary. La Cashilda was horrified to learn of the attempt against me, and promised to intercept anything sent Mary.

It was only a week later that La Cashilda brought me a newspaper from Bilbao that had been sent to her house for Mary. To intercept a newspaper seemed to me a rather excessive precaution, but when I read it, I found it contained an attempt against me very similar to the charge in the metal box.

The Bilbao newspaper contained a "fictional" narrative entitled "Shanti Andía's Duel." The story related my affair with Dolores in Cádiz, and told of my falling victim to the husband's wrath and of his challenge to a duel. The entire narrative was couched in such a manner that I was made to appear an utter cad.

The piece infuriated me by its vileness, and I determined to challenge Machín himself on the first opportunity.

Moreover, it was almost a year since Mary's father had died, and I was therefore bound by my promise to deliver the letter he had given me for Machín. My uncle had asked me to deliver it in person into Machín's hands, and I intended to carry out his last instructions to me. The occasion would furnish me a double opportunity.

The old doctor somehow got wind of my plans, and he came to tell me that he insisted on accompanying me whenever I went on my visit.

I made it clear that I was opposed to his coming, but at length he won me over. One day we set out together for Izarte, going by coach. We stopped in front of Machín's house and we both went up to his office. I was somewhat surprised by the appearance of my declared enemy at close range. He seemed to have grown suddenly much older. He had such an unexpectedly miserable air about him that my anger at him quickly passed away when it met this small resistance. He stared up at us with a somber and melancholy look, greeted us correctly, and asked: "What is it you would like?"

"This gentleman here would like to talk to you briefly," answered the doctor dryly. "And I would like to talk to you after he does."

Machín seemed taken aback by the tone of the doctor's voice. For a moment he seemed ready to answer sternness with violence, but he kept quiet.

"I had two purposes on coming here," I interposed. "First, I must hand you this envelope from Mary's father."

Machín was now completely astonished.

"An envelope from him for me?" he asked in obvious surprise.

"Yes, for you," I replied, taking out the envelope and placing it on the table between us.

"That's interesting," he muttered. "Thank you very much," he added.

"The other point of business was to tell you not to employ such vile measures against me," and I threw the newspaper from Bilbao on the floor at his feet.

Machín's pale cheeks took on a red flush, and the pupils of his eyes flashed briefly, but he said nothing.

"It is imperative that I speak to you privately," the doctor now put in hurriedly, in a tone of the utmost firmness.

"Very well. If you would like, I will come to your house this afternoon."

"At what time?"

"Will four o'clock suit you?"

"Good."

"I'll be there at that time."

The doctor and I stood up. We left Machín to his unaccountable depression and melancholy, and took our leave.

V. THE STORM

A few days later, one morning in October, I awoke to the furious sound of the wind.

The bay must be something worth seeing today, I said to myself, and though it was not yet dawn I got up and dressed, put on my raincoat, and went out into the street.

It was the dawn of a dramatic day, filled with the roar of a violent storm. The wind howled through the streets. The wives and children of the fishermen who had gone out in the predawn were already gathered on the breakwater, scanning the horizon with a look of desperation.

I made my way along the wharf, bucking the gusts of wind, and finally reached the round stone tower used by the lookout posted on the breakwater.

The old lookout, wrapped in his sou'wester and with his cap pulled down around his ears, was peering out one of the window slits of the shelter. In one hand he held a megaphone and in the other a telescope. He was on edge, for he sensed an impending tragedy.

"These fishermen are brutes," he muttered to me. "They always want to go out, whether the weather's right or not. They can't understand that it's better to suffer hardships at home than to be buried in the waves."

The old man went on muttering, and while we waited he outlined the events of the morning, relating them to the customs of the fishermen in case I should not be aware of their peculiarities.

"The fishermen keep in touch with some weather lookouts at Izarra and Aguiró, who observe the changes in atmosphere. If the signs point to good weather, the fact is passed on to the women who wake the crews of the fishing boats by rapping loudly on the doors of their houses. If the signs indicate stormy weather, the women don't make the rounds. If the weather is doubtful, on the other hand, the weather watchers don't send word to the women at all, but simply have the skippers of the boats summoned. Then, just before dawn, at the end of the pier, the skippers talk over the situation and the chances for good or bad fishing. If unanimity is not reached, then the decision is left to a vote; a wooden box divided into two compartments with two slots is brought out. A fishing boat is painted on one side of the box, and a house on the other. The boat indicates the side that stands for going out to sea; the house means staying home. The voting is absolutely secret. Each skipper puts his ballot into the slot marked by the boat or the slot marked by the house, and then the tally is made. If the majority is for going out, whoever wants to do so can go, but if the majority votes not to go out, then no one can go, and any fisherman who violates the rule will be fined and his catch confiscated, if he is discovered.

"Today," the lookout concluded, "after the skippers had argued the question, those in favor of going out were in a slight majority in the voting. But by the time they were ready to put out, the weather had so worsened that even some of those who had voted in favor of fishing changed their minds and stayed at home."

Even as the old man spoke, the weather was continuing to get worse. The wind howled more ferociously than ever. The waves, high as mountains, roared upon the rocks, washed up as far as the houses, tore at the doors, and dragged back with it everything it could sweep away.

Almost rhythmically the crests poured in the windows of the lookout tower, soaking the old man and myself, and then flowed back down the stone stairs with the noise of a cataract. From time to time the water dealt the walls a blow, as if an iron-gauntleted fist were knocking violently at our shelter.

The sea seemed stormier every second. According to the lookout, there were still four fishing boats outside port.

We could suddenly see two of them approaching through the waves. The lookout quickly called through his megaphone; he directed them to come to a halt; then, at the propitious moment, he ordered them forward, bellowing *"Avante!"*

The two boats, dancing over the water, disappeared into the spray, came on toward the bar, passed the two points of land, and entered the harbor.

"The other two are out there," said the lookout, indicating the direction. "It would be better for them if they went on to Guetaria, and tried to put in there. They must be exhausted. If they try to come in here, they're lost. . . Will you run and tell Larragoyen, the skipper, to get the lifeboat ready?"

"Of course I will."

I ran out of the shelter and crossed the breakwater. The sea dashed up on the quay as far as the houses, amid a noise as vivid as that of an earthquake. Fighting my way through the running streams, I reached the protected angle of the wharf and told the fishermen huddled there what the lookout had told me. The lifeboat was made ready. Larragoyen and some other sailors began to clamber aboard, despite the wailing of their womenfolk. The spectators looked at me as if to ask, "What will he do?" I jumped into the boat. Larragoyen, with a seaman's gallantry, told me to take command. The boat had no rudder; in a crisis it is better, in any case, to steer with an oar, a long oar tied to the stern. The women and children watched us with anxiety. It was a moment in my life that I had always anticipated having to live through.

Perhaps my destiny was to die at sea, in some heroic gesture, so that the children of my town should forever speak of Shanti Andía as a legendary figure.

My first reaction on entering the boat was one of suffocation; the sou'westers and rain gear worn by the fishermen gave off the mixed odor of linseed oil, fried fish, and sea water.

We stood by waiting to see what would happen: six seamen leaning on their oars, while I stood, ready to act as steersman.

One of the boats came in; the other, according to what we heard, was going down.

"All right, then, let's go on out!" I yelled.

We shot past the points of the land. The horizon was covered with black clouds whose forms changed every instant. Far off, near the water, there was the outline of a black bar with a coppery top. The waves, great yellow mountains, came from three or four directions at once and broke to form a whirlpool of spray.

In the midst of it all, Larragoyen took off his beret and bawled to the rest of us: "An Our Father for the first of us to drown!"

I must confess that this gesture had a very bad effect on me. All the others prayed; I stared off into the distance. The lookout was calling out to us, advising us not to go directly into the area where the fishing boat had capsized, but to go around it.

We did as instructed. The storm was a bad one, but we could still beat our way through it. The wind now blew from one quarter alone. The boat leaped like a dolphin over the waves.

Great and obvious dangers of this type take away one's fear, especially if one is forced to assume some responsibility. The peril is converted almost into a mathematical problem which must be solved. From the sea, the spectacle on land now seemed strange. The entire town seemed to be beneath the pounding waves and flying spray.

At intervals, an almost cyclindrical wave—as if it were hollow —would come rolling towards us, its volume greater than any of the other waves. Instead of waiting to receive it broadside, we would maneuver so as to meet it head on, or at least at the sharpest angle possible.

This defensive maneuver would force us to turn and get off our course. But at last we made a first turn around the spot where the fishing boat had foundered, and we picked up two of the fishermen; we made a second turn around the spot and saved another man; on the third turn, we found no one.

Still unaccounted for was Agapito, Genoveva's love, and three other men. Our oarsmen were exhausted. We approached the entrance to the harbor, and the lookout called out to us through his megaphone directing us to halt where we were.

I spoke to Larragoyen and said I thought it best to attempt a crossing of the bar as quickly as possible; it seemed to me it would be dangerous to head for Guetaria, in view of the condition of our men. Larragoyen did not answer.

To remain where we were was almost as dangerous as crossing the bar. After three strong waves, the three regulation sea knocks, as they were called, there was always a moment of relative calm. It was my opinion that we should take advantage of this moment to cross the bar; still, the men were already too exhausted to be depended upon for the final desperate effort.

Our uneasiness increased, and the morale of the men flagged.

I was kept going by a sense of responsibility. From time to time the wind would bring us the words of people on the breakwater; on the other hand, there were times when the shouts of the lookout did not reach us.

The sailors had lost their spirit. And the longer we waited to cross the bar, the less were our chances of doing so.

The sea, meanwhile, was continually wilder. The clouds scudded across the horizon in a dizzying fashion. Suddenly, one of those cylindrical waves that appear to be hollow inside came crashing down upon us, and came down on us so fast that there was no time to turn our prow around to meet it head on. It hit us diagonally, breaking over the backs of two of the rowers, hurling them down into the boat, and smashing over the rest of us.

There was no one among us but thought that our end had come. When I found myself still aboard the boat and above the surface of the sea, I was somehow provoked to anger and indignation.

"We're floundering around here like frightened idiots!" I yelled. "We've got to go in. Come on now!"

"Right, let's go!"

We were at last ready to make the final effort when, to our overwhelming astonishment, we suddenly caught sight of Machín's schooner; it was emerging through the harbor mouth, its jib filled, skimming along the water like a fantastic swan.

We were all struck dumb. The boat sailed out of the harbor, made a long turn, moving all the while with a spectacular speed. There were two men aboard: Machín and his servingman. The boat moved with admirable precision: a wrong move and the schooner would go to the bottom.

As it changed direction, we thought the boat was sinking; there was a moment when it was completely over, but gradually it straightened up and it came on towards us hauling the wind. Machín was stretched out on deck, hanging on tightly; as we came close, he threw us a line. One of the men at the bow caught it and made fast. Suddenly our boat gave a leap, as it was given tow by the schooner, and our prow sank into the waves.

Without waiting for any instructions from the lookout, Machín raced into the yellow waves over the sandbar, hurling himself and us into that area where sky and sea were lost in confusion, and he and we passed over the bar at a terrifying speed, as quickly at the summit of a mountain of water as cutting through its center.

Before we were fully aware of what had happened, we were

safe. Machín and his manservant lowered the sails and then we towed the racing schooner.

We reached the pier. At that moment the schoolchildren were returning from praying for us at the hermitage, and they stood before us now, gazing at us in wonder and admiration.

Machín was well aware that he was hated among the fishermen, and he had no intention of posing as our savior. He and his servant quit the scene at once. I stopped the manservant as he was walking away and said: "That was a splendid piece of work. You handled the boat like masters."

"Yes, it's a splendid craft," answered the servant.

"And the crew no less."

The man thanked me for my opinion, and disappeared behind his master.

Neither Mary nor my mother was aware of what had happened. I was getting ready to return home when the fishermen insisted that I go with them, and I was forced to promise them that I would meet them later, instead, at the *Guezurrechape* on the pier to comment the day's events.

VI. A TIRESOME SONG

When I told Mary that afternoon of our adventure at sea, she turned pale and then began to cry. She was grieved at the drowning of Agapito because of the effect it would have on Genoveva. Machín's behavior she found astonishing.

It was left to Mary and to me to communicate the sad tidings to the dead sailor's sweetheart. We took along with us on our mission a sister of Agapito's who was working as a servant in Lúzaro. On our arrival at the lighthouse, Genoveva came out to open the gate; as soon as she saw the three of us in our unjoyful silence, she suspected the truth and went away in tears.

I left the three women alone and went to visit the great Urbistondo, who immediately explained to me his ideas on the sentimentality of women; the serious air which he adopted was comical as well as absurd.

We returned to Lúzaro, leaving the lighthouse-keeper's daughter in the midst of her tears.

That night I went to the *Guezurrechape,* as I had promised. Larragoyen was there, along with all his friends, and they received me with shouts and applause. Everyone had already for-

gotten the men lost at sea. Such is life. They were alive, after
having been close to death, and they celebrated their good fortune. They were all in various stages of intoxication, and they
repeated to each other the details of the experience we had all
lived through. By and large, none of the fishermen put any faith
in Juan Machín's good intentions or his motives for having helped
us.

"But what possible ulterior motive could he have?" I asked.

"Who knows, Shanti, who knows?" they answered.

Someone even went so far as to suggest that Machín had put
out in his speedy boat in order to send us to the bottom all the
quicker. It proved impossible to change anyone's mind in the
matter, and so I kept silent. A seaman, especially a Basque seaman, can never be convinced of anything he doesn't want to
believe.

I was of the opinion that Machín was an extreme type, a violent man capable of large-scale good or evil, ready as quickly to
risk his own life for a man as to assassinate him. But I could not
convince even Larragoyen, who was a sensible man, of the value
of my judgement.

The sad details of the day were forgotten in favor of a general
rejoicing liberally moistened with wine. I sat among the fishing-
boat skippers and drank rum and coffee with them.

Shempelar, the shipyard man, launched into a ditty which he
repeated endlessly. The principal features, and the sole humor,
of the piece was that there was some reference to a sea captain and
some talk of a man named Shanti.

Basically the song said nothing; but what was the difference?
The truth is that, almost always, and absurd as it may seem, the
less a song says the better it is as a song. This ditty went as
follows:

> Ni naiz capitan pillotu
> Neri bear zait obeditu
> Buruban jartzen batzait neri
> Bombillum bat, eta
> Bombillum bi
> Eragiyoc Shanti
> Arraun ori.

(I am a pilot captain/ You must do as I command/ Put a bottle
on my head/ The largest bottle known/ And now another bot-
tle/ Shanti ply that oar!)

And this senseless song and its chorus was repeated over and
over again until midnight. Then, numerous other *zortzicos*

were sung; these were followed by selections on the accordion by a young fellow who played a bit of everything without interval or interruption: a waltz became a habanera, and the habanera closed on some bars from the "Marseillaise" or some hymn or other.

I soon found myself overcome by the alcohol fumes and tobacco, and my mind merely followed the pell-mell tunes of the monstrous recital.

From time to time I would mutter:

"Well, gentlemen, I'm going now," and I would stand up to go.

"No, no," everyone would shout.

"Don't go, Shanti," an old fisherman yelled.

"I've got to go."

"Not on your life! Throw that skipper in the water! Don't go Shanti!" came the chorus of yells.

When none of us could any longer sit upright or keep going on the strength of our spirit, we all quit the *Guezurrechape* and staggered to our different homes. It was raining, and the wharf was slippery with mud. I lost my way, and instead of going toward my house, I ended up on the breakwater. Thanks to the nightwatchman, who led me home, dawn found me in my room.

VII. MACHÍN DISAPPEARS

It had been some time since Machín had concerned himself in any way with Mary or with me. He was never seen around Lúzaro any more.

The day of my marriage with Mary was approaching.

One night, on coming home, I found Machín standing in my doorway. What could he be doing there this time?

"I must speak to you," he said at once.

"Very well, come in the house with me."

He did not seem bent on any attack or move against me, and I was stronger than he, in any case.

Machín preceded me inside, climbed the stairs ahead of me, and we entered my room together. He stood there looking about him, reading the titles on the books in my bookcases, and examining at a glance the paintings on the walls with evident curiosity.

"Are these paintings from your grandmother's house?" he asked surprisingly.

"Yes."

He studied them more closely. I watched him with marked impatience.

"You can say whatever it was you wanted to say. . ." I advised him.

"Yes. I'll tell you at once. You handed me an envelope from Mary's father. . ."

"True enough."

"Well, I have an envelope for you to turn over to her. You can give it to her the day of your wedding."

"Is this a trick?"

"No, no; you can rest easy on that score. Please tell her that it comes from her family. I can assure you that it can only constitute a pleasant surprise for you and for her."

I hesitatingly accepted the proffered envelope, which was a large packet. Machín returned to his gazing about the room with great interest. Then he suddenly asked: "Is your mother at home?"

"Yes, I believe she is."

"I would like to pay my respects."

"If you like. Come this way."

We entered my mother's room. She seemed startled at sight of Machín. He behaved very attentively and politely toward her, and they spoke together for some time. The incomprehensible visit made me uneasy.

What sudden change was this on Machín's part, and what did it conceal?

As we went out, Machín said to me:

"I intend to leave Lúzaro for good. Probably we will not see each other again. Will you continue to hate me?"

"No, despite the fact that I believe I have motives for doing so."

"Then I will say goodbye with the best of intentions and wishes."

He stretched out his hand, I extended mine, and he shook hands with great warmth.

On returning to my mother I found her somewhat excited by the interview.

"What upset you?" I asked her.

"Principally the fact that when he came in I thought it was my brother Juan come back."

"What!"

"Yes, it's true."

"And he resembles him that closely?"

"He looks just like him when he was young."

Machín was certainly a strange phenomenon: in his conduct, in his appearance and resemblance, in the sympathies and antipathies he awakened in people.

A few days later, on a very clear and beautiful day in autumn, Machín and his servant went aboard the schooner and sailed away. Days, weeks, years have come and gone: no one has ever heard of him again.

On the day of my wedding, after we were installed in my mother's house, Mary opened the large envelope Machín had left with me for her. A number of papers spilled out on the table. They were mining shares, government bonds . . . a small fortune. Among the papers was a letter that went as follows:

My Dear Mary:

The letter that your father sent me through your husband some time ago revealed that you and I are brother and sister, children of the same father. Shanti, whom I have hated in the past, is a close relative, almost a brother.

I am the son of Juan de Aguirre and a serving girl in our grandmother's house. I do not lay any blame on my father for having abandoned me to my own devices. Fate willed it so.

No doubt your husband and yourself are convinced that I am a perverse and evil man. I have not had the opportunity to be anything else. Everyone made me suffer when I was defenseless, and I have reacted by making others suffer when I became powerful enough.

Goodness is the force of the privileged. The sad envy of the well-being of others is a sickness of the spirit. And those who have struggled and striven in the caves where enemies bite are always contaminated by this sickness.

Not everyone can be sound, therefore, and not everyone can be good. I am still unable to be so, and since I cannot be good, in sending you this dowry, my sister, to help you set up your house, I console myself by thinking of it as my revenge, the revenge of the morally underprivileged man against the sound and healthy ones, the revenge of the despised and outcast of the family against the respected and pampered descendants of the same family.

Goodbye, dear sister. And congratulations.

                                                            Juan.

The letter paper was irregularly stained with the tears of the letter writer.

Machín, our enemy, had turned out to be our protector and our relative.

BOOK SIX

La Shele

I. THE OLD DOCTOR TALKS

A few days after our marriage, the old doctor, who was looking for me, found me in the street and told me that he had to speak to me urgently. He would be expecting me at his house after lunch. I went there, and he showed me into his study, which was lined with cabinets and whose walls were hung with rather disagreeably vivid anatomical prints. The doctor sat me down in an easy chair and then said: "As you know, Machín has left us."

"Yes, I was well aware of it."

"Do you know the reason for his change in attitude toward you and your wife?"

"No."

"Well, it was mostly due to something I told him the very day you and I went to call on him. I spoke to him later in this very room; he was sitting where you are now. At first he listened to me with an ironic smile, with that painful smile that is characteristic of him. But when I told him what I am about to tell you, he was transformed. And he finally cried like a young boy. I would not have thought that he was so softhearted. I was moved myself."

"And what was it you told him?"

"I told him about his mother and father."

"Did you know them?"

"Yes."

"Both of them?"

"Both of them."

And the doctor then launched into the story:

It's more than forty years now since I came here from Régil, where I had spent two years as a doctor. When I first arrived in Lúzaro, the town was not as it is now; four or five families ran everything, among these families the Aguirre and the Andonaegui were the most important and influential.

It was important for me, as the doctor here, to get along with these families; otherwise, I would simply starve.

I used to go to your grandmother's house very often; she had just been left a widow.

Your grandmother had in her house a young girl who was a godchild of hers, and whom we called La Shele. I always joked with her when I went to Aguirreche to drink coffee.

"How goes it, Shele?" I would say.

"Nothing new, doctor."

"When are you going to get married?"

"Whenever someone loves me," she would answer softly.

"Don't you have a sweetheart yet?"

"No."

"Well, what are you waiting for?"

She would smile as she filled the coffee cups. La Shele was very pretty, and very modest, and very fine. She was one of that type of Basque, slender and tall, who have something bird-like about them. I often think that our race is not a strong one. I never admit this in front of a stranger, or anyone from outside. But, our race, which is handsome and pure, is not strong. The people of central Spain have much more resistance; the Aragonese, for example, or the Castilians, or the people from Rioja. Ours is an old race which has refined itself and produced a pure type—though it has produced nothing very pure in the realm of ideas—but it has not much strength organically. You've probably noticed how a girl here will marry, and then after her first child will lose all her teeth, so that her nose will seem to grow longer over a gaunt face. . . I'm wandering from my theme, however. Let me return to it.

One lovely clear morning in winter I was called to Aguirreche. It was a few days after your Uncle Juan had left for Cádiz to pick up his ship.

"This place has turned into a hospital," your grandmother said to me. "We're all sick."

I examined your grandmother, your mother, your Aunt Ursula, and as I was getting ready to leave I was told there was still one more patient.

"Wait just a moment. La Shele is sick too."

The girl was brought in to me; she looked very pale and sad; she greeted me without lifting her eyes from the ground.

"Come now, you can go nearer to him than that," said your grandmother.

I could see that La Shele was suffering inwardly, and that the corners of her mouth were trembling with suppressed anguish.

"What's wrong with our little girl?" I asked pleasantly.

"She must be sick to her stomach," said your grandmother. "She has vomiting fits, and has circles under her eyes."

I scrutinized the girl, who let her eyes drop again; then I took her pulse, and said: "Let her come to my office, and I will give her a more thorough examination."

"All right, we'll send her. Do you think it's anything serious?"

"We'll see."

I took my leave of the family and continued on my rounds.

II. THE CONFESSION

I had just finished my coffee and was chatting with my mother and sister in the small glass-covered gallery that adjoins the garden when La Shele was shown in one day. I got up to meet her, led her into the office, and closed the door.

"Sit down," I said to her.

The girl sat down and I began the interrogation.

"Have you been in Aguirreche a long time now?"

"Yes, it's getting to be a long time."

"How old are you?"

"Eighteen."

"Your parents live in one of the houses owned by the Aguirre family, isn't that true?"

"Yes, sir."

"Do you feel affection for the people in your house?"

"Yes, sir."

"For the *señorito* Juan?"

"Also."

And here the girl blushed. I continued with my questions.

"You don't want to leave Aguirreche?"

"No, sir."

"Don't you trust me?"

The girl looked up at me in surprise, doubtless wondering why I asked this kind of question. I persisted.

"I asked if you trusted me. Do you think I'm a bad man?"

"A bad man! Oh, no, sir."

"Then you do trust me? You don't think I want to hurt you?"

"No, no, sir. I never said that."

"I know you didn't say it; I only bring it up so that you will know that I am your friend and that I have a good deal of affection for you. Do you understand?"

"Yes, sir."

Then I went on to tell her clearly what I had to tell her: "You and the *señorito* Juan have made love together, isn't that true?"

"No, no, sir."

"Why do you deny the truth? You and he have made love, and

what's happening to you now is a natural consequence. . . Don't you understand?"

La Shele kept quiet and lowered her head again.

"Did he promise to marry you? Did he deceive you?"

"No, he did not deceive me. He didn't promise me anything."

"Does he know the condition you're in?"

"No, he doesn't know."

"And why didn't you tell him before he went away?"

"I was ashamed."

The girl hid her face between her hands and began to cry in silence.

"*Ay, ené!* Oh, oh," she kept repeating, smothering a sigh.

I gazed at her, deeply moved.

"Come now, calm yourself," I said. "I am the only one hereabouts who knows of your condition. What do you plan to do? It will be best for you if you make up your mind at once, before your condition is noticed. Do you understand?"

"Yes, sir."

"What do you think we should do? Shall we write Juan?"

"All right."

"Do you know his address?"

"Yes. He's bound from Cádiz to the Philippines on a ship."

"Is that all you know? Haven't you more definite information?"

"No."

"You ought to find out the name of the ship at least."

"All right. I'll find out."

"And while the letter is in the mails and before he receives it—assuming he ever receives it—what will you do? Do you plan to go to your home?"

"No, not there. My father and my brothers would beat me."

"In that case, do you want me to tell the mistress everything, to see what can be done?"

"No, no. *Ay, ené!*"

"Well, what are you going to do? Where are you going to go?"

"I don't know."

La Shele gazed down at the floor and sighed. The tears ran down her cheeks.

I, suddenly growing impatient for some reason, stood up and told her: "Very well, then, you decide. I've already given you some idea of what is in store for you. I don't know what else to say to you."

The girl sighed deeply, and then, seeing that I was getting ready to go out, she detained me.

"No, don't leave me."

"What do you want me to do?"

La Shele thought a moment and said: "You write to the *señorito* Juan!"

"I'll write him, but it will be a long time before he gets my letter. If he has left Cádiz already, we can't possibly get any word back from him for at least a year."

"Then you can tell the mistress what happened to me. We can see what she wants to do with me."

The poor girl turned my heart. She handed herself over to her adverse fate like a lamb going to the sacrifice.

III. THE SALE OF THE CALF

On various occasions I insinuated to Doña Celestina, after I had told her the circumstances of La Shele's condition, that she herself should let her son know what had happened to the serving girl. But I soon realized that my attempt was bound to fail, and that as long as it was left up to the mother, nothing would be done in this direction.

I knew that Juan de Aguirre was on a ship running between Cádiz and the Philippines, but neither La Shele nor I was able to find out the name of the ship. Despite the lack of a proper address, I wrote him anyway; but the letter must never have arrived, for there was no answer.

Meanwhile, Doña Celestina and the vicar had together decided to get La Shele married. As you know, the marriages that are made up here among country people, with a financial end only in mind, are called "the sale of the calf." In the case of La Shele the sale was not an ordinary one but involved a sick and damaged piece of livestock, and it would be necessary to give a large dowry in order to get her out of the house and off their hands.

"We must get her away from here as soon as possible," said the vicar. "Let her go and live in some other town or some distant hamlet, and no one there will notice whether the little creature was born before or after the legal interval!"

"Yes, that would be most convenient," added Doña Celestina. "And what is your opinion, doctor?"

"I say the same as always: I would first consult Juan."

"Juan won't be coming here for four or five years."

"And in the meantime, how would we avoid a scandal?" exclaimed the vicar.

"No, no, it just can not be," rejoined Doña Celestina. "It's a waste of time to speak of Juan. The only point of concern here is to find her a husband and get her married."

"I believe the same as Doña Celestina," added the vicar.

"Well, then, let's see who would be the most propitious. I know all the families in the hamlets and settlements. . . Olazábal's boy has gotten married; Aspicua's son is too young; the Endoya boy has gone off to Somorrostro. . ."

"There's a young charcoal-maker in Iturbide. . ." Insinuated the priest.

"But those people are savages," replied Doña Celestina. "I don't want La Shele to have to go there. They would treat her very badly."

"And what about Machín?" asked the priest. "Machín, the Bachelor?"

"The one that lives in one of my houses?"

"Yes."

"But isn't that fellow a little foolish?"

"Ah! Naturally we're not going to find a man perfect in all respects, like the men envisaged by the Constitution of the year '12."

The vicar from time to time permitted himself a little jest at the expense of liberal ideas.

"Well, what shall we do? Shall we send for Machín?"

"I think it would be the best thing."

"The father, too?"

"The father and the son. We can explain to them what's involved and see what conditions they lay down."

"Very well then. We'll send for them."

I witnessed the interview, which was held in the kitchen. It was a sad scene; it gave one a pretty poor idea of humanity. Machín the father and Machín the son kept their backsides close to the fire.

"And so," announced Doña Celestina in an imperious voice, "I'll give La Shele a marriage portion of four ounces and two cows."

"And the hoes and harrow you mentioned," added old Machín.

"All right; and the hoes and the harrow. Are we all agreed now?"

"Well now, the thing is . . ." said Machín the father, scratching his head, "since the girl has been left in this condition, I don't know if it would be right . . . because people would say that. . ."

"I've already told you all that before. The girl is in the state she's in. We know all that. So make up your minds once and for all: yes or no. Or come right out and say that you want more."

"The truth is," mumbled the old man, "that there is a strip of land near the ravine that doesn't belong to our house, and my wife says it should belong to us—without a raise in the rent. I don't say anything about it, but my wife. . ."

"All right; that land will be for you."

The conversation went on in this vein, amid a wealth of details which served to illustrate that kind of country avariciousness which is so repugnant. When they finally reached a definite arrangement, Doña Celestina called out to her daughters:

"Bring in La Shele!"

La Shele appeared, her face pale, her eyes lowered and her eyelids purple.

"We have agreed among us that you should marry this young man."

"Very well, my lady," answered La Shele, in a weak voice, with something of a sob.

"Haven't you anything to say?"

"Nothing, my lady."

"Well then; now you know. The wedding will be held in a few days."

"Very well, my lady."

Machín the younger smiled, giving himself the air of a wicked fellow, while the old man continued to turn around in his head the thought of whether there was not something more that might be extracted from Doña Celestina.

This is the traditional morality of the rich. A life is wrecked, a child is left without a father, desolation is planted in a family, and it is said that the honor of a house has been saved—society has been saved.

IV. THE END OF LA SHELE

Whenever I thought of La Shele I had the presentiment, quite logical after all, that the whole affair would end very badly.

I would have been very surprised to learn that as the years went by La Shele had settled into a quiet, happy life with her husband.

Four or five months after the scene I told you about in which the marriage was arranged, I was summoned to the house rented from Doña Celestina by Machín. La Shele had given birth to a strong, robust boy, but she was sick.

On my first visit I found her very weak, and with the beginnings of a fever.

One day passed, and then another. The poor thing did not get better. Anything at all, the slightest remark, would send her into tears.

Doña Celestina called me apart, to speak privately.

"What's wrong with La Shele?"

"She's very sick."

"But doesn't she show any sign of getting better?"

"No."

"What is the matter with her?"

"First of all, she is in a constant state of excitation; and then I think she is suffering from a cardiac lesion, exacerbated by her pregnancy and the delivery, and by her bitter experience."

Doña Celestina changed color, because, though she was a proud and haughty woman, her intentions were good.

"Do you think her marriage to that man could have contributed? . . ."

"Quite possibly, though there is no sure way to tell, of course."

I did not intend to put her at ease. Let the brutality she had perpetrated weigh on her conscience!

I continued making daily visits to La Shele. There was no way of making her come around. She had obviously made up her mind to take a definite farewell of life. In the face of such a firm resolve to die, all the therapeutic plans come to nought. Within a fortnight, it proved necessary to give confession and extreme unction to La Shele.

Doña Celestina and her daughter went to see her.

They decorated the invalid's room in white, putting white coverlets on the bed and filling the place with flowers and religious pictures. At the moment she was given the Viaticum, the hallway was lined with women who bore lit candles.

La Shele was a very affectionate girl, and when she found herself being indulged, she was happy, and smiled.

The poor thing died early next morning.

The old doctor stopped talking and gazed at me attentively, as if seeking out my opinion.

"Yes, it's a terrible tale," I said. "That lack of respect for another's life is a terrible thing. How many people have been sacrificed to the idea of social position and status, an idea which, after all is said and done, is of no earthly use! A remnant of feudalism!"

"That's true enough."

"And what did Machín say when he heard the story from you?"

"He acted like a madman. He wept bitterly. 'Poor mother, how they made you suffer!' he murmured bitterly. Finally he cried out in wrath: 'I'd like to set fire to this whole town.' Later, grown more calm, he asked me to describe his mother, to tell him whether she resembled him or not. When I indicated that I thought his father had behaved badly he interjected: 'No, no. He wasn't to blame either.'"

"Machín told me that he had received a large envelope from you containing a lengthy manuscript written by his father, and he promised to send me this account."

"Did he send it to you?"

"Yes. And I've read it. I think you are the one that should have final possession of it, and I want to give it to you now."

He handed me the bulky manuscript, and I took it home with me. I began to read it at once.

BOOK SEVEN

Juan de Aguirre's Manuscript

I. A DESPERATE RESOLUTION

I was educated according to the severest principles. My mother inculcated in me the idea that my position obliged me to be more rigorous and inflexible than others. Basically I was a confused and harebrained youth, good-hearted, perhaps, but given to extremes.

I went to sea very early; on board ship, I quickly had to forget my mother's rules.

My life, during those first years of seafaring, was a very intense one. I was a member of the crew of the "Asia," a brig which sailed the China seas. The captain was an Australian, the mate a Basque. Our traffic was carried on between the Malay peninsula, Siam, Sumatra, Borneo, and the Philippines. The principal ports of call were Singapore, Batavia, Macassar, Hong Kong, and Manila. We were, in addition, constantly calling at places where the European had not yet established himself. Our captain, Sil Wilkins, was a maritime genius.

Often we were forced to fight, sometimes the Chinese marauders in the Gulf of Tonkin, sometimes the Muslim pirates who infested those latitudes and who gave proof of an astounding fierceness and daring.

Northeast of Borneo, near the archipelago of the pirates, we waged some ferocious battles against those armed ships called proas.

These proas are, in general, sharp-prowed vessels propelled by oar and sail, and they carry a number of men, usually armed with rifles. Most of these boats have mats hung over the deck to form a shelter, but some of the larger, three-masted ones even boast glass-enclosed decks and a battery of cannons. It is not easily possible for a merchant ship to match the speed and maneuverability of these launches, which are seaworthy in every way.

Sil Wilkins was not in the habit of running from these pirates, and he had always succeeded in beating them off.

He knew all their strong and weak points, as well as their classical stratagems. As a result we were able to wreak havoc upon them. Near the Celebes we sank, by cannon fire, three pirate craft that endeavored to close with us at the same time. We also gave some thieving Muslim a good lesson off Jolo Island in the Philippines.

Sil Wilkins was clearly an extraordinary seaman. I have never known anyone of such placid and calm bravery, or a man of greater generosity and understanding—even indulgence—towards the weaknesses of others. I was never able to make out whether in his heart he had an immense contempt or a great tenderness for mankind. Perhaps he felt both emotions at the same time.

Like all sea captains who have been at sea for years, he had spent most of his time on one ship; he knew what to expect of his "Asia," he knew what she was capable of, and he did not ask for more.

He also knew the China Sea like few men; and what he did not know, he guessed. Wilkins was an example of what a man can attain to when he applies all his intelligence and senses to one specialty. Despite his clear judgement of things and his long experience, it could be said of Wilkins that his innate talent was the least of his qualities.

Wickedness, baseness, envy, all these things he forgave and excused. In Wilkins' eyes, evil was merely the amount of shade necessary to make goodness stand out.

I spent nearly eight years sailing with Wilkins, until at the end of this time my captain retired, now an old man, to Sydney. I went on to Manila, and from Manila sailed to Cádiz. I was planning to enter the service between Cádiz and the Philippines. At this juncture, I received a summons from my mother and returned to Lúzaro.

It was then I met La Shele. She was the daughter of a substantial family who had fallen into ruin. She was a distant relative of my mother, moreover.

In our country, there is no stigma attached to domestic service on the part of a young girl who goes to serve in one of our local houses, and in the case of La Shele even less, inasmuch as she was a relative and a godchild of my mother's. Her position in our house could be considered half way between that of a maid and a poor relation.

La Shele was very young, and innocent; I was a sailor just returned from the solitude of the China Sea, filled with a desire for life. We lived life together, with all the usual implications. I do not know whether or not my mother suspected what was happening, but if she suspected and used a shoddy stratagem to get me away from La Shele, God will have understood and have pardoned her. But in any case, my mother received a letter from Cádiz, in which it was stated that the company judged my immediate presence in Cádiz to be indispensable. The writer of the letter was very vaguely identified to me. It was still a month away from the scheduled sailing of my ship, the frigate "Maribeles," but I did as I was told and returned to Cádiz at once.

When I discovered that the scheduled departure of the ship had not been advanced and that I was not really needed, I was on the verge of going back to Lúzaro. But I hesitated to do so, wondering what excuse I would give my mother for the double trip.

In the end I was moved more by fear of my mother than by any other feeling toward her. Moreover, I had no suspicion of La Shele's state. Had I any notion of what was happening to her, I would have returned at once and married her, whatever the consequences.

It was soon time to board the "Maribeles," and there to begin to forget even the memory of friends and acquaintances. It took us six months to reach Manila, and we remained in the Philippines for two additional months. I found several letters from my mother, and among much other news of more or less different importance to me, I learned that La Shele had gotten married.

When I read this report, it occurred to me that, as all the world says, women are fickle and ungrateful, and I supposed La Shele had simply forgotten about me in my absence.

I wrote a letter to one of my friends in Lúzaro asking for news about her.

Months later I picked up two letters in Cádiz from my friend answering my letter to him. In the earliest of the two, he told me of La Shele's getting married, or rather, of her being married off by my mother to the son of Machín, a stupid and drunken youth, to whose father my mother had been forced to give a sum of money and some land so that he would consent to his son's marrying La Shele, who had been pregnant. In the second letter, my friend wrote me that La Shele had just died, following childbirth, in Machín's farmhouse.

When I read of these facts, I was seized with a profound desperation. I resolved to quit the ship, but the captain sensed my perturbation and refused me permission even to disembark again.

The frigate soon weighed anchor, and I had to make the best of it and simply keep going forward. I spent six months of the voyage to the Philippines in complete despair. Sometimes my rage erupted in fits of semimadness, and a train of furious and violent ideas took possession of my imagination.

Little by little my wrath abated and turned into a profound and chronic melancholy. Everything struck me as sad; in the simplest thing I found reason for doleful reflection. In the end, these notions tormented me to such an extent that I began to get into the habit, whenever I was in Manila, of spending all my time in the taverns, drunk.

In one of these drinking places I met, to my misfortune, a certain Tristán de Ugarte, who proved to be for me one of those baneful men who appear in our path, with the apparent purpose of dragging us down to vice and ruin.

Ugarte was serving as mate on a slaver; he had left his post a few weeks before, and was leading a life of brawling and carousal. He had grown weary of the sea, of the agitated life of a slaver, and he wanted to rest up on the beach and spend some time under repair.

I told him how my wish was the opposite of his: how I longed for the agitated and precarious kind of life I had led aboard the "Asia" with Sil Wilkins, where I could fight every day, put to the sword every man that crossed me, and live in the hope of dying some day on the deck of a ship at the height of a battle.

"Well, listen to me, man; there's something we can do about that," Ugarte said.

"What?"

"We're going to swap our papers; we'll exchange our civil status. You go aboard the "Dragon," and your name will be Tristán de Ugarte. I. . ."

"It can't be," I replied. "They won't accept you on my ship with my papers or my name."

"That doesn't matter. I'm not thinking of going aboard your ship anyway. I want to buy some land here in the Philippines, and your name would make things easier for me."

"In that case, we can do it."

"That's all there is to it, then. From now on I'll be Juan de Aguirre. If you want to ship on the "Dragon" as mate and under my name, I'll write immediately to the captain, who's a countryman of ours."

"Good, write him. Where's the ship now?"

"In Batavia."

Tristán wrote the letter at once, and as soon as he finished, handed it to me. Then we exchanged papers. We were more or less of the same age and height, in any case. Since he was from

Elguea and I from Lúzaro, we had the same accent and manner of speech. The substitution of identities was easy enough.

I let the "Maribeles" sail without me, and a few days later I was at Batavia where I boarded the "Dragon" without any compunction.

II. SLAVING

Captain Zaldumbide was a French Basque. He received me amiably, led me to the poop quarterdeck, and there we talked together. He asked me about my previous experience, and he told me clearly about all the dangers connected with sailing aboard the "Dragon."

When he saw that none of his warnings deterred me, he was willing to take me on as mate. The two principal conditions for holding the job were to be a good pilot and experienced mate, and to speak Basque. I met both conditions. Once I was accepted, he showed me to the cabin that I would occupy next to his. He pointed out that both cabins were armored and that their portholes were barred.

There is no point in recounting in detail the ups and downs of my voyaging. They were more or less the same as those in the life of whoever goes to sea in search of action.

Captain Zaldumbide treated me with consideration. He was relatively a good man, though he was quite uneven in character, and very illogical. He normally acted with the greatest arbitrariness, but then, within his arbitrariness and his own point of view, he strove to be just.

His two outstanding characteristics were religious fanaticism and avarice. Despite the numerous brutalities and deaths he was doubtless responsible for during the course of his life, he refused to resign himself to the loss of his place in paradise. On the contrary, he held out for it with all his strength.

His avariciousness was something special. He had a metal-plated cabinet in which he kept his wealth, and a large number of small brass trunks reinforced by iron bars.

Once I began to joke about his hidden treasure, and he said to me in a secretive voice: "Don't let them hear you. They'd get the idea that I had a lot, and they'd kill me for it."

The crew was made up of gallows birds. Leaving out the Basques, who stood by the captain for the rewards involved and who were mostly peasant stock, and two or three others, the rest were a collection of drunks, thieves, jailbirds, the worst of the worst, the detritus of all the ports of the five parts of the world.

The Basques were something else. They were almost worthy persons. They were convinced that once they were out of their native town, once they were away from home, it did not make the slightest difference whether one transported for sale a family of Chinamen or Negroes, or whether one robbed other ships for a living. My countrymen figured, innocently enough, that at home, in their own towns, personal honor, good faith, and keeping one's word were absolutely indispensable attributes. Once at sea, however, they thought it more or less decorous to live by piracy, sacking, and robbery, and quite respectable if one grew rich by it.

Among the forty members of the crew of the "Dragon" there were men of all social classes: from types whose lives had been a continual series of criminal acts, such as Doctor Ewaldus, to simple men, such as the poor Irish lad Patrick Allen, who was a model of trusting goodheartedness.

Patrick Allen was one of those victims of blind fate. His father, a ruined farmer, had taken his family out of Ireland to seek refuge and work in Liverpool; there he had died, leaving a widow and a numerous brood to live in misery.

Allen was a fond and sentimental son, and he had a great love for the family, so that he suffered unbearably to see them sunken in their poverty. He hung about the docks looking for work, and he even began to haunt those seaport taverns where drunken seamen from all over the world congregate.

Allen had no marine experience, no papers or certificates, and no skipper would take the lad on. He watched his family going to pieces, and he could see the moment approaching when his sisters would be ready to enter those halls of cheap pleasure where seamen from everywhere get drunk on poor whiskey with a blond, painted woman at their side.

Allen was aware that in Liverpool, as in any other large port, there were men whose business was in human beings.

These agents in humans would pick up derelict sailors, furnish them with quarters in their own houses, even give them food and a little money, and when a sea captain came along looking for extra sailors, an agreement would be struck. The captain would pick out his men from the derelicts, and pay their debts by giving advances against the men's future wages.

Allen found himself one of these agents in human beings and sold himself for a few shillings to give to his mother. He was taken from Liverpool to Amsterdam, and there Zaldumbide ransomed him, paying his debts and putting him aboard the "Dragon."

Allen was a good lad, but not much of a sailor. Try as I might to explain to him the arts of navigation, I was not successful in teaching him. He looked on the sea as something lacking in interest. He had the spirit of a farmer.

Another basically good man was Franz Nissen, the helmsman. He spoke scarcely at all, and never about his life. But this silent man was a superb seaman. Zaldumbide told me his story: he had been serving in the navy—it was the Danish navy, I believe —and an officer had, unjustly, ordered him flogged; one night a short time later, Nissen had poured oil over the sleeping officer and around his cabin and then set the place on fire; he managed to flee the country afterwards, in some way or another.

Allen was my best friend on the ship. He knew all about my life, and I knew his. We were as close as brothers.

His friendship made my stay on the "Dragon" more tolerable. We used to talk together, and I perfected my English. I showed him what I could of our trade. And so months and years passed, amid a running accompaniment of danger.

We made numberless voyages, carrying unfortunate Negroes from Angola and Mozambique to Brazil and the West Indies.

I never grew accustomed to the spectacle of misery and horror involved in the slaving traffic. I usually hid myself in my cabin, to avoid seeing those unfortunates. Zaldumbide treated them well enough, but this did not prevent the entire spectacle from being repulsive.

The "Dragon" was not one of those classic slavers which were nothing more than floating coffins. The amount of air and water needed was carefully measured, and efforts were made to avoid contamination and infection. Zaldumbide was well aware, in short, that it was not good business to let the Negroes die on his hands.

From what everyone said, I understood that before my arrival on the ship the "Dragon" had done a great trade in "ebony" and that the crew had been most manageable. But in my time, the sailors were up in arms half the time, and the ship made its crossings almost by chance.

Three or four years after my joining the "Dragon" we were sailing one day off Cape Engaño on the northeast tip of Luzon, having left Macao behind, en route to America with some three hundred Chinese coolies, when a low-cut two-masted schooner, of the type known in the Philippines as pontins, appeared off our bow; aboard her was Tristán de Ugarte. He was a different man; a large scar cut across his face and completely disfigured him.

He complained loudly that my name had given him very little luck; his farm land at Iloilo had failed him. The truth probably was that he did not know how to administer it.

His restless character interfered with his making a living. He was a drunkard and dangerously excitable. I often wondered later if he were not mad, such were his habitual rages and flights of fancy.

We were crossing the Pacific when the Chinamen rioted on us, and either they or some crew members killed Zaldumbide and the Dutch doctor.

This uprising was followed by a series of encounters and frays between the two factions into which the crew was divided. At length they settled their differences, and I took over effective command of the ship.

My plan was to reach Europe, turn over the "Dragon" to its owners, and then go back myself to Spain.

One day, while we were still sailing in the Pacific, we encountered a ship without any sail which signaled us violently; when we came near, they asked if we had a doctor aboard. Failing to help them with medical advice, we sent them some water and tea as a substitute.

Almost immediately after this encounter at sea, the black vomit broke out on the "Dragon." We carefully searched the dead doctor's cabin again, and found a container of cinchona powder. From it we made up a potion for the sick. Of twenty men who came down with the disease, eight died.

Ugarte was seized with the notion of inciting some seamen to mutiny at the height of the epidemic aboard ship. He demanded that we change the name of our vessel and take up piracy. I was forced to put this madman in chains.

After a long and difficult passage, we reached the Straits of Magellan; because the wind was not favorable, however, I decided to keep a southward course and double Cape Horn.

The weather turned intensely cold, though it continued clear for a spell; but then shortly we ran into a dense fog bank, and we did not run through it for several days.

Prudence would have dictated that we lay to, but we continued on. There were several occasions on which we nearly ran into great blocks of floating ice. Managing to avoid them, we made use of the ice to replenish our water supply.

The crew was in a state of exhaustion; the men worked as if

they were victims of a fever; I was afraid that if they were once allowed to rest, they would not be able to rouse themselves again, and we would all perish in that stark and inhospitable area.

It was not until we reached the Bay of Solitude in the Falkland Islands that I called a temporary halt. Here we rested a while; once the crew had recovered its strength a bit, we set out for Europe.

We had reached the latitude of Saint Vincent when an English warship chased us; we got away, but the warship found us again and in the second chase destroyed our masts and rigging with cannon fire. We then fled the "Dragon" in our whaleboat; the ship's cook and some of his accomplices managed to get ahold of Zaldumbide's coffers as we were abandoning the ship, and they put them secretly aboard the whaleboat. As we fled, the "Dragon" began to sink; Ugarte bragged that he had opened a hole in the ship's bottom.

If it had not been for Zaldumbide's ill-gotten treasure, we could have disembarked at once on one of the Cape Verde Islands; but with that cargo it seemed dangerous to land there. We sailed northward toward the Canary Islands instead, and decided by common accord to land briefly somewhere along the African coast and bury the chests before going ashore in the Canaries.

We approached Africa near the Nun River; we entered the river mouth and went on to explore the banks on both sides. The dazzling white sand banks near the sea were blinding under the hot sun. A little further upriver, we began to come upon some elementary vegetation, brambles, and shrubs. Fifteen miles from the coast we found some ruins; they were probably the remains of the towers built by Diego García de Herrera, by order of the King of Spain. I did not think it wise to bury the chests too close to the towers, and I searched for the most appropriate spot, using them as reference. All the high points of sand along the river would probably shift eventually under the action of the wind from the Sahara; it would be best to fix on more stable points.

On one of the walls around the ruined fort, I found that someone had deeply engraved the portrait of an elephant in the rock; I placed myself so that my eye would be at the point where the elephant's eye was, and looked from what would be its line of sight. I saw that the shadow of a sharp rock situated near the river fell at that hour between two great stone heaps in front of us. At that exact moment the top of the shadow fell near the foot of an argan tree. It was at that spot that I decided to bury the coffers.

I fixed the place exactly, and since I assumed that before we reached safety we might be caught and searched by someone, I made use of a cipher: instead of drawing up a chart or other indication, I put all the descriptive details into Basque, and marked down the information by circling the appropriate letters consecutively in a prayer book.

The seamen had meanwhile encountered some nomadic Moors, and had bartered with them, exchanging a rifle for two lambs. But the Moors, instead of complying with their agreement, attacked us and killed several of our men.

We beat a retreat downriver, hotly pursued by the Moors, and soon were at sea again. Shortly after, we were in the middle of a gale. It was impossible to use our sail, and the enormous waves began to break over our boat. We had to bail out the water, using our caps and anything else at hand; the spray dashed across our faces all the time, and the wind blew out our lantern whenever we lit it to try and read the compass and even drowned out our shouts to each other.

We fought the rain and waves for two days, and on the morning of the third we sighted the island of Lanzarote, which appeared like a cloud on the horizon.

We thought we had reached safety at last when suddenly an English naval launch appeared from nowhere and made us prisoners; they took us aboard the warship which had chased us a few days previously.

We were suspected of piracy. As everyone knows, the laws against piracy are ferocious. The pirate is held to be outside the laws and rights of civilized nations, and English law condemns him to be hung by his neck until dead.

The English warship was called the "Argonaut." The medical officer aboard this ship was an excellent person; in the course of our voyage I found myself telling him the story of my life, without concealing anything. He gave good reports of me, and was no doubt influential in seeing that I, as captain of a pirate ship, was not immediately hung from a yardarm.

In short, the English treated me well during the passage from the Canaries to Plymouth. The only person to harry me was Ugarte, who kept recriminating with me for not having followed his advice when we were in the Pacific.

III. THE PRISON SHIP

We reached England, and were immediately led before our judges. The entire crew of the "Dragon" stood in the dock. The fact that we had not actively resisted capture, and the added fact that we were not clearly pirates, again saved us all from hanging.

We might even have gotten free altogether if the trial had not been held with such speed that we had no time even to organize our defense. We were condemned to various prison ships and distant prisons, those in authority on the "Dragon" for ten years, the seamen for five.

The seamen were sent to prisons in the interior of England and to the prison ships, or hulks, near Portsmouth and Chatham. The rest of us were sent to a prison ship in the far north.

We embarked aboard a cutter called the "Flying Fish"; our party consisted of Ugarte; Nissen, the helmsman; Old Sam, the bosun; the Irishman Allen—I had requested and obtained permission to keep him with me; and a group of Frenchmen, previously condemned by the court. As we started out of Plymouth, Old Sam threw himself into the water. We did not catch sight of him again. The soldiers on guard fired wherever they thought they saw movement. I turned away from the sight of that terrible hunt.

The next day, toward nightfall, the "Flying Fish" lay to, and a boat came alongside.

We descended into the boat, our hands manacled; guarding us was a party of soldiers under an officer.

The "Flying Fish" was soon lost to sight, and we neared land. Through the dense fog that surrounded us we could see only a river mouth looming up ahead. Then, under the misty polar sky we began to see gray headlands, bare of vegetation, and in front of us the land we were approaching, black swampland over whose stagnant water clouds of birds wheeled.

It was still twilight when we drew near the prison ship. It was a vessel without rigging, devoid even of masts, which loomed above us like a dark stain between a gray sky and a gray sea. Close up, the old ship resembled a Noah's Ark tied up with lines and chains; it was very high, and black smoke poured from its smokestacks; its bow figurehead was an image of Neptune.

The same gray neuter color was everywhere. In the twilight the yellow water was nearly indistinguishable from the sky.

I have never felt a greater sadness.

We passed under the taffrail; the poop boasted three stories above the water, with windows and galleries decorated in a baroque style.

The top of the taffrail must have been some thirty feet above the water, and from it hung a large lantern shining through the murk of the oncoming night.

The prison ship was an old vessel from the Trafalgar epoch, and its name was "Neptune."

Once aboard her and standing on the deck, we were forced to wait where we were for a long, cold hour. Finally, I was ordered to take off my clothes. I obeyed and was given some faded pants, an ancient waistcoat, and a jacket with a large number on the back. I had made up my mind not to protest under any circumstances, and it proved a wise decision, for other of my companions, Ugarte chief among them, immediately suffered double punishment—in addition to being deprived of their clothes, they were locked up to boot.

When I turned around I saw Allen standing before me; the two of us were now dressed like convicts, and we gave each other a long searching look, at the end of which we shook hands solemnly and swore never to forsake the other.

This was to be our home for ten long years. What a home and what a life it would be! Spring, summer, and winter would have to pass many times over this floating jail, always in the midst of this gray sea, these muddy swamps, with no more communication with the world outside than the sound of the waves and the sharp cry of the seagulls and wild ducks.

Life aboard the prison ship was horrible. We scarcely had room to turn around. The soldiers of the guard were quartered in the bow, and their officers in the poop. The prisoners lived between the lower gallery and the barracks constructed on deck, under the eyes of guards at both ends, and beneath them and above them.

It was most difficult to accustom oneself to live there, but in the end anything can be accomplished by perseverance and will.

I am convinced that I did not fall deadly ill in the first days only because of an extraordinary effort of will. I was constantly feverish and my head burned; at night I could never sleep and would merely fall into a state of complete exhaustion. At dawn, when the morning bugle sounded, I would get up with my clothes damp and my hair wet; I had pains in every joint of my body and felt completely prostrated.

Despite all this my will did not break; I could count on its strength, even tenseness, for some great effort. I was able to get a potion of cinchona and within a fortnight I was physically well again.

Men confined on prison ships were treated in the same manner as convicts. In case of disobedience, they were flogged, or put in chains, or confined in the black hole, where they were kept on bread and water.

Most of the men were allowed to keep pets: pigeons, birds of all sorts, squirrels, and other domesticated animals. Every man sought his own peculiar way of filling his idle time.

There was an English slaving captain among us, who, according to his own story, used to tie his Negroes, whenever they gave him trouble, to the mouths of cannon and then fire the cannon. When this captain was run down by his captors, he had put as many Negroes as he could into barrels and dumped them over the side. This brutal demon was now moved to tears whenever the rabbit he had domesticated seemed out of sorts.

Ugarte and a man from Marseilles were the chief trouble-makers. Ugarte was the eternal complainer: the bad food, the humidity, the cold, all the natural discomforts of a prison ship drove him wild, and his protest served only to keep him in chains or in close confinement all of the time.

He denounced me bitterly as an informer and a coward because I refused to protest. I was unable to convince him that a protest which served no end but the imposition of additional punishment was sheer stupidity.

The man from Marseilles, whose name—or nickname, I am not clear which—was Tiboulen, was a nuisance of a different style.

The quality which in Ugarte might have been called peevish dignity was in Tiboulen a form of patriotism based on hatred of the English. The man from Marseilles was one of those bitter Mediterranean personalities, excessive, farfetched, given to display; to his natural character he joined the petulant and hot-headed patriotism of the French.

Tiboulen was not a violent and bad man, like Ugarte; when he was alone, he proved himself amenable to reason, but with a public before him, he lost his head. Tiboulen felt a need to have people concern themselves with him, whatever the motive, and he fought with his fellow inmates senselessly and directed a thousand ridiculous threats at his guards.

This type of man, who lives for the gallery, brings down on himself first wrath and then contempt. Sometimes I went so far as to wish that the jailers would tear the flesh off such an idiot; at other times I felt pity to see him handed over, utterly defenseless, to the brutality of his keepers.

In the end, Tiboulen and Ugarte were assigned to another gang, and left us in peace for a while.

During the first few months, Allen and I spent our time systematically studying all the forms and possibilities of flight.

It would be extremely difficult: all the openings on the ship were barred with heavy iron; the doors all had elaborate locks. A gallery, or enclosed deck, ran around the entire ship; it was exactly at water level, and its portholes were placed so close together that no man or object could have passed before them without being seen by the sentries.

There was always a strong guard stationed in this gallery, and the rounds were made every quarter of an hour.

In addition, other prison ships were anchored in our inlet, and a system of mutual vigilance was maintained, so that at night numerous launches patrolled the area around the hulks.

From the conversations of my companions, I was able to deduce that a Masonic lodge, under the name Faith and Liberty, was functioning in our midst. The lodge had agents in contact with the prisoners on the other prison ships—and not only with the prisoners, but even with certain officers of the garrisons.

Allen and I expressed a desire to join the lodge, and, after submitting to the tests, we were admitted as brothers. The Venerable was an old Greek pirate, whose life had been a series of horrors.

By means of this Freemasonry we were able to learn some interesting facts of use in any possible flight. The estuary in which our prison ships was anchored was like a large lake, more than a league wide. There were a total of three prison ships anchored there, and our ship was in the middle.

The "Neptune" was situated approximately two miles from land.

A danger much greater than that of the sea, in case of escape, was the coastal swamps, more than a hundred yards wide. They were said to be equally impossible to walk or to swim across.

The greater number of prisoners who had escaped in the past had gotten caught in them, and had died there, to be converted into carrion for the birds of prey who lived on decay.

Once I saw the impossibility or futility of escape, I devoted myself to the study of mathematics. The recommendation given me by the doctor on the "Argonaut" continued to be helpful, and thanks to it, the commandant of the prison ship lent me various books on geometry, algebra, and physics. To these he added a Bible.

Allen, who was a fanatical Catholic, several times urged me not to read it.

The prisoners were sunken in their boresome apathy and each one sought his individual way of whiling away his time. I started to give lessons in mathematics, and I even earned a bit of money. Despite the fact that it was forbidden to have light at night, I managed to go on reading; I saved the bits of bacon that formed part of my ration, attached an oakum wick, and made use of it for the light I needed.

The indifference I felt toward everything, united to a stoical philosophy that I began to acquire, helped me to bear all my troubles with calm and without needless anger. Moreover, I had the hope that at the end of two or three years I would be sent to a penitentiary colony, where life would be more endurable.

Several times I endeavored to teach Allen mathematics, but he was not of a mind for it. He preferred to accompany himself with an accordion and sing the sentimental songs of his country.

IV. FLIGHT

At the end of a year I knew all the people aboard the prison ship.

I heard of some old convicts who had developed a curious business. They would skillfully bore a hole in the prison ship and then sell it to the highest bidder. These holes had to come out almost exactly at water level, between the level of the lowest gallery—which was patrolled day and night—and the water itself.

Ugarte, who had returned to plague us and who again spent most of his time in the lockup, importuned me to find out who would make us an exit hole so that we might both escape. He had money and would pay whatever was necessary.

A Dutch sailor, one of the crew of the "Spectator," a pirate ship which had been celebrated in its time, entered into negotiations with Ugarte, and agreed to make a mine in the ship and turn it over on completion. In the hope of eventual freedom, Ugarte became more tractable.

The Dutchman succeeded in making part of his passageway, but halfway through the operation one of the guards discovered the mine, and the work was lost.

Following this frustration, Ugarte would not leave me alone.

Every day he badgered me with one or two alternative projects. The idea of escape obsessed him; thanks to this fixed idea, he managed to achieve a certain tranquillity.

In truth, I was beginning to get accustomed to life on the prison ship. The idea of getting stuck in the swamp until the carrion birds took me away was not very seductive.

Ugarte got feverish and out of hand; he chafed again under his special punishment and he irritated me by taunts and continually asking me if I was afraid to make the attempt to escape.

I tried to point out that we should conserve our energies for the opportune moment, and not waste any strength in stupidly railing at the inevitable. I also laid down the principle that as far as I was concerned the primary condition for any escape plan was that it be simple. I would not listen to anything that was not. Our only guarantee of success would lie in the plan's simplicity.

In the end, Ugarte, Allen, and myself leagued ourselves together. We concentrated on the problem for several days, and finally agreed on a plan. It consisted of the following points: We would tunnel a hole in the wall of our sleeping quarters so that we should emerge directly on deck; next we would gain our way aft to the poop deck, which was about the length of half the ship, slip down a rope past the commandant's cabin, and so into the sea.

I insisted that one of the plan's conditions be that we not defend ourselves and under no circumstance kill anyone. It would be so difficult to traverse the swamp, gain the coast, and make good our escape that we must take it for granted that our chances of being returned to the prison ship were something like a hundred to one.

We set about the preliminaries. Ugarte had received a good sum of money, and he was willing to spend it. Through the agency of our Masonic connections we got ourselves supplied with files, a saw, a pocket compass, and some ends of hemp from which we could manufacture a line.

All of us slept in hammocks. It was wintertime, and we agreed to begin covering our heads at night, as if we were trying an extreme method to keep warm. The idea was to accustom the "master," when he made his tour of inspection, to see us in the same formless position, and also to convince him that we fell asleep at once.

We also agreed not to talk together in front of others. To make everything appear normal, I even urged Ugarte to feign an occasional fit of anger in his old style.

We began to make our mine on Christmas Eve. Every night we worked at deepening four grooves, in the form of a square, which were covered over with tar when the night's work was completed. The finished square was to be like a wooden plug in a wine barrel: it would be put back and the slots covered so that it would not be immediately noticed.

It took us several nights to complete. When we had finished, Allen sat down outside it and played his accordion, and from time to time, with his finger dipped in some tar, covered over the places where the openings showed in the wood.

The second difficulty, the crossing of the swamp, had given us much pause. These swamps could neither be walked across nor swum. Allen proposed we make wide wooden soles for our feet, in the manner of snowshoes, which we could tie on our feet with cords when we reached the edge of the swamp after swimming from the ship. Our only concern then would be to find the most solid part to cross upon.

Once this idea was accepted, we decided to make the shoes or soles of thin boards. Allen petitioned the "master" for enough wood to make two chests, one for himself and one for me, where we could keep our effects. The wood cost a fortune, for the caprices of prisoners had to be paid for. Ugarte's funds were reduced to very little. The petition aroused no suspicion, and Allen prepared six thin planks, which he stored in a corner of the poop deck by authority of one of the guards. The planks were a foot and a half wide and three feet long, and in the middle they were fitted with holes—which were concealed by stopping them with wax—so that we might tie them to our feet when needed.

Once the first two preparatory steps were completed, we stood by waiting for a dark night. The moon was on the wane, but the nights were still too clear.

As the decisive moment approached, I felt increasingly uneasy. I do not believe I am a coward, but as I looked over the ship's side at the frothy gray water, as I realized that we must soon throw ourselves in, I would feel dizzy and my heart would pound.

One Saturday, a few days after Twelfth Night, Allen was able to get a look through a telescope belonging to one of the guards, and he sighted a small boat tied up at a point along the coast. It had been left there, no doubt, by some duck hunter. The boat was on the other side of the swamp.

We made our decision at once, and began preparations. Each man was to carry his clothes, a file, and four or five shillings in a packet, wrapped in a piece of waterproof cloth, to be tied to his back. The cords to tie the wooden boards to our feet would be carried around our necks as we swam. The large rope we would have to leave behind tied to the taffrail on the poop.

We decided to make our flight on Sunday night.

Our fellow prisoners knew of our plans, and awaited the results, as if it were a theatrical function we were putting on.

The guard entered and took the roll, as always, before we turned in. It was customary for the "master" to come in later, with one or two of the guards, to check to see that each man was in his hammock.

Once the roll was called, Allen, Ugarte, and I took off our clothes; we immediately made them into bundles and wrapped them in the pieces of waterproof cloth. We then helped ourselves to some of the other convicts' clothes hanging on the common hooks and shoved them under our bedding. We left our caps hanging as they hung on other days. When the "master" came in, the three of us got on the floor, took out the square piece we had cut in the wall, slipped our bundles through, and then squeezed through ourselves on to the deck. We closed up the opening behind us. Outside it was terribly cold. Almost at our side, a sentry suddenly called out, "All's well!"

The night was totally dark; a vague reddish haze seemed to float in the air. We crouched down and ran along under the side of the ship; at length we were able to leap to the poop deck. There we waited for a bit, shivering, to see if we were discovered or if we should continue our flight.

I began to shake with the cold.

"Here, take some of this, and rub yourself with it," whispered Allen, handing me a chunk of tallow.

I began to rub myself down, and Allen smeared some tallow on my back. This coating of grease kept me from the cold. Ugarte and Allen did the same.

"And now, the wooden planks for our feet?" I asked.

"They're close at hand; I'll get them in a moment," said Allen.

We waited for the bed check to be made. If our absence was discovered then, it would be madness to go any farther.

The "master" and his men came out on deck in a routine manner. The sentries were changed. Our disappearance had not been noticed. It was time for us to act.

Allen ran along the poop and shortly returned, bringing with him our wooden sandals. We felt like crying out "All's well!" ourselves.

We made our way aft along the poop deck without the slightest noise. Our next job would be to leap to the rounded taffrail gallery, upon which the balcony of the commandant's cabin opened out. From there we would have to jump to an un-broken balcony, lower down and protruding less.

From one railing to the other there was a distance of some twelve feet.

If we tied our rope on the upper gallery, we could descend by it to the next, but how could we untie it afterwards for use in reaching the water? To cut it in half would not serve our purpose. We wanted to enter the water without any noise, for any sound might arouse the sentry.

On the sides of the poop, on all the salient angles of arrises there were chamfers faced with glass, behind which there were all manner of baroque adornments.

On old ships these chamfers were called garden chamfers. There was no way to scale them.

"Give me a file," whispered Ugarte.

I handed him mine. He leaned far down over the railing and determinedly jammed it into an opening; he pushed on it to see if it held, and then climbed down, using it as a step; we all followed suit, jumped down to the lower railing, and from there fell lightly to the deck with little noise.

The lower gallery contained three illuminated windows. Through the windows we could see two officers playing cards in the cabin.

From where we now found ourselves the drop to the water was some fifteen or sixteen feet. Under us, there was still the lower gallery with its round of sentries, but there would naturally be less vigilance at this end of the ship.

We could have lowered ourselves into the water by one of the chains which anchored the prison ship; but the chain on the poop had a lantern fixed to it at the top and was consequently well illuminated, so that we would have been plainly visible should any of the guards happen to look that way.

Allen tied the rope to one of the iron rungs of the railing; at the other end he tied the boards which we were to use in get-ting across the swamps. Then the Irishman let himself down the rope soundlessly. When the rope went slack again, Ugarte slipped down, and finally I went down the same way. At one moment during my descent I could have sworn that the sentry in the gallery was staring into my face, but it was doubtless an illusion of my imagination.

"Let's start out," someone called softly in the water.

We untied the boards and the three of us began our swim towards the coast. There was a good sea running; a strong north-easter was blowing and carried with it large drops of rain.

Ugarte set out with great energy; I called to him in a low voice to tell him to use more discretion, for otherwise he would soon tire. He paid heed to my warning and slowed down; from time to time, the three of us would turn over on our backs and float.

We all took turns carrying the boards, and they served as a float for whoever had them at the moment.

Soon we were passing one of the other prison ships. Looming up out of the mist, it resembled a gigantic and fantastic glow-worm. Then we left this lightship behind. Thanks to our system of methodic halts, we were able to swim for some two hours without exhaustion.

It must have been ten o'clock at night when we swam into the border of the swamp. The river current ran between the sea proper and the muddy shore. We swam across the river, which was nearly frozen, and ran into a muddy bog. At first we found it impossible to walk on that liquid silt; four or five yards from the water, however, it proved more solid. We slithered on, pushing our way deeper into the bog, until we had reached an area where the weight of a man was supported, although not sufficiently to allow walking. Sprawled in the muck, we tied the boards to one another's feet. Then the three of us stood upright, and began to plod our way in single file, holding on to the man in front. The swamp gave off a sickening and nearly over-powering stench. There were moments when one of us would sink down into a soft vicious hole; but, falling and pulling each other upright, covered with mud to our ears, we finally reached a sandy area which did not yield under our feet.

We set out along the coast. The boat was nowhere in sight; either it had been removed, or we had lost our way in the night.

Ugarte commenced to blaspheme, cursing his fate. Allen told him to be quiet, for Providence had so far favored us and to blaspheme was to challenge God.

Ugarte answered him sarcastically, and the two would have come to blows if I had not interposed to calm them.

"If you could see the ridiculous figure you both cut, wrangling with each other from behind a suit of armor made of mud, black as crabs, you would soon stop fighting."

We went around the sand spit on which we were walking and reached a beach where the water was clear. We washed ourselves off as best we could, rubbing ourselves with handfuls of grass to take off the covering of grease and muck that covered us from head to foot, and then we put on our clothes. We were uncertain as to what to do, whether to strike out or to wait for the dawn. Instinctively we would have liked to start out, but we were held back by the hope of finding the boat Allen had seen on the previous day.

In the end we decided to remain where we were and wait for day to come.

V. ADRIFT

Finally, after an endless night, the mist began to clear and the morning to appear—a sad, dirty-colored morning, enveloped in rain and mud. The ravens flew over our heads, letting out blood-curdling screams. They seemed to be lamenting the fact that they did not find us carrion, stretched out on the muck of the swamp.

Suddenly Allen caught sight of the boat; it was tied up at a nearby point. "There it is!" he yelled, and set out on the run.

Ugarte and I followed behind him. The boat was tied up with a chain. We had two files left to us, and we began at once to file away at the iron. The work took us a long time. Ugarte, always impatient, looked around for a rock; he found a large one, and gave the chain such a blow with it that it broke asunder. He almost succeeded in smashing the boat as well. It was not in his nature to calculate all the results.

The boat contained two oars. We got in and began to row at once. We took turns, and even found the labor invigorating, at first. But we soon began to tire, and then a fog enveloped us.

At midmorning, we sighted a coastguard cutter through the fog coming in our direction; we pulled in the oars and lay down in the bottom of the boat. Either the cutter did not see us or they thought we were sleeping duck-hunters, for they did not approach us but continued on at a fast clip.

I had memorized the map hanging in one of the guard posts on the prison ship, and knew that we could not be off any town until we had gone some five or six miles. The sun appeared for a moment, a pale sun that shone in the sky in the middle of an opalescent halo. The three of us gazed at each other. We presented a hideous picture; we reeked of prison, and the convict numbers could still be seen on our backs.

When I spoke of our numbers, Ugarte and Allen took off their jackets and pricked out the infamous numerals with the points of their files. I did the same.

We worked our way along, not going out too far from the coast. From time to time we shifted places, and one of us would rest. We had lost the habit of rowing, and so our hands grew swollen and the skin rubbed off.

The coast, which we could now see, was desolate, with low hills and swamps along the water's edge. In the distance, we would see the smoke of an occasional farmhouse, and from time to time the ruin of some castle.

As the afternoon began, fog again swept over the sea, and we had to go on blindly.

Hunger, thirst, and weariness drove us toward the land. It had now been more than twenty-four hours since we had eaten, and our hands were beginning to bleed.

We finally landed on a deserted beach, near a little town whose port we could see plainly.

I had heard it said that in some places of the Scottish and Irish coast the people eat the brown algae known as Laminaria, and our hunger was such that we did our best to swallow this seaweed; but we could not do it.

Allen found some barnacles, and we tore them off the rocks with our files; they were our first food of the day.

We decided to run the boat up on the beach and spend the night ashore. We did not dare enter the village, looking as we did, and climbed up the beach and over some sand dunes, out of sight of any chance passerby, and made our way a little inland until we found the town cemetery; stretched out between two of the taller sepulchers, protected by them from the wind, we lay down and were able to get some sleep.

Around midnight we were definitively awakened by our hunger and cold. We got up, quit the cemetery, and started out anew.

"Let's go into the town," said Ugarte, "and see if we can't find something to eat."

The sky had cleared and was full of stars; the puddles in the road were frozen over; the ground was made hard by the hoarfrost; a cold wind blew strongly. We were getting closer to the town, and the dogs barked in the silence of the night. As we passed in front of a humble cottage whose windows were illuminated, we decided to send Allen to ask for some bread, to buy it if necessary. He came back at once, saying that he could find no one about.

"There's no one about!" exclaimed Ugarte. "So much the better."

He dashed into the cottage himself, and came back in a few minutes with a loaf of bread and a slab of dried beef.

We had turned into common thieves. Ugarte next set his face toward the port.

"But what's the point of going that way? Wouldn't it be better to go back to the beach?" I asked.

"Let's have a stab at it," he answered.

We followed along to the port, and there Ugarte walked boldly up to a coasting lugger that was tied up to an iron ring, and stepped aboard.

"There's no one in here either," he called. "It's a beautiful craft! Come on, climb aboard."

"You mean to steal this ship?" I asked in surprise, for the idea had not entered my head before.

"Why not? What's the difference between stealing a small boat and a larger ship with sails? It's all the same thing."

Of course he was right. We undid the mooring line, and the three of us, pushing against the sea wall, worked the vessel out into the open. Then we noiselessly hoisted the sails, and set out to sea. The ship contained supplies and water to last for several days.

The next morning, we scratched off the name of the vessel, the "Betty," and baptized it with the new name we gave it, the "Rosa," out of Bangor, Allen's home town.

We sailed along all that day and all the following night, and meanwhile we were able to rest and eat. By Wednesday morning we were far enough away from the prison ship so as not to have to worry that the authorities would fall upon us. We had made good use of our time.

If the wind should continue favorable, we could make France. We lacked a chart, but to sail out of the Irish Sea, despite the fog, only a bearing was necessary.

I was hoping that we would soon reach some point or other where Allen and Ugarte could be separated. Once the two of them had found themselves out of danger, a furious and active hatred had sprung up between them. Anything one said seemed to infuriate the other.

I did my best to calm them down, but it was no easy task, considering the stubbornness of the Irishman and the irritability of my own countryman.

We struggled against strong winds for the next three days. The vessel pitched continually; it seemed to break the water, striking it as if it were a long knife, and this proved a nuisance to us all. On Friday night we were navigating through Saint George's Channel, between Wales and Ireland, a passageway that I knew well enough.

All night and all day we danced on top of the waves, enveloped in fog and unable to get on our course. The wind moder-

ated somewhat when the sun came out. When the sky grew clear
and the fog lifted, we found ourselves in sight of the Irish coast.
Thereabouts the coast was made up of rock cliffs. Then the
choppy sea began to grow calm, until it was nearly immobile,
and the wind failed completely.

We were by now short of water, and decided to put in towards
land.

To put into a port would expose us to someone's recognizing
the vessel, and might lead to our falling immediately afoul of
the law, and so we decided to land on some isolated beach.
Allen would go to the nearest village with the few shillings left
to us and there attempt to buy some food; meanwhile, I would
go in search of water, and Ugarte would stay behind to fish.

I set out and was not successful in finding any water supply,
neither a river nor a spring of any sort. A peasant I chanced
to meet finally told me that there was no water to be found thereabouts.

I returned to the ship and waited for Allen to return. He came
back bringing some food, which we devoured, and a bottle of
beer. When he was through eating, he said: "Now I must tell
you what happened, and about the offer that was made me. I
went to the town, and into the store to buy provisions. I was
immediately asked who I was, and from where I came. I talked
about a shipwreck and the shopkeeper told me, 'If you want
to work, there's a farm in the next town that's looking for help.'

"I followed the road and found the farm. A dark young man
interviewed me, and, when I saw that he created no difficulties,
I told him that two comrades would come with me. All of a
sudden, the dark young man said, 'You people are corsairs.'
'No, no,' I answered. 'Listen,' he said, 'even if you've escaped
from the hulks, it doesn't matter to me. If you work well, I'll
pay you the same as the others. Are your comrades Irishmen
too?' 'No, they're Spaniards,' I said. 'It's all the same to me,'
he answered. 'So long as they're not Englishmen, I'll take them
on.'

"I said goodbye," concluded Allen, "and came back as fast as
I could."

We debated whether or not we should accept the offer of
work, and decided that it would be the best solution for the
moment. Next we wondered what we could do with our
stolen vessel. To abandon it right there would be a giveaway
of where we had landed.

We brought the lugger around to one end of the beach; at

the moment there was a rather good breeze blowing; we hoisted the jibs and the fore-and-aft sail, tied the tiller, and then pushed the vessel out into the water, while we stood chest-high in the waves. At first the ship seemed as if it were disconcerted, surprised; it advanced a bit, retreated; it gave the impression of a person seized with indecision, wanting to take the leap and unable to make up his mind. At last it took the wind so well that it rushed away, leaving us suddenly stupified.

"She knows where she's going," said Allen with conviction.

We climbed a high sand dune and when we got to the top we turned around to look back. Our ship was sailing steadily on.

"Let's head for the farm," I said.

From the height we were on, two small villages were visible; one appeared to be a fishing town, the other an inland town surrounded with cultivated fields.

Traveling by night, and thus avoiding all sight of people, we reached the farm where Allen had been hired. It was located on one side of the highway and in front of it there was a leafy grove of very high trees. The farmhouse itself, large and dark, was of stone, and was surrounded by low brick buildings.

The overseer furnished us with some work clothes, and the next day we began work in the fields.

Despite his offer to treat us the same as the other workers, the overseer took advantage of our status as men without papers and presumed convicts to exploit us.

I was resigned, being fully aware that there was no way out of this situation at the moment; for his part, Allen, being Irish, got along well enough; Ugarte, on the other hand, who lacked this distinction, was always complaining.

"Let's get out of here," he would insist at every step.

"Wait until we're able to dress in some decent clothes and have a little money, and then we'll go," I told him.

He waited, amid noisy protests. With the first money I received I bought myself a jacket, a knapsack, and some high shoes and leggings. Allen dressed in the traditional country manner. Ugarte, when he slipped at last into his new suit, announced that we must leave at once.

It was his plan that he and I set out, leaving Allen behind; Allen, on the other hand, had thought of abandoning Ugarte. I would have preferred to go with Allen and leave Ugarte, but by now I had begun to feel pity for my fellow Basque.

"I think it would be best," I told them both, "if each one of us went his own way, and we met again in France."

"No, no; that won't do."

"Well then, the three of us can go on together, and share the same fortune; but we have to submit to some direction and authority; otherwise, the whole thing's impossible."

"You give the orders," they both said. "We'll follow them."

"You mean you want me to be in charge."

"Yes."

"In that case, I want to warn you both that I will part company with the man who doesn't follow orders, whether on the road, on sea, or wherever it is."

Both men promised to follow orders blindly.

The next day, I spoke to the farm overseer. I told him that he had guessed right about our having been in a prison ship; that we had been there as political prisoners; that we had lately seen a man we took to be from the English police loitering around the farm, and that we therefore must leave at once. I added that we had been quite happy at the way we had been received at the farm, and only requested that if he were asked about us he deny all knowledge.

The overseer, who was one of those Irishmen who hold a furious grudge against everything English, promised that not only would he say nothing but that if he caught an English spy on the farm, he would dump him in the pond.

We quit the farm soon after. We planned to head south, along the coast, until we reached Wexford, where we could look for a boat that would take us to the continent.

We started our trek on a melancholy day in autumn; the sky was dark and lowering, and a light rain fell; the ravens swept cawing over our heads. The trees shed their reddish and yellowed leaves, strewing the fields; gusts of wind blew them hither and thither across the road; a pervasive autumnal odor of dead grass, wet ferns, and dank leaves hung over everything.

We trudged along the seacoast, ascending and descending a succession of low hills covered with brush. In the distance, looking inland, we saw the blackened ruins of several castles, a string of farmhouses whose chimneys sent forth columns of smoke into the air, fields still green, and some thick, heavy woods.

On the afternoon of the first day, the warfare between Ugarte and Allen broke out anew. They fought over any point at all. As was only natural, the Irishman, since he was in his own country, knew it better than we did and got along better at every turn. Ugarte considered this eminently logical development a direct insult flung in our faces.

I warned them both that if they continued fighting I would

part company with them both and go on alone. They desisted again, and finished the day in peace.

At dusk we approached an enormous flock of sheep. Allen fell into conversation with the shepherds, and we accompanied them to a roadside inn called the Bluebell. Its entranceway overlooked the sea and the cliffs and rocks of the coast.

In the days following, the presence of Allen saved us from any number of difficulties.

Before entering a town, the Irishman would go on ahead and reconnoiter alone; if he detected anything he took to be suspicious, he drew a cross with a stick of charcoal on the first house on the way in; if everything seemed in order, he drew a figure eight.

We, following behind, would note the marking. If the sign warned against entering, we would circle the town; if the indication was favorable, we went on ahead to the nearest tavern, where Allen would be waiting for us at the door. There we might order some hot soup, a bit of boiled meat, and a glass of beer; then we would lay down for some sleep in an odd corner or in the hay.

Every morning before setting out we would buy some provisions for our lunch on the road. Ugarte would gather the firewood, I would build the fire, and Allen would cook.

VI. THE PRIVATE HOSPICE

We had gotten to within a few miles of Wexford when night overtook us. We stopped in a village and went to seek lodgings in the inn. The village inn proved to be a small house, back from the highway, with an arch at the entrance and a small model of a dolphin painted in loud colors atop it. Both sides of the arch contained windows, and under them were placed two stone benches.

The woman who kept the tavern, a vigorous example of Irish femininity, told us her establishment was filled, and that she could not lodge us. We succeeded, at Allen's insistence, in getting something to eat. While she was serving us our supper, the Irishwoman asked us: "What are you people?"

"Seamen. Our ship sank off the coast a week ago, and we're walking to Wexford."

"If you're seamen, you can go to Captain Sandow's house. He'll take you in."

"Who is Captain Sandow?" I asked. "A military man?"

"No; he's an old sea captain. And old madman who lives with his daughter. He's put up shipwrecked sailors in his house before."

We left the inn accompanied by a young boy, who showed us the way.

Sandow's house was an old castle, guarded by a square gray-stone tower covered with ivy. Various buildings of unequal size surrounded the main house. A number of chimneys, grouped together like the pipes of an organ, lent a fantastic appearance to the place; a second series of chimneys, running in a zigzag, resembled flexed arms. An exterior staircase led up to the central floor. The buildings were surrounded by a muddy terrain, the site of old, abandoned gardens now grown to wilderness, mysterious and dramatic, especially in the white light of the moon, as we first saw it all.

There was no definite walk leading from the entranceway in the surrounding wall up to the castle proper; the path was almost erased by the weeds and shrubs.

Light shone from two of the castle windows; they seemed like melancholy eyes watching from behind the foliage. The garden contained thick-topped elms, resembling giant sentries, and numberless rose bushes still bearing blown white roses.

We pulled on a cord that hung from the gate and heard the sound of a bell in the distance.

An ancient maid came out to the gate, and Allen told her briefly that we were shipwrecked seamen.

"I'm going to tell the captain. Wait a moment."

The old woman disappeared, and shortly afterward one of the illuminated windows was thrown open and the figure of a man stood outlined in the light as he cried out: "Ahoy, the castaways! Come forward!"

We pushed on the gate, went on into the garden, and entered through a courtyard at either side of which stood a dog carved in stone. We climbed an old staircase and arrived in a hall that had an air about it halfway between abandoned and seignorial; it was a place without light, humid and cold.

Captain Sandow was a thin old man, yellow of countenance and white of beard; his daughter was a delicate, pale girl with black hair and blue eyes.

Allen began to recount in Irish a narrative he had invented to suit his taste, dealing with our supposed shipwreck. But the captain interrupted the well-learned discourse before it was half over to tell of his own voyaging. We listened to him attentively, and he invited us to supper; we supped with him, and he invited us to stay. As we prepared to retire, he told us: "You can stay here as long as you need to rest up."

Then, preceded by the old woman, we climbed a set of winding stairs leading into the tower; it was necessary to walk carefully over the damp steps, which were slippery and broken, and to lower one's head to prevent cracking it.

At length the old woman opened a door and the three of us came out into an abandoned library, on the floor of which were various straw mattresses; and there we slept.

The next day I suggested to Allen he tell Captain Sandow that in order to compensate for his hospitality we would do some work around his house.

Ugarte thought it simple-minded to offer to work when no one had suggested it, and Captain Sandow replied that he did not want us to have to do anything. But, on Allen's insistence, he agreed that we might straighten up the garden a bit.

The captain had bought his castle for very little money, and he had no intention of putting it to rights. Everything about it was old and ruined: the walls were crumbling beneath the blackish ivy, the chapel was in a complete state of abandon, the halls were falling in, the library was filled with damp old books, and the staff consisted of four servants as old and ruined as the house.

The swallows had built their nests in the eaves and rain spouts, and the taller trees sheltered crows and owls that uttered sinister shrieks in the night. The abandoned garden contained a mysterious and somber pond, around whose edges the poplars, shedding their leaves for years now, had deposited sheets of silver.

The day after our arrival, Allen, Ugarte, and myself began to uncover the old paths in the garden, to pull up the weeds that surrounded them, and to strew sand on the walks. Next, we started to clean off the pear trees, which were growing in fan forms spread out on the walls. On Sunday, we heard mass in the chapel of the old mansion, and afterwards I went to the library to look through the books. The library was a large, fantastic room under a caissoned ceiling which showed holes in several places. There were bookcases filled with damp books, and above the bookcases were piled torn and blackened paintings. There were a great number of hunting trophies in the room; these, apparently, merely annoyed the present master of the castle. An exit through a paneled door, now worm-eaten, from which hung a rusty lock, led to a gallery filled with the nests of bats and swallows. At the end of the passage a vault with small windows was set into the thick walls. This vault was occupied by busts of antique personages, all of them mutilated and chipped, and by a series of wall clocks of all sizes, their actions stopped and the majority of them broken.

I searched through all the corners and found several of Walter Scott's books and a copy of the *Poems of Ossian* by Macpherson.

I dried them in the dining room, in front of the chimney; then I fixed up their bindings and brought them to the captain's daughter.

"Where have you found them?" she asked.

"In the library. There must be more."

Sure enough, I found a goodly number of interesting and diverting books. Together the two of us read *Rob Roy, Ivanhoe,* and *Quentin Durward,* and we discussed at length the characters created by the great author. I found a certain resemblance between the captain's daughter and Diana Vernon, although Ana Sandow was undoubtedly more melancholy than Walter Scott's heroine.

Ana lived a life dependant on the caprices and whims of her mad and egotistic father, who did not allow her to talk to anyone outside the house.

Allen, meanwhile, had struck up a fast friendship with the maid and even with people in the vicinity. For my part, I was forced to listen, without any show of impatience, naturally, to the seventh, the eighth, the ninth recounting of Sandow's adventures. Ugarte, after a brief feint at working in the garden, would lie in his bed on the floor, bemoaning his fate.

I began to feel a friendly affection for Ana Sandow. The poor girl, so joyful and lively by nature, was a victim. The captain did not want his daughter to marry or to establish a real friendship with anyone. It was for this reason that he had shut them both up in the castle and had threatened the servants with immediate dismissal if they allowed any strangers into the grounds or house. Despite his stated desire to be cut off from the world, the old egotist was bored and desired the company of a selected few—but only to distract and amuse him.

Ugarte had noticed that the young mistress of the house showed sympathy toward me, and, carried away one day by a fit of rage and jealousy of the type to which he was subject, he wrote to Captain Sandow, telling him that I had formed a liason with his daughter, that the three of us were pirates, and that we had escaped from a prison ship in England.

Captain Sandow summoned me, and I told him our story without concealing anything. From his face and manner I realized that he was badly put out, and so I assured him: "Do not concern yourself over us any further. We will leave this very day."

"I am glad to hear it," he answered me, "not because of you, but so that I won't have to see the informer."

After I had promised him that we would leave at once, I could not understand his continued bad humor and sulkiness. But, from what Allen told me the next day, I was able to deduce the explanation. Sandow had questioned Allen concerning the account I had given of our wanderings, and, finding that what I said was true, he felt humiliated because his adventures, in comparison to ours, were completely ordinary.

VII. HATE EXPLODES

I informed Allen and Ugarte that we must leave at once.

"Why is that?" asked Ugarte, pretending to be surprised.

"For no reason at all. Only some well-intentioned person has told Sandow what kind of people we are and where we came from."

"Who could it have been?" he asked brazenly.

"That's something you know better than anyone else," I answered him in Castilian Spanish.

Allen was listening to our exchange, well aware of Ugarte's falseness.

"I don't know what you mean by that," muttered Ugarte now. And then, seeing that I did not deign an answer, he added cynically: "The truth is that the little note has gotten under your skin."

"I should think so!"

"And what did the captain say to you?"

"He told me that informers make him sick with loathing, and for that reason alone we should go."

Ugarte turned pale. Allen, who now understood everything, exclaimed: "Ah! Is he the one that denounced us?"

"You stay out of what doesn't concern you, animal!"

The Irishman burst out in invective, and I had to struggle with him to keep him from hurling himself on Ugarte.

On the last night we spent in Sandow's house, I wrote a long letter to Ana. The three of us were in the library; Ugarte and Allen had stretched out on their beds, but they were awake.

When I had finished writing, I left the library, stuck the letter into a book, called the maid, and told her to see that the captain's daughter received the book. I was afraid that if I stayed away from my companions too long, I would return to find them in a deadly struggle.

None of us was able to fall asleep. Allen was burning with indignation against Ugarte. Before dawn, we quit the house without taking leave of anyone. It was a cold day outside. We followed the highway and walked along the coast, plagued by a thin rain.

Allen and Ugarte refused to address each other. To avoid all communication between them, Ugarte spoke to me in Castilian and Allen addressed me in English.

"That we should have to slog through the rain because of a dog like him!" Allen muttered between his teeth.

That night, soaked to the bone, we found an inn, half tavern and half cottage, called the "Hunter's Rest." It was a simple cabin, with walls and roof completely covered with ivy, and two windows with red curtains, illuminated by an interior light. From outside, it looked like the shaggy, bristly head of a monster with two red eyes.

Though we were now quite near the city for which we were bound, we decided to spend the night where we were. We sat down at the table and ordered supper. Ugarte began to mimic and mock Captain Sandow and his daughter. At first, his ridicule made me indignant; but I soon felt pity and a kind of shame for Ugarte, aware that he was falling into another of his fits of mad spite and aggression. But he kept on talking so much and hurling such insults that at last I asked him in some surprise: "What have I done to you that you should hate me in this fashion?"

"You're in my way," he screamed. "One of us is more than enough in this world."

And in a paroxysm of rage he began to insult me furiously, screaming that he wished me dead, because I was his downfall and his bird of ill omen.

Allen, pale with anger and hatred of Ugarte, cried out: "I wouldn't stand for it."

"You dare butt in? Stay out of it, you dog, you cur!" yelled Ugarte.

And, in his fury, he pulled out one of the files that we had brought with us from the prison ship, which he still carried, and jabbed at the Irishman, striking him in the cheek.

Allen jumped up, grabbed the bench he had been sitting on, raised it high in the air, and brought it down on Ugarte's head with such force that he left him dead on the floor.

The Irishman continued pounding the corpse and even the table like a madman, with the insane and mechanical force of a wounded elephant, until at length the bench broke and he was left with a fragment of wood in his hand, gazing at it like a sleep-walker just awakened. Then he threw the broken bench to the floor and broke out in tears. Everyone in the tavern had witnessed the affair, and sided with Allen.

"Come on," I finally urged him. "We've got to get out of here."

"No, no. What for?"

I was forced to remain at his side. Luckily, the wound on his face was a slight one.

"You go on. I'll stay here."

"No. I can't abandon you."

"There are witnesses here to what happened. It's best if you escape. You can help me more if you're free than if you're in jail. Take the money I've got left, and if you get to France, write the maid at Sandow's house about what happened."

I did as he said, and left the tavern; as soon as I was on the street, I began to run. There was a wind in my face that held me back somewhat; it was a humid wind, filled with the odors of the sea. I could hear the sound of voices in the distance, of people who also seemed to be running. Perhaps it was the police, who might have been alerted. I hid beside the highway for a while. Then I began running slowly again, and continued until I reached the city, where I made my way along a small narrow street. The wind wailed at intersections, the dogs howled, and the rain began to come down in buckets. I decided to stop at the first inn or eating house that I chanced upon. The first one that I encountered had a sign with a horse on it, and was called the White Horse. It was one of those quiet, unfrequented places that are to be found in the British Isles, and which are characterized by cleanliness and respectability.

A very lively girl came to ask me if I had yet had supper; I told her I had, and she led me to a room; a little while later, she appeared once again, bearing a large warming pan to warm the bed.

Outside, a veritable deluge was falling.

"I'll pay you now," I told the girl, "because I want to leave very early tomorrow morning."

"Just as you wish."

"Will the door be open at dawn?"

"Yes, it's usually open from about that time."

I paid her what she asked, and went to bed. It was still raining heavily outside; the water lashed the windows, and the wind whistled furiously, with surprisingly high, piercing notes. I fell asleep very quickly. It was a little before dawn when I awoke with a start, and peered out the window; it was no longer raining, and I dressed rapidly. When I went downstairs I found the door was not open. It immediately occurred to me that someone had told the people in the inn to close the door. But then perhaps they had secured it because of the wind.

I went back up and looked out the window. The distance to the ground was not too great, and so I jumped down, without mishap.

Finding myself alone, without the company of Allen and Ugarte, I felt driven by a greater energy and a more pressing fear of being recaptured. I would have preferred anything to being returned to the prison ship. The memory of those black headlands, the gray sea, the muddy swamps horrified me.

I spent a night in the fields, and the next morning, as the sun was coming up, I walked into Wexford port. I soon found a schooner getting ready to sail for Saint-Malo. In speaking to the captain about taking me, I found I had to overcome strong resistance. I handed over what money I had, and promised to pay him more when we reached France.

The captain was the image of an ill-tempered bear.

We made a horrible crossing, in the foulest type of weather and in a stormy sea. The captain apparently did not make a practice of concerning himself with his ship and its navigation, for as soon as we were at sea, he disappeared into his cabin and proceeded to get drunk on whiskey. Within an hour he appeared on deck in a state of drunkenness, his nose inflamed and his speech slurred. In view of the raging storm, he began to talk of changing his course and putting into England. After a while he seemed to forget it; we told him it would be absurd to change course, and, since he was rather muddled in his head, he did what he heard was best. At length we reached Saint-Malo.

I wrote immediately to Ana Sandow telling her what had happened after we left her house and asked her to intercede for poor Allen.

After a while I received a letter from Ana and a clipping from a newspaper, in which there was an account of the death of Ugarte in an inn near Wexford called the "Hunter's Rest."

Only, the dead man was given the name Juan de Aguirre, and I, whose whereabouts was listed as unknown, appeared as Tristán de Ugarte.

From what Ana wrote, Allen's situation was favorable, considering the circumstances; all the witnesses had declared in his behalf; the fact that the dead man was a foreign adventurer and he a native of the country worked in his favor.

As for me, I had a difficult time finding employment. Inasmuch as all that part of France, that is, Normandy and Brittany, carried on its principal commerce with England, and since I felt no attraction for the air of perfidious Albion, there was no ship's berth that suited me. Finally, I found work in a warehouse in Le Havre.

My life was animated by one enthusiasm: the woman who thought of me. I wrote her constantly, and I wrote Allen, to whom I regularly sent part of my wages.

Allen was imprisoned for a very short time. As soon as he was released he went to visit Ana. Captain Sandow was increasingly brutal and despotic in his relations with his daughter. Allen and she decided to act; and so one day, to my great astonishment, I looked up to see them both walk into my house.

Ana and I were soon married. Eventually, we had a daughter, and we called her Mary.

With my daughter's future in mind, I determined to find out what was going on in Lúzaro; I wrote my mother, and she wrote back to tell me that they had thought me dead and had even held funeral services for me.

My life with Ana might have been a happy one; but my wife's health was very delicate. That sweet and fragile creature, so simple, so ingenuous and so innocent, died in my arms at the end of a slow and tortuous battle with life.

I always recall her in the somber house of her father, and to the memory of her I join always the memory of Walter Scott and his most feminine heroines. I read the novels of the Scottish author in the days that I first knew her, and I can not ever separate my beloved from the literary personages of that great author.

When she died, I decided to leave France and return to Lúzaro with my daughter and Allen, who had made up his mind to link his fate to mine.

This, then, has been my life. Errors, faults, I have committed in plenty. And who has not?

So read the manuscript of my uncle, Juan de Aguirre.

VIII. PATRICK ALLEN AND ZALDUMBIDE'S TREASURE

One autumn day, towards nightfall, two suspicious-looking foreigners appeared in Chiquierdi's inn at Lúzaro.

They descended from the diligence, entered the kitchen of the inn, and, while they ate, made pointed inquiries about Don Santiago Andía. The woman who ran the inn told them that I had not lived in Lúzaro for some time, but was now at Izarte; when they learned this fact, they asked the distance from the town to our settlement.

The next morning, the mailman, who brought me the newspaper, furnished me with the facts of the visit and told me that the foreigners would certainly call on me. I waited for them, somewhat intrigued, and just before noon I saw them approach the house.

One of the pair was tall, red, heavy; the other was small, black-haired, and boasted a pair of lively eyes. I watched them from between the curtains of my room. At first glance, they did not seem to me at all suspicious-looking.

They rang at the door, and the maid showed them into my room.

The tall, heavy man seemed rather confused; the other man, smiling an insinuating smile, spoke up at once, with an Andalusian accent.

"Could you grant us a half hour of your time to listen to what we have to say?"

"Gladly, sir. Please be seated."

"Thank you," answered the short man. Then he added in English, addressing his companion, "Sit down, Smiles."

The two of them sat down.

"Aren't you Spanish?" I asked the dark-haired man.

"No, I'm English. I was born in Gibraltar. I'm a rock scorpion, as the English call people from the Rock. My name is Small, Richard Small. My father was English, my mother from Cádiz; that's the reason that I speak Spanish fairly well."

"Not fairly well, but very well; better than I speak it."

"Thank you very much! I will tell you, in the fewest possible words, the reason for our visit. Until a few months ago, I lived in Liverpool in humble circumstances; I worked in a shop and was on the point of getting married, when I met an Irish-

man of advanced years, the brother of my girl's mother, an Irishman by the name of Patrick Allen."

"Patrick Allen!" I exclaimed. "The man who lived here for
so many years!"

"The same man. Allen came back to his sister's house and told
us all the story of Captain Zaldumbide's treasure; he told us how
you had given him the exact location of the burial site, which
had been written in Basque in a prayer book. From that day, the
day Allen told us the story of the treasure, my girl's house was
turned upside down; my girl, her brothers, the entire family saw
nothing but millions in every direction. They urged me to find
a rich man who would contribute the necessary funds to under-
write a search for the treasure, and I found Mr. Smiles."

"Present!" unexpectedly called out the tall, red-faced man, as
he saluted in military fashion.

"That'll do, Smiles," interjected the dark young man. "As I
was saying I found Mr. Smiles, who owned a saloon in Liverpool.
Mr. Smiles leased out his saloon, I gave up my job, and, in the
company of Allen, the three of us, fully equipped, went to Las
Palmas in the Canary Islands. There we rented a schooner, with
crew and all, and headed for the Nun River. The skipper of
the schooner had orders to stand by for a week to wait for us
at the mouth of the river; if we did not appear, he was to
return at full moon for a period of six months. We disembarked
from the schooner and ascended the river in a small boat until
we were off the ruins of a hilltop fortress. We tied the boat to
a tree on the river bank, and carefully made our way, watching
and hiding every so often among the rocks, until we reached the
ruins. We had met or seen no one en route. From what Allen
said, we had to find a wall with an elephant drawn or incised
on it. The first to see it was myself: 'There it is!' I cried out.

"Allen ran up to the wall, stood with his back to it, and took
out a small spyglass from his pocket. Smiles and I were anxiously
watching him when we suddenly saw two white men creeping
around a wall to get a better view of what Allen was doing.
They quickly realized that we had seen them, and the pair
rushed us, followed by a dozen or so Moors who had been in
hiding. We had no opportunity to make use of our weapons,
and were made prisoners on the spot.

"Allen knew the two men: They were Ryp Timmermans,
cook on the "Dragon," and a Dutch sailor named Van Stein.
The two of them had been searching for the treasure for more
than a year, but had been unable to find any trace of it. Some

other former members of the "Dragon"'s crew, released from prison, had also appeared on the scene to make excavations in all the rises of the ground along the river bank, but Zaldumbide's coffers still lay buried, as far as we could tell.

"Ryp and Van Stein, more persistent than the others, had remained on the spot; they had renounced their religion and, becoming converts to Islam, had married Moorish women; they were the chiefs of a little settlement established in a small oasis which contained some brackish wells and a few palm, honey-locust, and argan trees.

"The two renegades and their Moors led Smiles, Allen, and myself to the oasis. The settlement itself consisted of a few wretched cottages, constructed of tree trunks, stones, and clay, covered over with a fabric made of camel or goat hair. They shut us up in a hut, and Ryp and Van Stein began to question us. Smiles and I told them the truth, which was that we had heard that a treasure was buried thereabouts and we had come to look for it.

"Ryp assumed that we had some special information on the matter, and he asserted that we would not be released until we had told all we knew. Allen was determined to tell them nothing. Smiles and I could not tell them anything, because we did not know anything of importance.

"We were kept in that hovel for a month; as food, we were given a little bread, salted fish, milk, and honey.

"Most of the Moors in the settlement were real savages, of mixed Negro blood. The women were the only ones who worked. The men, licentious dogs, spent their lives with a rifle on their shoulder, idly prattling. The women meanwhile cultivated the ground and stored the harvests, smoked and dried the meat and fish, and made fishhooks and arrows.

"Though the men would not work, they did occasionally hunt, pastured the goats, and would buy and sell tanned skins, capes, brimstone, camels, and oxen.

"Every year, at a certain season, the entire band would make a trek inland for a couple of months, on a Negro-stealing expedition. On reaching a Negro village, they would surround it during the night, and then, at a signal, would commence firing shots in the air and screaming wildly. The unfortunate Negroes would panic and begin to run out of the village, where the marauders would catch them like rabbits. Grouped into caravans, the prisoners would be sold to slave dealers, who would send them to Fez, Marrakech, and Tafilelt.

"It was difficult to see how Ryp and Van Stein could have

gained mastery over that band of bloodthirsty Moorish bandits; nevertheless, the truth was that they held the Moors in the palm of their hands. Those jackals would have been happy to tear us to pieces, but Ryp protected us. The cook was sure that Allen possessed the exact instructions for finding the treasure; he had him searched, of course, but nothing was found. He next tried to reach an agreement with Allen, whereby they would share equally in the treasure, if Allen could find it.

"Allen was terribly changeable in this arrangement; he made the agreement, then changed his mind, then agreed again to a division, and then announced he would have no part of it. He had reached a point where he placed greater importance on the treasure than on his life. 'You want me to tell you where the treasure is, so you can get it and then get rid of me?' He would say to Ryp as an argument. 'No, my boy, nothing doing.'

"Smiles and I urged him to come to agreement with Ryp; for my part, I was increasingly anxious to get out of there on any terms, even with empty hands. Allen, however, could not be pushed.

"One day he announced again that he was willing to work with Ryp. He called the ex-cook of the "Dragon," and we made an agreement to go to the river bank in a body, the five of us white men escorted by a party of ten armed Moors. We reached the ruined fortress, and Allen insisted that he be left alone. He spent a quarter of an hour by himself, and then he marched toward the river; he walked up to a certain stone, reached out and touched it, and said: 'Here it is.'

"The words were scarcely out of his mouth when Van Stein drew his pistol and fired point blank, killing Allen on the spot.

"Smiles and I started to run furiously, sure that our lives were at stake. Luck was with us, for the rest of the party did not trust each other long enough to pursue us, and they all began to dig in a frenzy, thus giving us a chance to get away. We arrived at the edge of the sea in a state of exhaustion; we were in the middle of an immense beach, formed of sand dunes that the wind had made and unmade. The two of us hid, for hours and hours, with every sense on the alert, in a crevice formed in one of the dunes.

"Of a sudden, in the calm of the night, we heard voices around us. It was Ryp and Van Stein.

" 'Can you see anybody down there?' asked Ryp.

" 'Nobody.'

" 'Maybe they crossed the river.'

" 'What do we care what they've done?' said Van Stein.

" 'What do we care? Why I wouldn't be surprised if the dark one knew where the treasure is," yelled Ryp.

"Smiles and I listened to the conversation; when the two voices could no longer be heard, Smiles said:

" 'They didn't find anything.'

" 'No doubt about it.'

"I did not know whether to be glad or sad; since they had not found the treasure, they would make some attempt to find us. As soon as night had fallen, we left our hiding place, and started down the wide beach. Where were we bound? We did not know; we had no objective. Smiles suddenly exclaimed:

" 'Damnation. There's a full moon tonight. If it clears a little, we'll be visible for miles.'

"Sure enough, a little later a full moon shone down on us, lighting up the beach so that every rise and crest was plainly outlined.

"A moment later, I recalled the fact that the skipper of the schooner hired in the Canaries had agreed to appear off the mouth of the river at the full of the moon for a period of six months. We were still in the fifth month. If he had kept his word and had brought the schooner to the river mouth we were saved. Inspired by the thought, Smiles and I began running and leaping over the shifting sand dunes, and ran towards the river mouth.

"There was the schooner. But she seemed on the point of putting out to sea!

" 'Help! Help!' yelled Smiles and I.

"At first they must not have heard us, but then we saw the ship sailing straight for us, its sails unfurled and gleaming white in the moonlight.

"Ryp's people, too, had apparently heard our shouts, for we began to be fired upon from further down the shore. Smiles and I dived into the water and began desperately to swim for the schooner.

"A few moments later, when I found myself on the ship's deck, I swore never to set foot in Africa again. We were soon back in the Canaries, and from there we went on to Liverpool. I was sure that the family of my future wife, once they learned of Allen's death and heard from us about our adventures, would find themselves cured of their passion for finding a treasure, but such was not to be the case. Quite the contrary.

" 'You've got to go,' my future mother-in-law urged me, 'to see that Spaniard, the one that can tell you where Zaldumbide's treasure really is.' And that's why we're here. We beg you to make known your conditions."

"I don't have any conditions," I said. "I'm well off; I don't need a thing. I'll be glad to give you the necessary information. Fortunately I have kept the piece of paper upon which I first jotted down the secret, word by word. I only hope you have better luck than everyone else connected with the treasure."

"But still. . ."

"No, no, no. I want nothing."

I gave them the directions translated from the Basque of Allen's prayer book, and the two Englishmen went away, after thanking me effusively.

A year later, I received a letter from the young man, Small, together with a package. The letter read:

The treasure has given us bad luck. We went back to the Nun with an escort of fifteen well-armed men. We found the treasure at once. But when Ryp's men, from their hiding place, saw us actually bringing up the coffers and getting ready to take them away, they attacked us with desperation. In the battle that followed, Smiles and Ryp were killed. Van Stein was badly wounded and two of our men fell prisoner. I caught a fever, of which I'm still not cured.

The accompanying package contained two large pearls sent me by Small. The thought of having them in the house was repugnant to me. I did not even want to show them to my wife, and, climbing Mount Izarra, I threw them into the sea.

They will make a nice ornament, I thought, for one of those undines Yurrumendi knew.

EPILOGUE

Many years have passed, years of normal, easy, everyday life.

Juan Machín has never appeared among us again. Perhaps he is wandering the seas, lost in some far corner. As if upholding a family tradition, he has become the restless Aguirre who is lost somewhere on the face of the world. Is he alive? Is he dead? Will he return to us? I do not know. I must confess that at first I would not have wanted him to come back; now, I would; I would be happy to see him and to shake his hand.

As regards me, I am a little ashamed to say that I am happy, very happy. It is true that I have not deserved happiness, but nevertheless such is the case.

When I think of my wife, I, too, recall the heroines of Scott, especially Diana Vernon in *Rob Roy*. But I do not, like my Uncle Juan de Aguirre or Scott's hero, have to think of my heroine as dead, but rather can look around and find her alive at my side. Today, with her fifty years and her gray hair, she seems to me more enchanting than ever.

My mother lives with us in our house in Izarte. She likes to spend her time in the kitchen, gossiping with the maids and with my daughter, putting wood on the stove, and murmuring against my wife.

Basically the two of them understand each other perfectly. But my mother must quarrel a bit; and so she accuses my wife of being bossy and of always wanting her own way.

All my children have been rocked in their grandmother's arms, and it will not be long before my mother can rock her first great-grandchild.

Every day I am becoming more indolent and more distracted. Often, in the early morning, when the weather is good, I get up very early and follow the open road, listening to the rumor of the fields. The birds sing in the groves, a brilliant sun pours over the earth.

On my return, I stand outside my house and contemplate it, standing as it does atop the garden which serves it by way of pedestal. The red geraniums shimmer along the wooden balcony; in the midst of the vegetable garden the sunflowers stand about on their giant stalks. I climb the staircase and come out on the balcony. The cows are at pasture in our meadow; my children follow them, protected from the sun by large straw hats. In front of me I can see the scattered houses of Izarte, which seem like play houses, spouting smoke from their chimneys; farther off lie the mountains.

My wife knows that sometimes I must wander a bit, and she leaves me to my devices. She used to accompany me on my walks, and sometimes, when we would watch the evening star, she would recite that poem of Ossian, which the two of us had read in a book belonging to Ana Sandow, and which begins in the following manner:

> Star of twilight, shining sovereign in the East,
> Radiant face appearing from behind the clouds
> As you stroll majestically atop the peaks:
> What do you see through the foliage?

I would listen to the verse with tears in my eyes. Ossian's songs to me seemed wondrous. Nowadays my wife has too many cares to allow her to roam in the country. Our clan has increased, and she is the administrative authority. I believe she is a fine tyrant, an intelligent dictator, the representative of the ideal government for the idle and lazy.

I am the vagabond of the family.

As the seasons change I feel the nostalgia given off by the sea's profound peacefulness, its solitude and abandon. Then I go to stroll along the Beach of Souls, and there I gaze, as if it were for the first time, at the three-pronged spray of the waves as they break on the sand.

Spring arouses deep joy in me, and autumn a profound sadness; but the sadness is of so strange a nature that it seems to me that I would be most unfortunate not to feel it from time to time.

On those November days, when the mist and rain and the dominion of gray returns, when the vague and blurred lines everywhere appear, when the sharp winds whistle, when the arroyo of Sorguiñ-Erreca turns into a torrent, then I like to walk along the beach and become saturated in the enormous melancholy of the sea and be soaked in the profundity of sadness.

Later, when I am saturated with the sound and sense of spray, and the waves, and the howl of the wind, I climb along the Crest of the Dogs up to the highest point and walk through the corn fields. There below lies the quiet village where I live, there live those that belong to me. I walk toward my house; my family, gathered around the fire in the kitchen on these winter days, is waiting for me.

Back in the kitchen, I recount my adventures to the younger children, embellishing the stories with details taken from my imagination. I have told all the stories so many times that my wife reproaches me in a mocking tone for telling them again.

Sometimes I have wondered if any of my sons will turn out to be a sailor or an adventurer. I have searched for signs in them of a sailor's devotion to the sea.

But no, they have no inclination for the mariner's lot, and I am happy. . . And yet. . .

In Lúzaro now, no one cares to go to sea; the sons of well-to-do families become engineers or doctors. The Basques are retiring from the sea.

Oh, gallant riggings! White, white sails! Haughty frigates, with prows on high and a figurehead on the cutwater! Round hookers, swift-sailing brigantines! How sad it is to think you will all disappear, that you will soon no longer be seen!

Yes, I am happy that my sons will not be seamen. . . And yet. . .

The Cabbages in the Cemetery

The house was on the way out of town, to the left of the highway: an ancient, one-story house, upon whose rain blackened walls various letters majestically formed the following phrase: "BLASIDO'S WINE SHOP."

The artist who had done the letters, not content with the elegant tone imparted to each letter, had striven to exceed himself, and above the lintel of the wide door he had painted a rooster with long, erect feathers, balancing its two claws upon a large heart, wounded and shot through by a treacherous arrow: a mysterious hieroglyphic whose significance no one knew.

The spacious entranceway to the house was narrowed by two great wine casks at each side, which left a small passage between. Behind them was the shop, which, in addition to being a tavern, was a tobacconist's, a stationer's, an establishment dispensing hot chocolate, and a few other things besides. In back of the house a few tables stood under a bower, and there the worshipers of Bacchus gathered on Sunday afternoons to drink and play ninepins, while those of the cult of Venus dropped in to assuage their ardors with refreshing blackberries.

Justa, the owner's wife and barmaid, would have made out well enough if she had not been burdened with a lazy husband, a wastrel and loafer, who, besides treating all the spirits his wife dispensed with sentimental familiarity, also possessed the fertility of a stud horse.

"*Arrayua,* Blasido! Whoa!" his friends would yell at him. "You mean your wife is that way again! How the devil do you do it. . ."

"What do you expect?" he would reply. "Women! They're just like sows. And mine . . . The mere smell of it, a whiff . . . eh? All I have to do is hang my underpants on the bedpost, and she's pregnant. The soil's good, the seed's good, the season's good."

"Drunkard! Pig!" his wife would scream when she heard him. "It would be better for you if you worked instead of talked."

"Work! What ideas these women get in their heads!"

One day in January, Blasido, who was drunk, fell into the

river, and though his friends hauled him out in time to save him from drowning, he had to go to bed as soon as he got home because he was having chills. Later he developed double pneumonia. While he was sick he sang all the *zortzicos* he knew. And finally, one morning, when he heard the drummer talking in the tavern, he called out:

"Chomín, will you bring in your fife and drum?"

"All right."

Because he thought highly of Blasido, Chomín brought in his fife and drum.

"What shall I play?"

"The *Aurrescu,*" said Blasido.

But then, halfway through the drum roll, Blasido turned around and said: "The end, Chomín, play the end, for I'm going now."

And Blasido turned his head back to the wall and died.

The next day, Pachi, the gravedigger, dug a magnificent and commodious grave, three feet deep, for his old friend. Justa, the barmaid, who was pregnant, struggled on, with her seven little ones and her tavern, and the advice of her dead husband's friends.

Of these friends, the most devoted was Pachi-zurra, or Pachi-hell as some called him. Pachi was a man who might have seemed tall if he had not been so heavy; seen from the rear he was square, from the front he was round, and in profile he was simply big-bellied. His face, carefully clean shaven, was of a hue between red and violet. His eyes, small and joyous, were circled with fleshy borders. His nose, which, it must be confessed, was not Greek, might have been handsome, if it had not been so large, wide, and highly colored. His mouth contained no teeth, but even his enemies could not do less than admit that his lips parted to produce the most sumptuous of smiles, and that his beret, wide as a platter and always pulled down over his head, was in exquisite good taste.

Evil tongues, the eternal old ladies, said that Pachi had had a stormy and dubious youth. Who could have guessed, said some, that those hands (aided by a modest blunderbuss), had stripped travelers of their wealth, over toward La Rioja, when the railroad line to the North was being built? Others detected in him the classical escaped convict; still others, a seaman from a pirate ship; and there were even those who, following logically from deduction to deduction, supposed that Pachi had petitioned for the job of gravedigger in order to melt down and render the fat of dead children. But all these suppositions (for the sake of the truth we must admit it) were not true.

Pachi, on returning to his native town after lengthy travels in America, found that on some property of his—a bit of land on a hillside, land that had come down to him by inheritance—a cemetery had been established. In the town they had thought Pachi dead. When Pachi demanded the return of his land, the municipality made attempts to buy it from him. But Pachi would not accept the offers made him and proposed in turn that the deeding of the land to the municipality be made conditional on his being given the post of gravedigger and the right to construct a small house in one of the walled angles of the cemetery, where he, with his beret and pipe, could go and live.

His proposition accepted, Pachi built a little house and went to live in it and watch over the cemetery. The dead surely must not have minded that Pachi had been given charge of their tombs, for he decorated them with fragrant plants and beautiful flowers.

Despite the care lavished on the tombs by the good Pachi, the townspeople looked upon him as a reprobate; all because some Sundays he would forget to go to mass, and because whenever he heard the village vicar eulogized he would wink his eye and say: *"Esaguna laguna,"* which in Basque literally means: "I know you, my friend"; with which phrase it was assumed he was making sly reference to a false tale—though the story was not without its vestiges of truth—which recounted the details of how the vicar had fathered two or three children in the neighboring town.

Such was the terror Pachi inspired that mothers, in order to frighten their children, would say to them: "If you don't keep quiet, *matitia,* Pachi-hell is going to come and get you, and take you away with him."

The aristocracy of the town treated Pachi with scorn, and the druggist, who thought himself a clever fellow, attempted to make mock of him.

Pachi and the young village-doctor got along splendidly; whenever the doctor performed an autopsy, the gravedigger acted as his assistant, and if some curious rubberneck got too close and then gave sudden signs of horror or repugnance, Pachi would wink knowingly at the doctor, as if to say: "This fellow's frightened because he's not in on the secret . . . He, he!"

Pachi paid little attention to what was said about him; he was satisfied with being the oracle of Justa's tavern. His audience was made up of the road-mender, who was the only liberal in town, the substitute judge, who when he was not substituting for anyone kept busy making rope-soled sandals, Don Ramón, the former schoolmaster, who brought his supper and a bottle of his own wine to the tavern, the drummer, one of the workers in the public granary, and a handful of others. Pachi's words attracted and held them.

When, having outlined his views of the *ignis fatuus,* the will-o'-the-wisp, he added, "No one need be frightened of them; it's simply a matter of ' 'lectricity,' " everyone would turn to his neighbor, searching each others' eyes to see whether or not the other had plumbed the profundity of this phrase.

And Pachi was the man for a phrase—not all great men have the gift—and he gave vent to aphorisms worthy of Hippocrates. His philosophy was encompassed in these words: "Men are like weeds: they are because they are, they appear for no reason; some weeds have red flowers and others yellow, and just so are there good men and bad; and whoever is a drunkard is fated to be one."

He would moisten his lips with water, and, as if this act of daring had frightened him, he would immediately follow it with a giant swallow of brandy; for the gravedigger always had his water served in a small shot glass and his brandy in a large tumbler—it was a standing joke on his part.

At repartee, Pachi was a phenomenon. One day, a mine operator, a wealthy young man who gave himself airs as a Don Juan, was recounting his conquests.

"I have a child in Olozábal," he was saying, "and another in the house of Zubiaurre, and one in Gaztelu's house."

"You'd be alright now, if you had one in your own house," said Pachi philosophically, "and if your wife's children were your own."

When Pachi recounted his adventures in South America, the smoke of his pipe warming his red nose, his words met with a chorus of exclamations and roars of laughter.

Pachi's adventures in America were of the highest interest. He had been a gambler, merchant, stockbreeder, soldier, and a dozen other things besides. As a soldier he had been forced to burn alive a goodly number of Indians. But it was as lover that Pachi's stories took on a truly suggestive air, when he told of his amorous adventures with Negresses, Indian and Negro half-breeds, mulatto women, and yellow damsels. He could say, without exaggeration, that his love had run the chromatic scale of women.

The barmaid and now tavern-owner was of such a lively disposition that a week after giving birth to her eighth child she was up and about as if nothing had happened. But that night she was forced to return to her bed with a fever, which turned out to be puerperal, and which carried her to the cemetery. The widow had fallen behind in her accounts, and so the tavern was sold, and the eight children were left in the street.

"*Hay que hacel algo por esoz niñoz,*" said the mayor, speaking almost in Andalusian to cover up his Basque accent: "Something will have to be done with those children."

"With those children something will have to be done," murmured the vicar in his suave voice, lifting his eyes to heaven.

"There's no alternative," said the pharmacist resolutely, "something will have to be done about those children."

"Children . . . Charity. . ." added the town secretary.

And the days passed and the weeks passed, the older girl had gone to serve as a maid in the postman's house, where she was happy enough, and the infant in arms was being nursed with great ill-will by the farrier's wife.

The other six—Chomín, Shanti, Martiñacho, Joshe, Maru, and Gaspar—ran barefoot about the highway, begging.

One day in the morning, the gravedigger came into town with a little cart, put the six children in it, took the suckling infant from the farrier's wife and tucked him into his arms, and led the entire troupe to the cemetery. On the way, he stopped at the general store and bought a nursing bottle for the infant.

"What a humbug!" said the Mayor.

"What an imbecile!" exclaimed the pharmacist.

The vicar modestly lifted his eyes to heaven, withdrawing them from the sight of such misery.

"He'll abandon them," prognosticated the secretary.

But Pachi has not abandoned them, and he is bringing them up. And, since he now has so many mouths to feed, he has left off the brandy. On the other hand, he is filling up the cemetery with garden produce and covering hallowed ground with crops in a lamentable fashion. And since there is now a market in town, Pachi has contracted with a friend of his, who owns the farm nearest the cemetery, to sell his cabbages and artichokes for him in the public square.

The cabbages of Pachi's friend, which are the cabbages from the cemetery, have a reputation in the public market for being delicious and especially tasty. What the people that buy them don't know is that they are quietly feeding on the substance of their grandfathers.

The Abyss

The landscape was of a sullen severity. At the edge of the horizon, beneath a sky inflamed with red clouds which were fused by the last rays of the sun, ran the chain of mountains of the sierra, like a lead-blue wall of China, crowned at the top by prodigious crags and striated further down with flutings of snow.

A goatherd and his grandson were pasturing their herd of goats on the mountain, at the top of Stone Hedge, up near where Crow Peak looms like a giant granite sentinel.

The goatherd wore a long yellowish coat over his shoulders, leather chaps over his knees, a cloth cap lined with goatskin on his head, and a white shepherd's crook of wild hawthorn in his black hand which resembled an eagle's talon more than a human hand. The goatherd was a rough, primitive man; his cheeks, as wrinkled as the bark of an old oak, were partly covered by the stubble of a beard, whitish and dirty, which he had not shaven in a number of days.

The boy, blond and freckled, roved behind the mastiff; he made his sling hum as he whirled it dizzily above his head, and he joyously answered the distant voices of the shepherds and cowherds with a strident yell like the neigh of a horse, ending in a long, clear, silvery note, a mocking laugh which the mountain echoed around.

From their mountain height, the goatherd and his grandson could see hillsides and hilltops without trees, wastelands dotted with round, black patches representing thickets of furze, and beds of violet and purple thyme and lavender in flower.

In the hollow of the mountain, beside a river bed filled with dried leaves, there were trees of a dark green foliage, and clumps of heather, swamp oak and dwarf oak.

Dusk was coming on, and a light wind was blowing; the sun was slowly sinking behind the mountain tops; reddish snakes and dragons swam in the blue mother-of-pearl sea of the sky; then, as the sun lost its color, the clouds turned white and lost their hue, and the snakes and dragons turned into immense crocodiles and gigantic whales. The mountains grew furrowed with shadow, and the valleys and hollows filled and overflowed with the twilight.

Far off, the cow bells could be heard as the cattle were driven home, and the barking of dogs sounded in the air. All these distant rumors, joined with the indefinable sounds of the country, resounded through the immense desolation of the countryside like mysterious voices born of the solitude and silence.

"It's time to go back," said the goatherd. "The sun is getting ready to hide."

The boy ran furiously to left and right, waved his arms, brandished his crook, pounded the ground, shouted and hurled stones until he had succeeded in rounding up his goats in a corner of the mountain. The old man got them in order: a he-goat, with a large bell around its neck, acted as guide, and the flock set out on the descent to the plain. As the herd of goats spilled out over the grass, they were like a black wave flowing into a green sea. The joyous ringing of the bells around their necks sounded its regular rhythmic unison.

"Did thou look to see if old Aunt Remedios' billy goat is in the flock?" the old man demanded of the youth.

"I seed 'im, grandfather," said the boy.

"Thou hast to keep an eye on that animal. Wickid divils take me, but I've got nothing but ill will toward that beast."

"And why is that so, grandfather?"

"Dost thou not know that Aunty Remedios has got the name for bein' a witch, all over the place?"

"And can that be true, grandfather?"

"That's what the sacristan said the other night when I was at the place. They say she smothers people and animals, and gives potions. They say they've seen her cutting across the sky, betwixt bands of snakes."

The goatherd went on talking about what the people in the town said about the old woman, and thus chatting they descended the mountain, from the path to the trail, from the trail to the road, until at length they stopped in front of the gate to an enclosure. From this spot they could look down and see the great depth of the valley, with its silver semicircle of river shining in the distance; near the river, the town stood among the mists; a little closer, on the slope of a mountain, was the ancient ruined castle which had belonged to the lords of the town.

"Open the wattle, boy," the goatherd called to the boy.

The boy withdrew the removable sticks from the picket fence, and the goats began to troop in through the gate to the enclosure, pressed and jammed against each other. Suddenly one of the animals bolted in fright and, jumping to the other side of the road, began to run swiftly downhill.

"Run, run after him, boy," yelled the old man. In the next breath he set the dog after the fleeing animal: "Go on *Wolf*. Go git 'im!"

The dog gave a muffled bark and started off like an arrow.

"Go on! Git 'im!" the goatherd yelled again. "There he goes."

The escaped billy goat jumped from rock to rock like a rubber ball bouncing from one object to another. From time to time it looked back, standing straight up, marked out by its black coat and its devilish goatee. It hid among the bushes and brambles, and rushed and leaped along, in and out of sight.

The dog ran behind it, gaining ground slowly. The boy followed behind both animals, aware that the chase must soon come to an end, for the craggy part of the mountain ended shortly in an open field sloping gently downward. As he reached the dividing area between crags and open ground, the boy caught sight of the billy goat, now running desperately to get away from the dog; he watched it draw near a pile of rocks and disappear among them. Near the rocks there was a cave which, according to rumors, was of a profound depth; in the suspicion that the billy goat had fallen in, the boy peered cautiously over into the mouth of the hole when he came up. There, on a small shelf of the cavern's rock face, stood the goat.

The boy stretched out face downwards at the mouth of the opening and leaned down to grab at one of the goat's horns; but the maneuver proved impossible, and he returned to the goatherd's side and explained the situation to him.

"Damnable beast!" muttered the old man. "We'll go back there in a little while; first we have to get the others in."

The two of them went to work to get the goats put away for the night, and then the goatherd and his grandson went back down toward the place where the crags ended, and approached the side of the abyss. The goat was still standing between the bushes on his small shelf. The dog barked at it and growled a muffled growl.

"If you give me a hand, grandfather I'll a-go down," said the boy.

"Be careful, boy. I'm terrible afraid thou'lt fall in."

"Don't worry yourself, grandfather."

The boy pushed aside the growth at the mouth of the vertical cave, sat down a moment at its edge, turned himself over on his hands, and then hung almost over the abyss, until he could get in position to slide his feet along the walls of the hole and secure them in one of the salient edges at the top. Finally he was able to get a hold on one of the goat's horns, and he pulled on it. When the animal found itself being pulled, it jerked backwards so sharply that it lost its footing. It fell, and in its fall dragged the boy with it down into the bottom of the abyss. Not a cry was heard, not a lamentation, not the slightest whisper.

The old man peered over the mouth of the cavern.

"Boy! Boy!" he yelled in desperation.

Nothing, no sound could be heard.

"Boy! Boy!"

In the murmur of the wind, amidst its soft whistling as it rose from the bottom of the abyss, a painful bleating now seemed to be mingled.

Crazed, beside himself and terrified, the goatherd was at a loss what to do, until it occurred to him to seek the aid of the other goatherds, and he set out at a run toward the castle.

The castle loomed so large that it seemed to be at hand, but in reality it was half-an-hour's walking distance away, even when the shortcut was taken. It was an ancient and ruined ogival castle, rising over the open country from the top of a high elevation. The twilight hid its ruin and devastation, and in the equivocal light it appeared to take on larger and more fantastic proportion.

The old man was now forced to a walk, panting as he went. Night was falling, and in the sky the stars were beginning to shine. One particularly bright star shone like silver light over a mountain in the distance, a soft and dreaming eye watching all that happened in the valley.

As the old man came abreast of the castle, he climbed up to it along a narrow raised way; he crossed the ruined escarpment, and went in the gothic door, into a patio filled with debris and surrounded by the four creviced walls, which were all that remained of the ancient seignorial mansion.

In the hollow of the stairway to the tower, in a shed made of pickets and straw, the light of a smoky candle revealed ten or a dozen men, rustic figures, all shepherds or goatherds, grouped around a few burning embers.

The old man stammered out the story of what had happened. The others got up at once; one of them got a rope from the ground nearby, and they all set out from the castle. With the old man in the lead, they headed toward the open terrain where the cave was located.

The chance circumstance, that it had been precisely the billy goat belonging to the old witch that had dragged the young boy to the bottom of the cave, was beginning to assume extraordinary proportions in the minds of the other goatherds.

"And supposing this beast is the divil's own?"

"It could well be," replied another.

The men all looked around at the last speaker and felt a shudder of fear.

The moon had come up. Dense black clouds, like a flock of monstrous beings, ran across the sky. A confused jangle of sheepbells could be heard; the bonfires of the shepherds were visible in the distance.

The men reached the dividing area between the open field and the crags, and approached the abyss with palpitating hearts. One of the men lit a dry branch and brought it close to the mouth of the cavern. The fire illuminated the beetling walls, faced with rough boulders and ledges. A cloud of frightened bats rose from the aperture and whirled blindly in the air above.

"Who will a-go down?" asked the old goatherd in a choked voice.

Everyone hesitated, until finally one of the younger men indicated that he would descend into the abyss, since no one else would do so. The youth tied the rope around his waist, and the others handed him a torch they had made of dried pine branches; he took the lit torch in one hand, walked to the edge of the great hole, and disappeared from view. The men above lowered him bit by bit; the cavern must have been very deep, for the rope kept playing out and still the youth gave no sign of having reached bottom.

Suddenly, the rope began to jump wildly, desperate and muffled cries were heard from the hole, and the men began to haul in on the line; quickly the young man was brought up, more dead than alive. The torch he still carried in his hand was extinguished.

"What did you see? What did you see?" everyone clammered.

"I seed the divil, all ruddy, all ruddy."

The terror of the survivor was quickly communicated to all the other men.

"Will nobody a-go down," murmured the old goatherd in despair. "Will ye let the poor lad die?"

"Look you, grandfather," said one man, "this cave belongs to the divil. A-go down yirself, if ye want."

His decision at last taken, the old man tied the rope around his middle, and he approached the edge of the black hole.

At that moment a vague and distant murmur, like the voice of a supernatural being, could be heard on the wings of the wind rushing around the abyss. The legs of the old man would not move.

"I don't dare . . . I don't dare either. . ." he sobbed, and began to cry bitterly.

The goatherds, silent now, gazed at the old man somberly. As the late-appearing flocks of sheep came down from the pastures on their way towards the town, the shepherds guarding the flocks joined the group of goatherds around the abyss, and, informed of the sad event, silently prayed, crossing themselves several times. Then they continued on to the village.

Men and women had come up to swell the group at the opening in the earth, and they filled the night with the sound of their whispers as they commented on the affair. Filled with curiosity, they would peer down into the black mouth of the cavern, and entranced, they would listen as the sound of a vague, distant, and mysterious lamentation came to their ears.

The night was now well advanced. The people stayed on, a prey to their profound curiosity.

Of a sudden, there was the sound of a hand bell, and the people hastened toward a high point to see what it meant. They saw the village priest ascending the mountain with the sacristan, in the light of a lantern held by the latter. A goatherd had found them on the road, and told them what had happened.

When they saw the viaticum, all the men and women lit torches and kneeled down. In the blood-red light of the fire-brands, they saw the priest draw near the abyss. The old goat-herd sobbed with a convulsive hiccough. His head bent towards his chest, the priest began to read the office of the dead; the men and women, murmuring in chorus, answered in a sad and mo-notonous chant; the smoking torches crackled and sparked, and from time to time, in an interval of silence, the mysterious complaint, far off and vague, indistinct and wavering, could be heard escaping from the cave.

When the prayers were done, the priest withdrew, and behind him went the women and men, who supported the old goatherd in their midst, drawing him away from the cursed spot.

And for three days and three nights, laments and moans—vague, distant, and mysterious—could be heard arising from the bottom of the abyss.

The Way I Write *

One of the things that would have made me happiest in this dog's life would have been the ability to write fast and well, with all the syntax which is said to be necessary to a littérateur; and it is not only for the sake of the glory that I would have liked this, but also for the sake of the quiet, relaxed, and gentle life which must be the lot of man who dedicates himself to covering a paper with scribbles as he invents graceful, entertaining tales, entangling the Marchioness with the page boy, causing the Marquis to roar, bringing haughty nobles upon the scene, and peopling the stage with innocent girls, unappreciated artists, and a whole flock of beings who certainly do exist, even though their existence is denied by those modern writers who, lacking lively imaginations and the fantasy to invent, call themselves psychologists.

But, since I have not an ounce of syntax in me, my uncle, the ex-Cabinet Minister Don Ramón Paredes de la Fumarada (Raymond Smoke-Walls) has always been opposed to my being the official chronicler of his family, which is my family as well, and has attempted to pit me against another. I am well aware that my prose does not compare with that of his former secretary at the ministry.

He never makes mention of the other man's style because, as he says, political activities have not allowed him time to polish it; besides, the other man feels contempt for literature and the arts.

A cousin of mine, a madcap of a fellow, claims that Don Ramón himself is unable to write a letter; but I find that hard to believe, especially coming from such a scandalous chap, because it is scarcely possible that Don Ramón, if he were that thick, could have been paraded before the eyes of the country as one of the most serious and brainy men of our epoch and a profound sage in educational matters; nor is it possible that, without any merit whatever, his speeches would have been preserved in

* This Introduction to *La Busca* (which was translated into English as *The Quest* by Isaac Goldberg in 1922) was supplied by Baroja to the newspaper *El Globo*, in which this novel of Madrid low life was published in 1904.

the *Register of Sessions* of both Chambers as finely wrought blocs of parliamentary eloquence. For all that people say, I believe that in Spain no one is prominent except those who deserve to be, and my uncle surely could not be an exception to the general rule.

With syntax or without it, I am determined to go ahead and write, and to write the history of my family in its various phases, in its different stages of splendor and misery, of misfortune and felicity. I am impelled to the task, first of all, because I'm good for nothing else, and secondly—why not admit it?—because of a desire to irritate my respectable relations a bit.

How did I become convinced of my absolute uselessness for all types of work? I will set down the facts in case anyone should be interested in an investigation of my ineptitude.

My father was an original man. I say was, because since we have had no word of him since he went to explore the Amazon with his friend Diz five years ago, I assume he is dead. My father was, as I say, an original man, one of those who insist on bucking the current.

Once, when the two of us were strolling in Moncloa Park, he said to me:

"Every natural, social, or political condition among men or animals—and even the ants have religion and politics—is a point on a circumference, related to a point higher up and one lower down, or, if you like, a point on the left and another on the right. To take an example: grass feeds on the earth; the grass is eaten by plant lice; the ants eat the lice; chickens eat the ants; men eat the chickens; women eat men; and everybody is devoured by the earth; and then the grass grows again from the earth. So the way I imagine everything, though it might not be correct in all particulars, is in the form of a circle, and in any direction you look you'll find circles, circles everywhere. Now what conclusion would you draw from this?"

"Well, it seems to me that the higher you are on the circle the more comfortable you are."

My father, who had been intending to draw a stoical conclusion, looked at me fixedly, and, with his natural stoicism, said nothing.

My father, as I have indicated, held ideas different from those of anyone else. He believed, for example, that in order to become a good doctor a man should begin as a male nurse; an architect should begin as a mason; a military man as a soldier; and a priest as an altar boy.

When I finished my secondary schooling, my good father looked at me very seriously and said:

"You've now finished studying a lot of things that will be of no earthly use to you. Think of what might attract you, explore your inclinations. You'll go around with me for a few days, and you can let me know what you like best among the activities we see."

The first day we went to a foundry, where we saw a steam engine around which some balls went whirling, a set of ovens, a conveyer belt which ran along near the ceiling with a whistling sound.

"Would you like to work in here?" my father asked me.

"No, papa, I wouldn't like it at all," I answered him.

Two or three days later my father took me to San Carlos; I saw the dissecting room, with its white marble tables on top of which there were human arms and legs. It made me turn cold. Next we went to a laboratory where there was a man, skinny, dark, and ill-tempered, who was using a glass rod to stir a kind of casserole in which, I swear to God, I believe there was a mass of phlegm.

"I like this less," I said, turning green.

On the following days we visited a sawmill, a number of warehouses, and various types of factories and industrial establishments.

When he realized that I did not at all like what I saw, my father told me in a funereal voice:

"Look. Since you're not good for anything, you can study law."

I did so, and, thanks to the recommendations furnished me by my uncle the ex-minister, I was able to keep passing the examinations. I took my degree in law, and in the course of my first case I realized I was no good in court; my throat went dry and I could not vociferate properly or loudly enough for the gentlemen with the sashes and caps to interest themselves in what I was saying.

As I revolved in my mind the sad fate of the man who has no money and who, moreover, is good for nothing, it occurred to me that I might very well make a littérateur.

"What do you think of it, papa?"

"Very well," answered my father, shrugging his shoulders; "that profession undoubtedly harbors the greatest number of idiots. Small as your talents may be, you could expect to do something in that field. It's always easier to turn out a bad novel or a bad play than it is to turn out a bad lock."

"So you don't think it's a bad idea, then?"

"What would you have me say? You have one advantage on your side, in any case."

"What's that?"

"The fact that we live in a country of leftovers."

"Of leftovers? I don't understand."

"Yes, a country of leftovers, of perpetual liquidation sales. Spain strikes me as a country which buys its institutions and its civilization in a secondhand shop. Spain is in the same situation as we Spaniards: it buys old ideas in the way we buy used coats in a pawnshop."

"In short, you think it would be a good idea for me to become a writer?"

"Psch! I'd almost rather you'd become a bullfighter."

I realized that my father was not overfond of the idea. But since I hadn't been able to think of anything else, I began at once to write symbolic dramas and musical comedies. My uncle protected me, giving me fifteen duros a month to bring him his correspondence and accompany him on his strolls, and with this little salary, and a few additional pesetas I got from the illustrated periodicals from time to time in return for stories and verse, I bumped along more poorly than well.

Ambition, the desire to ascend along one of those circles of life that my father described, shadowed my future. I cultivated my uncle with a warm affection merely for the sake of those miserable duros. The great preoccupation of this gentleman was, and if he is not dead, probably still is, to pass for a nobleman.

"We Fumaradas are," he used to say to me, "older than the Albas or the Medinacelis. The first Fumarada appears on the genealogical tree in the seventh century. And there is no blot on our escutcheon."

The Fumarada coat of arms boasted an infinity of quarters containing kettles, water pots, bridges—sometimes on a field of gules, sometimes on a field of vert.

Once when my father went to ask Uncle Ramón for some money, he told him (I don't know whether to flatter him or to laugh at him) that he had heard a distant relative assert that the surname Fumarada came from Fumareda, the name of a castle belonging to a Christian knight who preferred to set fire to his mansion rather than hand it over to the Moors, and that the true coat of arms of the family was a cloud of smoke (*humareda*) on an azure field. But later I heard my father say that if there were clouds of smoke anywhere in the family they came, rather than from the blaze set up by the knight of desperate measures, from the practical fire sent up from the oven of some honest charcoal-maker in the family.

I can not do less than confess that something definite drove me to publish my little writings: a sense of revenge.

I would perhaps not have written down even these notes if my uncle the ex-minister had not played a dirty trick on me, dismissing me from his house on the pretext that I was making love to his daughter.

Now that I have freed myself from the yoke of the fifteen duros, I can reveal that my family's genealogical tree is a hoax and that the ancestors of the Fumaradas were simply a set of bums and hungry tramps, people who, as my landlady says, washed themselves in the river with a stone because they didn't have the money for a bar of soap.

I had suspected the truth for some time; but, since I would earn nothing by divulging my suspicions, I kept them hidden. It was a chance train companion—the poor fellow was caught in one of those circles of life and found himself at the very bottom as a consequence of having knifed his girl, so that he was under guard when I saw him—who revealed, completely, the vanity and smoke of the Fumaradas' aristocratic ambitions.

It happened in the following manner: I was returning from Hendaye one summer in a third-class coach; at a stopping-place near Vitoria, four prisoners climbed aboard, tied wrist to wrist and herded by Civil Guards. In the same compartment with the prisoners rode two girls, with whom I had struck up a conversation.

In all the time that the prisoners were on the train neither they nor their guards spoke a single word. When we halted at the Burgos station, the four bound prisoners got off, and we who remained behind immediately began to talk and comment on the fate of those unfortunates.

One of the girls, holding up a gray-colored envelope by the flap said to me: "Look at what one of those prisoners left on my lap."

I took the envelope and tore it open and from it withdrew a photograph and a letter. The text was a declaration of love, copied from one of those books which provide models for that sort of thing. The declaration of love was followed by a note, written in a less exalted style, which explained that due to a misfortune, bad luck connected with thrusting a knife into some lady—affairs of the heart!—the writer found himself in prison.

The letter finished by saying: "Write me! Write me." It was signed Francisco Fumarada y Paredes, and his address was: "Number 184, Burgos Prison."

I can already see my uncle raging like a wild man when he reads these remarks of mine, and swearing that *those* Fumaradas have nothing to do with the *real* Fumaradas, and that the former are foundlings, exposed waifs; I can just hear him fulminating about patents of nobility and about his genealogical tree.

Some sharp critic may think there is something about this mordancy of mine—after all, it is terrible—something that indicates that I harbor a certain resentment against the comfortable classes; but if the sharp critic draws this conclusion, he is deceiving himself; the truth is that my only intention is to irritate my uncle's family. Those who know me are well aware that I do not hate—quite the contrary—the idea of wealth, and that I would put no obstacle in the way of my having some of it for my very own.

When I found myself without the fifteen duros and began to revolve in my mind the question of how I was to earn enough to keep from being a burden to the landlady, a good woman, whose protection is worth much more than my uncle's, I said to myself: "I could sit down and write the history of my family, a family that includes prisoners, bums, honorable men, ex-ministers, even priests; there is enough material to be found among the Fumaradas, the Paredes, the Pintos, the Alcázar, the Coreras to fill volumes; there will be plenty of piecework, I'll have enough types for everything; if I'm missing one, I'll invent him; if I have one too many, I'll eliminate him: I'll just shuffle the cards, mix some things with others, and, who knows?"

I was considering my plan when a friend of mine, to whom I had communicated my projects and who knows a couple of long-haired youths, asked me: "Listen, what technique do you intend to use in your books?"

I was puzzled. I had heard that in order to write, one needed syntax; but technique—I had not thought of that.

My friend explained to me that the word "technique" included the manner of proceeding, the plan of the work, and even the tricks of style.

"The plan I intend to follow," I explained, "is to portray my family in its development, in the different social strata in which they have lived, in the city, the country. How does that strike you?"

"Admirable!"

"In Madrid, I'll begin with the bums and wastrels, and work upwards, passing from the workman to the small merchant to the large merchant to the social climber, until I've reached the aristocrat."

"I see that you want to be the Galdós of Spanish life."

"That's it. You have understood my purpose. Do you like the plan?"

"It's magnificent. But, can you count on enough types, enough characters from this great cycle? Because it *is* a cycle."

I, though I was none too sure what a cycle was, answered yes, that he had certainly gotten the gist of the idea, and in direct answer to his question replied:

"Pshaw! . . . What types and characters I don't have at hand, I'll invent. It's easy. For example, I'll bring together the bad temper of one with the greed of another and join it to the sullenness of still another and I'll have a character made to order."

"That's synthesis," observed my friend. "The characters you construct in a composite manner can be binary, ternary, quaternary."

"True enough. I'll make others in the opposite way. When I notice a fat glutton who acts like a brute I'll make three men out of him: one a glutton, another fat, and a third brutish."

"There you have analysis," exclaimed my friend.

"Right again," I replied. "As to the manner in which I will compose my novel I remain in some doubt. As you know, my uncle had some works of merit in his library; he had almost all of Ortega y Frías and Pérez Escrich; in foreign literature, he had the works of Viscount Alincourt, of Ponson du Terrail, and in addition to these, the novels of Jules Verne; and then he possessed all the serials published by *Las Novedades,* and those put out by the *Correspondencia de España.* As you will understand, I can not make up my mind easily what orientation to follow amid such a wealth of genius. For this first work of mine, I incline toward the technique of Jules Verne."

"Very good! But I mean very good! And you'll begin at Madrid?"

"Naturally."

"And what will you call your work?"

"La Busca."

My friend shook my hand warmly and predicted that the laurels of triumph would soon crown my brow.

The Renegade Friar

In 1820 there appeared in Cádiz an enterprising, daring and turbulent man who quickly made himself popular. His name was José Joaquín. He was, according to himself, a doctor; he had been in America, and he held radical ideas. This man, a friend of demolition and in league with Masonic elements, immediately gained fame among the people of Cádiz. He preached irreligion, the liberty of customs, and free love.

He was not, like the Abbot Marchena, a literary and academic atheist; instead, he mocked literature and all academies. Don José Joaquín spoke to everyone: he gave advice and counsel to men and women, examined sick children, and recommended hygiene and herb infusions on all sides. He was sympathetic, effusive, and energetic.

Don José Joaquín, half naturist, half revolutionary, wanted a tribunal from which to expound his extremely novel ideas, and some Masonic friends set up a printing press for him, and there he began to issue a newspaper, the *Diario Gaditano*. The press called itself the Sincere Union, and was listed as being under the direction of Citizen "Clara Rosa."

"What the devil does "Clara Rosa" mean?" people asked each other. The doctor himself explained that he had lived with two women: one called Clara, the other Rosa, and that in memory of them both, almost in homage, he signed himself with their names. An amateur in ethnography might have taken this gesture to be a survival of matriarchy.

Citizen "Clara Rosa" published various small works: *Voyage to the Subterranean World; The Concordat Triumphant; Man and Brute,* and some others.

The collector José María Azcona, with the informed intuition of the bibliophile, had succeeded in bringing together all these tracts, as well as a goodly number of copies of the *Diario Gaditano*—but he did not reckon with blind chance. For when he was on his way to the binder's with them, his car was robbed and the suitcase that contained them taken, while he was in a bookshop on Jacometrezo Street, and he never recovered them.

I had hoped to read these tracts so that I might have a clear and even rosy idea of "Clara Rosa"; but I have not been able to read a one. The opinions which the director of the *Diario Gaditano* merited from his contemporaries do not inspire me with confidence. Reference is made to him in his *Memoirs* by Alcalá Galiano; by Le Brun, in his *Political Portraits of the Revolution;* and by Menéndez y Pelayo in *The Heterodox.*

Don Antonio Alcalá Galiano says that beginning in 1821 a newspaper appeared in Cádiz which became famous by reason of the eccentricities of its editor and publisher, the protection furnished it by certain influential persons, and the wide acceptance and credence given it by the common reader. Rumor had it that the chief contributor was a writer who had once belonged to a monastic order and who signed himself with the extraordinary pseudonym of "Clara Rosa" because—as he himself related—he had had two mistresses, one named Clara and the other Rosa.

Also according to Galiano, this man was of the most ignorant type and scarcely even knew anything about Spanish grammar; but he made up for the paucity of his poor thought and for his awful style by an incredible audacity.

"He devoted himself to upholding the most farfetched doctrines, if it can seriously be said that doctrines of any kind at all were upheld in his newspaper. He spoke against the government with a violence which bordered on the seditious; often he went beyond this borderline, so that he appeared useful to certain elements and endeared himself to the worst and most numerous class of newspaper readers, a class which in Cádiz was synonymous with the herd."

Somewhat similar words were being used against the writer of the above, Alcalá Galiano, at that very moment by the Absolutists.

For his part, Le Brun asserts that "Clara Rosa" was the incarnation of popular delirium, personified in its newspaper form.

"He was a Liberal, but his liberalism was so patched up with rags and tatters that it is impossible to describe it. His education was something he might have picked up in the garbage cans around town and then laid out on a piece of paper; it was made up of pieces of everything: theology, liberty, faith, partisan history, and an infinity of orations against everything that had ever been or ever would be, which he modified and graduated to his ends until they suited.

"Since he was not one to halt at barriers, and since he imagined that liberty meant smashing all existing restraints and limitations in society, his plan was to knock the head off every puppet in the play, whether in the field of religion, law, custom,

science, art, public decency or whatever had been established in
tradition; he felt that everything should be brought to the
ground, without a moment's hesitation, just Bang! and it's all
over, the entire past: saints, the mass, churches, sacraments,
authorities, tribunals, laws. They were all fruitless worries, and
he was for the New Life. But what a Life!"

Despite all Le Brun's astonishment, such is the nature of revolution, and such is the more or less successful way of new doctrines with old doctrines that are going by the board.

Le Brun goes on to say:

"'Clara Rosa' grew so insolent that there was no longer any
curbing him, and in his ravings he would just as soon tear God
out of the sky or pull down all those who did not agree with his
opinions as he would throw away a squeezed orange. He took
care only that each insult, each anathema, each folly ended with
the word 'Liberty'."

The tracts and newspapers authored by "Clara Rosa" must
have caused a fine scandal in Cádiz and its environs. It must
have been something like the storm set up eight or nine years
before by Gallardo's *Diccionario critico-burlesco,* though there
was a great deal more literature and craft in Gallardo's produc-
tion.

"The municipal authorities," adds Le Brun, "the other journalists, the Masons, the *Comuneros,* the old women, the Bishop,
who is another old woman, in short, everybody, came to verbal
blows, and insolences and charges and countercharges, and
libels flew through the air, and soon threats grew into action,
and blows were exchanged and knives were drawn.

"Complaints were made to the Court, juries were appointed
to investigate, sentences were passed, and a certain Castro, who
was in the death house as a traitor (and who was freed by order
of King Ferdinand because he really *was* one and deserved
hanging as much as a saint deserves two candles) proved to all
and sundry, out of pure malice (for no one asked him to do it),
that 'Clara Rosa' had been a friar and had apostatized, that he
had gone to America where the inquisition caught up with
him and had him arrested and sent back to Spain, that he
was consigned to a monastery, from which he escaped, that he
became a doctor in Portugal, that he married and had children,
and that he came to Spain to seek his fortune upon the
proclamation of the Constitution, bringing with him his wife
and children and his swindle of a liberalism, as well as the name
'Clara Rosa,' under which he lived and died. This Castro spent
a good deal of money and time in proving all these things, and

he did it solely for the sake of ruining the man, and because he was himself, as he announced, a person of deep conscience. But 'Clara Rosa' died, and so did his accuser a short time after he was freed by the king from the scaffold, to which, despite Ferdinand's wishes, he had been brought by public opinion."

In *The Heterodox,* Menéndez y Pelayo writes that the Masonic Chapter in Cádiz was led by an apostate friar called "Clara Rosa."

"Of this already forgotten personage," he says in a note, "it is worth adding that he was called Fray José Joaquín de Olavarrieta. He lived in America for a long time, and had been tried by the Holy Office on the charge of false doctrine."

José Joaquín de Olavarrieta was from Munguía (in the province of Vizcaya). He had been a Franciscan friar in the monastery of Aránzazu, near Oñate, and he was very fluent in Basque. He traveled in America, where he was condemned by the Inquisition as the author of a tract titled *Man and Brute.* He was returned to Spain as a prisoner, then escaped to Portugal, where he practiced medicine in a hamlet until he was able to go to Cádiz following the Revolution of Riego.

I cannot imagine Olavarrieta ("Clara Rosa") as one of those lean, tall, long-nosed type of Basques. Instead, I visualize him as being rather heavy and chubby, careless of his clothes, pale-faced, with black whiskers. That was the typical aspect of the two or three renegade priests I have known, one of whom was H. Ardieta, doctor, ex-priest, and friend of my father; he had been to America and had written a book on *Biological Chemistry,* which was published in Barcelona, and a small book for a collection called *The Mutiny.*

I do not, as I say, have a direct knowledge of any of the tracts issued by "Clara Rosa." The irritation shown by the writers of the epoch cannot be taken very seriously, given the pedantry and smugness of Spaniards at that time.

To a Basque, it seems strange that one of the most violent, most extreme writers of the first Spanish revolution should be from the Basque country.

The commonplace supposition is that all Basques are conservative and reactionary. The black flag of Saint Ignatius Loyola has been given such importance in the world that its folds have been draped over the entire race.

But common opinion is not strictly accurate. Among all nations and in all peoples, even in the smallest and even in those that have the most deficient culture, one tendency is always matched by its opposite. Thus, for example, among the Basques we find such examples as Saint Ignatius Loyola, and Saint-Cyran (whose father's name was Echeverri and who was born in Bayonne), the founder of heretical Jansenism. Equally Basque were Zumalacárregui and General Eguía, and their opposites Espoz and Mina and the republican Harispe; just as much Basque were Don Juan Bautista Erro, philologist and learned minister of the first pretender Don Carlos, as were Domingo Garat, Minister of Justice in the French Revolution, who read the death sentence to Louis XVI wearing a pair of spectacles which are conserved in his home at Ustáriz.

There have been many types of revolutionary Basques throughout history, most of them obscure figures, a few better known. In France: Garat, Basterreche, Harispe, Mauco. In Spain: Echave, Lazcano, the father and uncle of General Urbiztondo, Aviraneta, and an ex-priest, Arrambide by name, from the Jacobin Club at Bayonne, whose tracks I have not been able to follow.

To return to Olavarrieta, or "Clara Rosa": he wanted his newspaper to emulate the tumultuous popular glories of *Père Duchesne,* Jacques Hébert's virulent journal in the French Revolution.

According to Alcalá Galiano, the Sovereign Chapter of the province of Cádiz protected "Clara Rosa," whose very bad writing had entranced the mob. The ex-friar was defended by the Frenchified Reinoso as well as by Istúriz. Several of the Masonic leaders, however, were suspicious of him because of his continuously increasing hold over the public.

At a Masonic junta held in January of 1822 certain explanations were apparently demanded of "Clara Rosa," for he seems to have made a reply.

"The ex-friar was slow to explain himself; he was even ignorant of the formulas used in the Society to which he belonged," writes Galiano, "for in speaking of others he used the *Don,* instead of using the designation Brother, though sometimes he mixed them both; still, this was the least of his irregularities, for his speeches were studded with others."

Galiano's reproach is of little consequence to anyone except a pedant, for the use of *Don, Señor,* Brother, or Comrade, is a matter of formal and superficial treatment and means nothing.

"He made up in audacity and brazenness for whatever capability he lacked. Invective and sarcasm did not move him one iota as far as his insolence was concerned."

It is perhaps natural that "Clara Rosa" should not have felt like addressing the people around him in the Masonic mum-

mery as Brothers, if he was attacked with "invective and sarcasm."

The ex-friar was imprisoned, and from prison he apparently
denounced some of his friends for having urged him on only so
that they might abandon him. He was a sick man by then, and
he died shortly after his imprisonment. As he took leave of
life in his obscure prison he might have jestingly thought, with
the Emperor Adrian, of his small, wayward, and tender soul; in
any case, he refused to be intimidated.

He left instructions to be buried with the book of the Constitution opened at the article covering the sovereignty of the
people, requested that his body be exposed to the public for one
day, and asked for the exclusion of all clergy, crosses, and
candles at his funeral, preferring instead that national anthems
be sung for him until he was put away in his niche. This gesture
doubtless contained as much demagogic fanaticism as jovial
Basque irreverence.

The unfortunate end of the outlandish "Clara Rosa" excited
his friends, and the Society of the *Comuneros* adopted him as
their own and launched a violent campaign against Istúritz,
the Masonic leader, whom they held responsible for the ex-friar's
end.

The *Comuneros* decided to give the body of "Clara Rosa" a
funeral without precedent. A description of the ceremony will
be found in the journal *The Voice of Religion,* in a number
for the year 1838.

The cadaver was promenaded through the streets of Cádiz:
the body was left plainly visible, with a quill pen placed in its
hands. An enormous multitude gathered, bringing olive leaves
with them and singing marches and hymns to Liberty to the
accompaniment of a national orchestra, which converted the
funeral into a patriotic function.

According to Galiano again, the funeral party, instead of following a route from the mortuary house direct to the cemetery,
proceeded to the plaza called San Antonio or Constitution and,
after certain honors were paid to the stone which was to be
used as marker (it was the custom in those days to render a
cult to the gravestone), the party appeared under the balconies
of Istúriz' house, where they passed slowly back and forth, by
which they let it be known that they considered the inhabitant
of that house responsible for the dead man's misfortune.

"He died in prison in 1822 as a result of an offensive article
he penned against the authorities of Cádiz," says Menéndez y
Pelayo. "His burial was the occasion for a Masonic and irre-

ligious manifestation. His body was dressed in a long white shroud and led through the streets in an open coffin, with the book of the Constitution upon his chest. The Liberals of Cádiz marched along beside him carrying branches of myrtle and laurel in their hands, while the band played patriotic music. Speeches were made in the cemetery. These reports," adds Menéndez y Pelayo, "I owe to Adolfo de Castro."

José María Azcona has written, he has told me, a biography of "Clara Rosa" containing numerous details; when it will be published I do not know.

"Clara Rosa," friar, Basque, anarchist, demagogue—jovial and sloppy—may or may not deserve to figure in the literary, or even libertarian, Pantheon of Spain. But he certainly would have been in his element in a wineshop in Bilbao, or Gaztelupe, or San Sebastián, or among the "Chapelaundis," the "big berets" of Irún.

Gálvez the Absurd

Pedro Luis de Gálvez was an absurd man; I think he was a pathological type. He had been born in a village in the province of Málaga, and had been a seminarian. According to the story he told, he had written a satire in verse against one of the professors or tutors, hinting at nefarious vices, and he had been expelled for this reason.

He turned up in Madrid. At the beginning of his residence in the capital city he apparently had some resources to count on; he married and fathered several children.

He was a Bohemian by nature and could not accustom himself to any sort of regulated life. I do not believe that he was an extremist in politics, or even strongly opinionated, and yet he began to be known as a republican and syndicalist. Shortly, he was in jail in some Andalusian town. Next, when he got out, he consorted with certain republican politicians, spoke before a meeting, said some impertinent things about the king, was thereupon arrested and tried, was found guilty of the crime of lese majesty, and then, instead of availing himself of the help of the leaders of his party, who surely would have been able to save him, he let himself be taken to prison.

It seems that he served his time in Ocaña, and later he related in detail the horror of his life as a prisoner; doubtless, from some psychic perversion, he was attracted to these horrors.

Gálvez told terrible stories, especially about homosexuality in prison, where bullying became sadism and the most refined cruelties were practiced upon the weak, all accompanied by the greatest hypocrisy. He would tell about it with a certain morbid delectation.

He next passed through a Bohemian epoch, and one heard many extravagant tales about him. It was said that once, when one of his children died, he wrapped him in newspapers and took him around to the cafés, to solicit money for his burial. The same thing was told about a certain Milego, a great white-bearded character and friend of Manuel Sawa who did not, however, have anything to do with that other Milego, a

Valencian who distinguished himself as an orator and was later a professor in some city in Galicia.

Gálvez, who read an anecdote about himself that I recounted in a book called *The Cavern of Humor,* reproached me not for having recounted it but for having called him Carlos Luis instead of Pedro Luis, for he felt that in setting down that particular combination of names I had obviously been thinking of Carlos Luis de Cuenca, an identification he found offensive.

Following his Bohemian period in Madrid, Gálvez disappeared from the Court city; when he returned some time later, he said he had been traveling in Germany and the Balkans, and that he had served as an army officer in one of the Slav countries. I doubt the truth of this assertation.

Gálvez told me he had met and talked with Gorki and Sudermann and that both of them had asked after me. That might have been true or it might have been the flattery of a professional sponger.

Time passed, and a writer by the name of Modesto Pérez proposed to my brother-in-law, the publisher Julio Caro, that he issue a series of biographies of the writers belonging to the so-called Generation of 1898. Don Modesto himself wrote the biography of Unamuno, and Gálvez turned up at the publisher's with an offer to do mine.

It did not take me long to realize that Gálvez had not the slightest interest in his work. He got no more than fifteen or twenty pages of the biography done, and then he could go no farther. I would say to him:

"Put some stuffing into it and you'll have the book finished in no time."

Gálvez attempted to collect his fee for the book before turning the manuscript over to the printer. He was given an advance: but he wanted the entire sum. He was undoubtedly incapable of finishing the book, even by putting in bits copied from here and there.

I warned him:

"If you like, write the biography of someone else, anyone you like, and if you finish it, I'll see that you get your money at once; on the other hand, for not writing anything, nothing doing."

He would reply: "Don't say that to me; you make me so sad I could cry."

"Well, my friend, in that case you're going to spend your life in tears," I answered. "For I don't believe you'll find a publisher anywhere who will pay you for work you don't do."

"I have a different sensibility from the others; I put my soul into literature. I see that you haven't read my verses, and that makes me very unhappy."

Everything he said was make-believe: the truth was that he did not like to work.

At this time he told me how he had gone, six or seven times, to a place at some distance out along the highway to Extremadura, in the heat of summer, to fetch some cheap boots that were being distributed at a charity center and which were probably worth some twenty or twenty-five pesetas at the time. And yet he was not capable of sitting for three hours in a row at a table, writing an article for which he would have been paid rather more than the boots were worth. Anyone would have thought it was more comfortable to do it the easy way, but not he.

From time to time, Gálvez would disappear from Madrid altogether.

During one of these periods it was said that he was in prison, and then that Pedro de Répide had helped to get him out.

Répide had gone on a tour of Ocaña prison one day along with some other journalists. He caught sight of Gálvez there, and exclaimed: "What are you doing here?"

"I've been here for three years," Gálvez answered.

"But why haven't you written? We all thought you were out of the country."

Répide used his influence with his friends, and Gálvez was soon out of prison.

Then the tales began again. It was said that he had written books that other men had signed.

The books mentioned included Larreta's *The Glory of Don Ramiro,* and one by Ricardo León.

None of it sounds very likely, for the simple reason that Gálvez was lazy.

But I don't know what was fact and what was fiction. It all seems like fantasy to me. It is possible that Gálvez may have done some work for Ricardo León, correcting galleys, for which he would have been paid. This would not surprise me, for I heard Gálvez speak badly of almost every writer in Madrid, especially of those who presumed to be stylists, but I never heard him say a word against Ricardo León. Later it occurred to me that this was a singular fact. I also heard that he often went to León's house to eat, and that he was given money there. The two men were from Málaga, and of about the same age.

It was also reported that the painter Zuloaga presented

Gálvez in one of the most aristocratic houses of Madrid, and that he had impudently remarked: "Here you have the best poet in Spain."

Someone told me that during the dictatorship of Primo de Rivera, Gálvez had called at the home of a well-known writer who was then living in great state. Without a doubt he went there to ask for money.

The writer's manservant showed Gálvez into an elegant sitting room with shining mirrors and big heavy velvet curtains. Gálvez waited, and then, when he saw that the other man did not appear, ground his cigarette butt into one of the mirrors, by way of leaving a calling card, and marched off.

As he reached his fortieth year, Gálvez already presented a worn and haggard aspect. At the time when he was thinking of doing my biography for my brother-in-law's small publishing house, he brought them a photograph of himself taken in his prison cell in an Andalusian mining town—Pueblonuevo del Terrible, I think it was—which showed him writing at a table covered with bottles, and wearing the garb of a modernist poet, complete with long hair.

Of Gálvez' writing I never read anything but a few bits of verse without much personal character.

He also said that his verse was his best work; but since he knew I was not a great reader of verse, he never sent me any of his books.

He considered me a writer ruined by a methodic bourgeois life.

For his part, he led the most unhinged life conceivable. He accepted anyone into his household. If he, on the other hand, once wormed his way into another man's house, that man could consider himself lost. There would be no way to get him out again. He doubtless thought that this was the normal way of life.

One man would put up in the house of a second, the second would take away the first man's wife, a third man would keep the children, etc., etc. Any other course of conduct Gálvez considered mannered and routine.

Gálvez married an actress, as I remember, and then he lived with a French woman who owned a perfume shop.

The only activity for which he felt an affinity was the making of sonnets. He manufactured them as someone else would turn out doughnuts, and a number of them, some people said, were very good.

One anecdote concerning Gálvez and a Catalan publisher I thought pretty funny:

The Bohemian from Málaga had convinced the Barcelona

publisher that he should publish his books; the publisher also agreed to furnish the poet three or four hundred pesetas every month so that he could go on living. One day, as the two were walking on the Ramblas, Gálvez said to the publisher: "Pardon me a moment."

The publisher watched Gálvez go up to an unknown man and engage him in a heated conversation. Finally, the man reached in his pocket and handed something over to the Bohemian.

When Gálvez returned to his side the publisher said:

"I'll bet you just hit that fellow for a loan."

"Yes, that's true."

"And how much did he give you?"

"He gave me forty *céntimos.*"

The publisher exclaimed: "Why you're a pig, a shameless pig; I've given you enough to live on and you accept swill from others."

Gálvez answered this objection with an insinuating and endearing gesture: "No, no, you don't understand. I did it, you see, to keep from getting stale."

In short, so that he would not lose his touch. Gálvez was a dilettante at sponging. He took whatever he could get: a five-peseta note, or double that amount, or half it.

He hung around my brother-in-law's publishing office, and engaged the publisher and Don Modesto Pérez in conversation.

After a while, I lost sight of Gálvez.

During the Civil War I heard nothing of him until the end, when I learned that he had been shot by a firing squad.

With the outbreak of fighting, Gálvez had adopted a terrifying air and acted like a man capable of anything.

"This week I have personally accounted for two hundred men," he would say.

Perhaps all the talk was no more than show and bluster, that he did nothing more than talk, a terrible case.

I have no firsthand knowledge of my own, but I think that the hatred that welled up in Gálvez during the war was a sadistic consequence of all the suppressed humiliations that had fermented in his soul. This kind of reaction is the most repulsive part of any civil war. Hatreds based on frustrated vanity, on low and miserable failures, are stirred up. The fact that a person might have a safe and commodious position is often not enough to prevent this kind of odium.

The spectacle of humanity when these sentiments are aroused is not a very pleasant one. It is, rather, shameful and sad.

From what I was told, I gathered that Gálvez, toward the end, had become a spiritualist, and that when he was in the death house, he told a fellow prisoner, a young man whose father had already been shot, that he expected to see the father within a few hours and that he would give him news of the son. He said all this, according to the testimony, with the greatest serenity and conviction.

In the course of the war, Gálvez had given several bookshop owners some bad scares. He appeared once in Melchor García's bookshop in the guise of a Red officer, carrying a pistol, and told the clerk, Anacleto: "All right now, how much money is there in the till?"

The clerk told him that there were very few sales those days, and Gálvez told him to hand over what he had and that he would see to it that the Red militiamen did not bother him.

He seems to have carried out the same operation in Pueyo's bookshop, demanding the money in the till, and then all the money that could be found in the house.

It was said later that Gálvez did not behave badly toward his friends and that he had protected Emilio Carrere and Ricardo León as best he could. León was in hiding, changing his place of residence continually. It was said that Gálvez took him one day to a Red commissariat, and introduced him there as a friend from Málaga who had trapped the real Ricardo León, whom he had ordered shot.

Gálvez was as lazy as a Turk, and by now an inveterate alcoholic. He went around vaguely repeating that he had written novels that other men had signed and thereby gained their fame. I don't know how much truth there might be in this assertion: I do believe that Gálvez was incapable of any consistent or continuous labor.

Gálvez was condemned to death. In jail at Porlier he was like a madman, with his long white hair falling to his shoulders, his beard down to his chest, and wearing dark glasses. He stooped in walking and made use of a cane.

He went about talking with this one and that one and taking a drink whenever he could, and then he wrote a sonnet on his Last Hour, which he passed to one of the prisoners. A guard took the sonnet away from the other prisoner and tore it up.

The Tale of a Wig *

Descartes's axiom *Cogito ergo sum* seems false to me.

No one need make a spiritual detour to ascertain that he exists. He knows he exists because he hears, sees, walks, feels, and so on. He has no need for entelechy.

The Abbot Galliani was a small, thick-set man, only four and a half feet tall, but he was one of the most amusing men of his time and the idol of the purest-blooded *dames* of Paris by reason of his wit and joyfulness. Naturally, he was a Neapolitan. In spite of the fact that he was addressed as Abbot, it appears that he was not a priest. I have in my library two volumes of his Correspondence—with Madame D'Epinay, I think—filled with ingenuities. I am not sure, but I believe it was in the prologue to this work that he relates the following anecdote.

The Chief of Police of the City of Paris had invited Galliani to a great ceremonial banquet. The abbot needed a new wig, and he ordered one from his wigmaker. The day of the feast arrived, but the wig had not been delivered. A manservant was sent to fetch it.

The wigmaker made his excuses: his wife had been in child-bed, the child had died, and his wife was not yet well; it was not strange, therefore, that he had not been able to finish his work; but he would himself deliver the wig that very afternoon. That afternoon the wigmaker arrived at Galliani's house carrying a hatbox. Carefully he opened it up, and disclosed the baby that had died the day before.

"Good heavens!" shrieked the wigmaker, clapping his hands to his head, "the priests have made a mistake: they've buried the wig."

Anyone can make a mistake and bury a wig instead of a dead child; but it's not the usual thing.

In writing these *Memoirs* it has not occurred to me either to twist the facts or to tell lies. What would be the use? There are people who have said: "There are some things he doesn't tell." A person setting out to narrate events that to him seem inter-

* "The Tale of a Wig" and the preceding two vignettes are from *Memoirs: From the Last Turn in the Road*.

esting or characteristic is going to omit what he considers vulgar and emphasize what is rare. That is only natural. Would anyone underline the common, everyday, pedestrian things? Is a writer supposed to set down that he has just met John Jones? What for?

PLAY:

The Legend of Jaun de Alzate

The Author Speaks

You will all pardon me if, by way of prologue, I appear on the stage before the representation of my work and salute you. I am the author of this *Legend of Jaun de Alzate;* I am also a village poet, a humble poet, from a humble country, the country of the Bidasoa River.

The principal object of my *Legend* is to sing of this land and this river. Our region is small, it is true, without large horizons; and so my song will also be small and without large horizons. I am not sorry. I have more sympathy for small things than for the enormous and colossal.

I am going to present to you, along with the legend of Jaun de Alzate and the slight scenic, comic, lyric, fantastic accompaniment, scenes from the life of my Basque country.

As a countryman I possess no knowledge of the theatrical art; I don't know how to manipulate the puppets onstage and I don't expect to have a real public, but I would like to believe that such a public exists, so that I may feel free to act like a traditionalist in literature and begin my work with this form of prologue.

And thus, my kind and entelechial public, though you may not have any objective reality, as we philosophers say, I am going to furnish you with some explanations regarding this legend. I call it a legend, but the truth is I am not sure what it is; I have not had any model in mind as I write it, and I am going about composing it by happy chance, throwing into my grab bag everything that strikes my imagination. My hero is Jaun de Alzate, that is, the lord and master of Alzate. The Jaun de Alzates were among the most ancient ancestors of our Basque country; they were a family as old as Mount Larrun.

And now, a slight etymological disgression, if you please:

In Basque, Alzate means "abundance of alder," and the alder is a magical tree in Central European mythology. From the alder comes woman, as man comes from the ash tree. A Basquophilic friend of mine, though, has pronounced himself against this alderic etymology and supposes that the Basque word *alza, alça,* must have originally meant the generic idea tree, just as the very similar Sanskrit *alka* also means tree in general, and in that case Alzate would mean something like an abundance of trees, a stand of trees, a grove.

And now a slight geneological divagation, if you will:

According to a geneologist, the first Alzate was named Eguzqui ("Sun"), and his mother Illargui ("Moon"). Another investigator adds that a grandfather of our hero in his youth slew a dragon that used to hide in a cave of Mount Labiaga. With this data as a basis, one savant has treated Jaun de Alzate as a solar myth. We place no faith in him: for our part (and we speak in the plural, as if there were several of us), we believe that Jaun de Alzate actually lived and had a real existence in the world of phenomena.

Who *was* Jaun de Alzate? In his time, Jaun de Alzate was a courageous warrior and a wise man; a noble man with a noble spirit.

Today, the ancestral house of Alzate has been brought low. Three white houses, like three doves in an eagle's nest, occupy the site of the ancient castle on the banks of the Lamiocingo-erreca, the rivulet of the Lamias, which flows toward a juncture with the Bidasoa.

Of the ancient house and castle of Jaun only ruined walls and moss-covered stairs leading down to the riverbank remain.

For long years the house of the Alzate stood in abandonment, slowly caving in, its thick walls turning black and becoming covered over with ivy, its roof of tiles scummed with lichen, its windows broken by wild climbing vines, and its chimneys falling in. Its lower rooms, their ceilings and floors pierced with holes and cracks, served as a shelter for vagabonds, gypsies, and wandering vendors; the attics were used by the rats and owls.

Long ago the memory of Jaun de Alzate disappeared from the minds of men; his image was lost in the obscurity of time, just as the water of Lamiocingo-erreca is lost in the Bidasoa, and after that, in the ocean; but the humble poet has saved this history from oblivion, has gathered it from the sea of old papers and dusty parchments, and will present it before your eyes with a few, more or less arbitrary, interpolations.

The *Legend of Jaun de Alzate* is a legend of the Middle Ages, a legend to which the author has perhaps not known how to give its proper medieval character. It takes place in Alzate and in Easo. It is true that I have little enough data to go on in regard to events in Alzate and Easo in the flood tide of the Middle Ages, but I put my faith in intuition. Who will know whether I have succeeded or failed? Nobody, most likely.

Someone will say: "There are enormous anachronisms here."

Of course. Thus, for example, in the first part of my *Legend* I speak of the corn harvest, despite the fact that the majority of experts assert that this plant comes from America. In place of the harvesting of corn, I could have said the harvesting of millet, for that was a seed cultivated by the ancient Basques. But to my mind the suggestion that the Basques ate millet would have given the impression that our ancestors were goldfinches or canaries.

Finding myself on the slope of anachronism, I have let myself slide down without any protest. In this, too, I put my faith in intuition.

And now, just as the ancients used to enumerate in the prologue the themes and arguments of their works, I could do the same here; but I don't think that by so doing I would excite your curiosity. Intuition, again. And so I will not enumerate beforehand the incidents of my hero's destiny, but will rather indicate them as they unfold in time.

I have composed and written my work quickly and unceremoniously, in the short intervals of joy and the long intervals of pain: sometimes with the trace of a smile, sometimes with the trace of a sob; thus the story is sad and joyful—more sad than joyful—but always changeable, like the mad days of our land: cloudy, rainy, and shot tnrough with some shafts of sunlight.

Before the time comes when dams and artificial waterfalls have disfigured the Bidasoa, the tiny river of our tiny country, before posts have come to substitute for trees, and cement walls for hedgerows, and screws and bolts for flowers, before there are no more legends left than those associated with the plaques of the Sacred Heart of Jesus and the Union and the Spanish Phoenix, before all this happens, I would like to sing of our land in its natural and primitive state and to express, though it be in a deficient and awkward manner, the charm and grace of this sweet and lovely land.

No, it's not that I am one of those mummies who pray for the immobilization of the world, nor am I one of the confraternity of nincompoops who deprecate Science, that admirable Science which creates, which imagines, which invents—the only religion for Europe; but I *am* one of those who abominate the stupid and imbecilic industrialization carried out for the benefit of building contractors.

In short, before our country has lost all its character and all its charm, I would like to represent before your eyes, in the *Legend of Jaun de Alzate,* some scenes of Basque life in remote times.

It is certainly true that our corner of the Bidasoa does not possess a brilliant culture nor a resplendent history: there are no great mountains, no great valleys, no magnificent cities. But that does not stop the nightingales from singing in the branches of a summer evening nor cause the larks to stay silent in the meadows on sunny mornings.

For us, the enthusiasts of this land, the country of the Bidasoa is like a sweet song, graceful, familiar, always old and always new.

The inconstant and changeable climate harmonizes with the tone of our spirit: its versatility gratifies and entertains us, and we much prefer it to the severe and heavy immobility of other lands and other climes.

Yes, our land is a humble land, but it is a smiling and open land, and when the autumn sun illuminates it with its golden light, when on Sunday afternoons the country people dance in the plazas of the towns to the sound of the whistle and drum, for the poet it becomes a land of enchantment.

And now, in order to continue literary tradition, allow me to conclude with an invocation of the type that is standard in all the old prologues:

O Lamias! O Sirens! O Spirits of the woods! O ancient Thor, Thor of the cauldron! Lend to my hoarse voice a bit of sweetness and harmony! Lend freshness to my dulled imagination! Lend me a little breath and courage, so that I may represent before your eyes in the *Legend of Jaun de Alzate* some scenes of Basque life in remote times.

Intermezzo

THE CHORUS: Dawn begins to lighten the sky. The village is deserted. Who is that ferocious figure with fierce eyes and red beard who is drawn in a cart yoked to he-goats? Why does he wear a cauldron on his head? Is he a man or a god? . . . Why, it's Thor, Urtzi Thor, son of the Earth, the strongest of the gods! Urtzi Thor is stopping and looking at Alzate's houses. He speaks, sadly. Let us listen. Let us listen to what he says!

URTZI THOR: Farewell! Farewell Pyrenees beside the sea! Rolling luminous mountainsides! Green and temperate valleys! Sonorous resounding towns! Farewell proud and ancient Basques, and joyous youth with eagles' beaks! Farewell joyful, dancing girls! I am returning to my frozen wastes. Farewell! Farewell!

The Tranquil Life

I. IN JAUN'S CASTLE

The Alzate quarter of Vera-on-the-Bidasoa is, in this epoch, an independent hamlet, governed by Jaun, its master. The quarter is formed around a street of great old dark-hued houses, their balconies covered with flowers, their roof tiles covered with moss, their narrow doors resembling the doors of a fortress.

Jaun's place, on the banks of a rivulet called Lamiocingo-erreca, is in form somewhere between a large house and a castle, and its aspect is one of disorder. The entrance is over a a small bridge that spans the stream, and through a low, Gothic door which bears the shield of the Alzate: two black wolves on a field of gold. The door leads to an entryway paved with stone and boasting two columns, two benches, and a number of large iron rings for tethering horses.

There is also a wagon in the entryway, together with a heap of hay and a number of tilling instruments. On the left of the entryway stand the first steps of an oaken stairway railed with thick cross-pieces; on the right is the kitchen; and in front, the door to the stable, from whence issue the lowing of oxen.

The kitchen is spacious and dark, with rafters supporting the ceiling. There is a large table in the middle of the room and a fireplace with a great stone hearth.

Under the flaring funnel of the chimney there are two wood benches. A fine fire of oak stumps is burning in the fireplace. The old woman of the house, Jaun's mother, is seated on one of the benches, spinning golden flax; the spindle moves in her hand with great speed; from time to time she scolds the cat or the dog as they warm themselves at the fire, and from time to time she interrupts her work to throw an armload of broom and dry furze on the flames; the broom and furze perfume the air with their scent.

Two young boys, her grandsons, run to their grandmother every other minute to ask her something.

Apples are roasting on the stone of the hearth, as are chestnuts in a large iron cylinder; every so often the chestnuts explode with a loud report.

It is night time in the fall of the year. Jaun, his mother, his wife Usoa, his two grown sons and their wives have just finished supper.

Jaun is tall and well-built, forty-five years old. He has clear blue eyes, fine color, a beard beginning to turn white, and a daring and determined air. When he enters or leaves his house he whistles like a thrush; when he wants to summon his friends and comrades at some secret and deserted spot for purposes of war or rapine, he sings like an owl or howls like a wolf.

He abides by the precepts of the naturist religion of the Basques, accompanying the priest Arbeláiz to the top of a mountain to make a bonfire on certain days, and dancing in a forest clearing with his neighbors in the light of the full moon.

USOA: Our neighbors are coming tonight to shuck corn with us.

JAUN: Fine! Is that why you have chestnuts and apples roasting at the fire?

USOA: Yes, that's the reason.

JAUN: Have you brought up the wine?

USOA: Yes.

JAUN'S MOTHER: Wine! Nowadays everybody in the world drinks wine. There's no shame!

JAUN: Didn't they drink wine in your time, mother?

JAUN'S MOTHER: No. I should say not. But now there's nothing but vice.

THE BOYS: Grandmother! Tell us a story.

JAUN'S MOTHER: All right. I'll tell it to you now. . .

Meanwhile, the young people, lads and maidens, begin to come into the kitchen; they set down large bundles of corn on the floor and attach a torch and a lamp to the wall. The owner of the house, Jaun, his friend Arbeláiz, and a few others, all older men, are installed in front of the fireplace; Jaun's wife and the other married women are seated near them; the young men and women, no friends of the light, sit in a group at one end, and begin shucking the ears of corn on the heap. The young people break into peals of laughter from time to time: the older men and women are never sure exactly why.

After a while, as the shucking operation draws to a close and heaps of gold and red ears, large and small, are piled on the floor, the young people begin to move about. The girls eat chestnuts and apples and drink cider in wooden glasses; occasionally one of the boys will offer them strong liquor; as soon as the girls take a sip, they make a great scene, hawking and spitting it out at once. The ears of corn are piled up in the corners, and the large table is pushed over to the wall. A young man brings out a bagpipe; another takes a fife out of his pocket, and dancing begins. The rhythmic footfalls of the dancers are matched by the snapping of their fingers.

A VOICE: Zagarra, lori, lori,
                        Dembora denian
                        Gasteac ancac ariñ
                        Soñua jotzian.

(When it's time for the fat, fat apples, the young move their legs very fast.)

JAUN: How those girls leap, friend Arbeláiz! Youth, youth! It's something wonderful.

ARBELÁIZ: And something that passes very fast.

Arbeláiz is a tall man with a long beard and shining eyes. He is the village priest, the one who makes the auguries for the village.

JAUN: When I see that girl Pamposha, so lovely and fair, I feel my age like an attack of conscience.

ARBELÁIZ: Which one is Pamposha?

JAUN: Balezta's daughter.

ARBELÁIZ: Ah, yes!

JAUN: I also think with envy of the right that some of our feudal lords still reserve for themselves.

ARBELÁIZ: The right of the lord to every marriage bed!

JAUN: Exactly! What cynics those fellows are! The truth is that when one sees these lovely girls one regrets not being more feudal. Don't you think it might be possible, Arbeláiz, to go back a bit and re-establish these sound medieval customs?

ARBELÁIZ: Bah! It seems to me that you haven't left off being a rooster, even if you're not feudal.

JAUN: Do you believe it?

ARBELÁIZ: Well, let's see now. . . I know of at least four households where one of the boys has exactly your eyes.

JAUN: I know of some other houses, not your own exactly, where the Arbeláiz strain runs strong.

ARBELÁIZ: Lies! Calumny! . . . Me, a poor priest.

JAUN: Humbug! As if we didn't all know of your conquests!

ARBELÁIZ: Follies of youth. Still, now that I'm old I can under-stand it.

JAUN: Well, the fact is that I still feel like a young man, ready to set out on new adventures and journeys.

ARBELÁIZ: Nevertheless, you're all of forty-six.

JAUN: This Larrun air seems to keep me green. And then you have to admit that in our time women were freer than they are now, though they claim the opposite is the case.

ARBELÁIZ: Yes, I believe that's true.

JAUN: I've heard my grandfather say that in his grandfather's time the sons considered themselves to belong more to the mothers than to their fathers. The woman stayed at home, and the man, being a shepherd, would come and go as he pleased.

ARBELÁIZ: What we have now is better.

JAUN: It seems more respectable. But in that bygone age a man lived a looser life. . .

ARBELÁIZ: That would naturally appeal to you. . .

JAUN: Ah, I should say!

ARBELÁIZ: It's time now to rest, Jaun; and you haven't lived a tranquil life, like most men. You've fought in France and Spain . . . you've traveled. . .

JAUN: Yes, and I've sailed a bit too.

ARBELÁIZ: Have you been to sea too?

JAUN: Yes, with the Normans of the Point of Bayonne Bay.

ARBELÁIZ: With those terrible pirates?

JAUN: In my time they were good fellows. They were the ones who taught me to read, and taught me a bit of Latin as well.

ARBELÁIZ: That's incredible!

JAUN: At that time Bayonne was a beautiful city, busy, cultured, and prosperous. Now it seems to have fallen away.

ARBELÁIZ: The truth is that you began life an adventurer.

JAUN: And I'm ending it like a good sedentary countryman.

ARBELÁIZ: Who knows? There's still time.

JAUN: No, no. I talk to you now and boast and brag about my adventures and voyages, but don't pay any attention to me.

ARBELÁIZ: A goat naturally makes for the high places.

JAUN: I'm prepared not to have any more adventures or do any more fighting or make any more love. No, no; I don't want any restlessness or trouble; I only want to live monotonously with my old Usoa, and take care of my flocks and work my lands. I don't want anything else. Neither new friends, nor new knowledge.

II. CONVERSATIONS

The girls and boys are now dancing frenziedly and with abandon in the kitchen of Alzate's house. Among the men, Barrendegui, Ezponda, and Lizardi stand out by reason of their

*sprightliness. La Arguiya, La Belcha, and La Pamposha are
the most admired among the girls. La Arguiya is tall, clear-
eyed, white-skinned, with blond braids; La Belcha is a brunette, olive-skinned, with black, melancholy eyes; La Pamposha
is neither blond nor brunette, but she is enchanting: she possesses the agility of a serpent, eyes that shine, and lips that
smile with a gracious and mocking smile.*

LIZARDI (*to Pamposha*) : If you only wanted me as I do you! Why
don't you say yes?

PAMPOSHA: Me! . . . Ha, ha. . . !

LIZARDI: Is it someone else then?

PAMPOSHA: Someone else. . . ? No, my boy, no . . . ha, ha. . . !

LIZARDI: You seem to like them all well enough to laugh with,
and dance with.

PAMPOSHA: Naturally. And why not. . . ? Ha, ha, ha. . . !

LA ARGUIYA (*to Ezponda*): You've got to tell your mother that
we're sweethearts.

EZPONDA: Yes, yes. I'll tell her soon enough.

LA ARGUIYA: But when?

EZPONDA: Shhh! When it's time.

LA ARGUIYA: You're always telling me the same thing. You're deceiving me, I already know it. You don't do anything but stare
at La Belcha and the other girls.

*Basurdi (the Wild Boar), Jaun's manservant, a big-headed fel-
low with small, piercing eyes, a fat glutton and a girl-chaser,
is talking to La Illopa, who is somewhat foolish.*

BASURDI: How about going to the barn later?

LA ILLOPA: No.

BASURDI: Why not? You go there with others.

LA ILLOPA: I'll go if you give me something.

OLAZÁBAL'S GRANDMOTHER: Here, drink this, a little touch of
thantha, just a drop. It's good for ills of the stomach.

ZARRATEA'S GRANDMOTHER: A cup or two, that's my limit; I'm in
the habit of taking no more. More would be a vice.

OLAZÁBAL'S GRANDMOTHER: Yes, but at our age it goes good. And
with this humidity. . . !

ZARRATEA'S GRANDMOTHER: And the sorrows one has borne!

OLAZÁBAL'S GRANDMOTHER: A little does one good . . . to drive
away the gas.

ZARRATEA'S GRANDMOTHER: And the gloom . . . because with the
misfortunes one has had to bear; and then, life has become . . .
so expensive.

OLAZÁBAL'S GRANDMOTHER: It's a fright . . . I don't know where it will all end. Have you noticed these young things, what hussies! In our time we weren't like that.

ZARRATEA'S GRANDMOTHER: Naturally not! We would have had too much shame.

OLAZÁBAL'S GRANDMOTHER: On the other hand, the young men have become more handsome. How gallant they are!

ZARRATEA'S GRANDMOTHER: I don't understand how they can pay any attention to such shameless girls, girls who don't, after all, have much to offer.

OLAZÁBAL'S GRANDMOTHER: Absolutely nothing. That Pamposha isn't good for anything.

ZARRATEA'S GRANDMOTHER: And La Arguiya, with that hair which looks like tassles of corn!

OLAZÁBAL'S GRANDMOTHER: And La Belcha, with that awful color!

ZARRATEA'S GRANDMOTHER: Yes, the truth is that men have very strange tastes.

OLAZÁBAL'S GRANDMOTHER: Shall we have just another touch of *thantha?*

ZARRATEA'S GRANDMOTHER: Just a drop, no more . . . just enough to taste it.

OLAZÁBAL'S GRANDMOTHER: Don't be afraid of it. With this humidity. . . !

ZARRATEA'S GRANDMOTHER: And the sorrows and misfortunes one has borne!

   The two of them drink.

THE OLD MAN OF FRIXU-BAITA: What beauties these girls are, friend Lecu-eder!

THE OLD MAN OF LECU-EDER: I think they're more lovely than the girls were in our day.

THE OLD MAN OF FRIXU-BAITA: Yes, you're right. On the other hand, the boys aren't the likes of us. We were much more gallant, more . . . obliging. These fellows have chucked all the forms.

THE OLD MAN OF LECU-EDER: Petulant squirts, senseless fellows without an ounce of grace. It's incomprehensible how they can get these girls to pay any attention to them.

THE OLD MAN OF FRIXU-BAITA: Yes, that's true, it's incomprehensible.

THE OLD MAN OF LECU-EDER: How the world has degenerated!

A VOICE: Baratzaco picuac
                      Iru chorten ditu
                      Nesca mutil zalia
                      Ancac arinditu
                      Ancac ariña eta

Burua ariñago
Dantzan obeto daqui
Arto jorran baño.
Ay, Ene! Nic ere nainuque!
Ay, Ene! Zuc naibazenduque!

(The fig trees in the orchard have three branches: The girl with
a taste for men moves her legs, her legs very fast and light and
her head even faster and lighter, for she can dance much better
than she can ever weed corn rows. Ay, Ene! I wish I could too!
Ay, Ene! If you only would!)

The people go on dancing.

III. FRIENDS: DRINK, SING, DANCE!

JAUN, *who feels rather gay, addresses his people:*

Drink, sing, dance, my friends! Life is short, and youth is a
passing thing.

I am your patron, protector, chief, and comrade, and I rejoice
to see you happy and joyous. We are all humble folk, and ignorant too, but we are people of large hearts, who despise mean-
ness and hypocrisy, and love all that is great, noble, and strong.
In the wars against our neighbors we have fought side by side,
and in peace we have worked the land with the same oxen.

Drink, sing, dance, friends! Life is short and youth is passing.

We none of us aspire to do more than live out our obscure life
with its small incentive of momentary joy and fantasy. That is
our nature in Alzate: a little sensual, a little poetic, a little fantastic. Let us fill the cup again and drain it to the dregs.

Drink, sing, dance, friends! Life is short and youth is a passing
thing.

Here is all our philosophy. Tomorrow death will come in war
or peace. And we will meet it bravely. But joy is good and laughter also. Be joyful, and laugh, you are all young!

Drink, sing, dance, friends! Life is short and youth is a passing
thing.

IV. THE CALM OF NIGHT

The dance is over. All the people at Alzate's, lads and lasses, have gone to their houses. A few wild cries, irrintzi, have resounded in the distance. The night is warm, the village sleeps in the darkness. The stars shine in the sky, light clouds trail among the trees, the dew falls upon the flowers, the oxen low in their stables, and the stream of the Lamias appears bent on telling over its own secrets to itself.

V. A FALL AFTERNOON

Some weeks later. An afternoon in autumn. The sky is blue, with rosy mother-of-pearl clouds. A yellow sun gilds the slopes of the mountains, and the ferns and leaves on the trees turn red. Nature, passive and dreaming, allows the twilight caress without stirring. In the upper zones of air, lit by flashes of sunlight, clouds of insects are visible. In the sky, slow-flying buzzards cross and recross majestically. There is something deeply tranquil and idyllic about the end of the afternoon.

There is an odor of humidity, of dry leaves—the smell of autumn; the warm wind carries with it a sweet languor; and the rose-colored clouds, which loom up over the crests of the mountains like triumphal banners, have an air of nostalgia about them.

Across the foothills the bonfires send up puffs of black smoke.

A great calm reigns in the orchard of Alzate's house. The fruit trees are beginning to lose their leaves, and in the meadow the apples drop silently upon the grass from time to time and roll down the slope.

In an arbor of his orchard Jaun is seated on a stone bench next to the wall, under the shade of an apple tree and a fig tree, both loaded with fruit.

A stream, the Lamiocingo-erreca, runs near the wall. At this moment, the stream gives off a reddish, almost scarlet, glow; the dragonflies, with their iridescent tulle wings, their thin straight bodies, and their bulging eyes, skim the water with great speed. From time to time a kingfisher flies by.

Jaun stares out at the fields without thinking. The orchard is full of white butterflies swarming, red-breasted birds singing, horseflies buzzing, lizards running along the walls, and complicated spiderwebs like lacework dancing in the sunlight. The cat stalks the birds, stretching and then drawing in its limbs with the movements of a panther.

There are still some roses left on the rosebushes; they have very few leaves around them; some other late-blooming flowers are visible in the small garden beside the arbor.

This garden, red in the autumn light, is the color of the hair of certain blond women.

In a nearby farm plot, two of Jaun's workers are gathering various colored squashes, baskets of apples, and bundles of string beans, which they will spread out on the long balcony in the sun.

USOA (*coming out on the balcony*): Will you come in, Jaun?

JAUN: Coming.

Jaun crosses the orchard and traverses the wine cellar on his way to meet his wife.

The pale light, screened by the greenery of the fields, penetrates into the large rooms inside the house.

The afternoon is drawing to a close, and the gauze-like clouds of autumn cross the slopes of the mountains. From the chimneys of the neighboring houses blue smoke begins to emerge, slowly and effortlessly, and quickly turns to tenuous wisps in the air.

With the coming of night, the black chimneys take on the appearance of phantoms, melancholy and pensive. And the blue smoke coming from the village chimneys has something of the quality of the incense used in prayer; it speaks of the humble lives of the villagers, of the country folk, of the grandmother who piles branches on the fire as she rocks the cradle of the smallest child and hums a song to it, while the man of the house leads the oxen to drink in the stream and the wife brings feed to the animals in the corral.

VI. PROJECTED VOYAGE

JAUN: Why have you called me, Usoa?

USOA: I have been thinking that you ought to go to Easo, Jaun.

JAUN: What for?

USOA: We don't know what our daughter Ederra is doing there.

Besides, you have some money to collect in the town. So you can have a good time, too.

JAUN: I don't need to have a good time. I'm fine here at home. I don't feel like leaving the house.

USOA: Yes, but you ought to go.

JAUN: The truth is that I'd rather not go.

USOA: You're getting very lazy.

JAUN: We're both getting old.

USOA: You don't look it. . . Well then, you'll go, eh?

JAUN: All right. We'll tell Arbeláiz so that he can make the augury for the trip from the flight of the birds.

USOA: He's already made it.

JAUN: What? Was the augury favorable?

USOA: Yes. He's going with you. Basurdi will go too.

JAUN: A brave beast! Basurdi isn't good for anything.

USOA: We need the other man for the cider press.

JAUN: All right. I'll go with Basurdi, though I'd long ago made up my mind never to travel with him again.

USOA: I've got to put some presents for Ederra in a basket.

JAUN: If Arbeláiz and Basurdi are going, why do I have to go?

USOA: Listen, the truth is that I'd like you to go because I've been told that Ederra has a boy friend, and I understand he's a Castilian and a Catholic. It would be best if you met this fellow.

JAUN: All right, I'll see him. Wouldn't you like it if our daughter married an outsider?

USOA: No, I wouldn't. I'd rather she married someone from our own country and of our own beliefs.

JAUN: Ah, of course!

USOA: La Pamposha, from Baletza, is also going to Easo.

JAUN: Ah. . . ! La Pamposha is going. . . ?

USOA: Yes. She's going to Easo, and from there on to Sara.

JAUN: Oh? La Pamposha is going to make a trip to Sara?

USOA: Yes.

JAUN: And what is she planning to do in Sara?

USOA: I think she's going to get married.

JAUN: And are we so badly off in men here that she hasn't found one to her taste?

USOA: Doubtless.

JAUN: Well, how long am I to stay in Easo?

USOA: As long as you want . . . a week or two.

JAUN: That's good. You can't say that I'm not an agreeable man. Have you anything else to tell me?

USOA: Don't drink any wine or hard liquor. You know it's bad for you.

JAUN: I won't drink.

USOA: I'll get your baggage ready. Would you like to start out tomorrow morning?

JAUN: All right.

USOA: We'll send word to Arbeláiz and to La Pamposha, and you can tell Basurdi to get the horses ready.

JAUN: All right.

VII. PRESENTIMENTS

JAUN: I have a presentiment, a terrible presentiment that this trip is going to go badly for me. Ah, perhaps it's only a foolish apprehension. La Pamposha's going and I'll accompany her. That will be nice. But why do I have this presentiment?

CHORUS OF SPIRITS: It's useless for you to oppose your destiny, Jaun. Everything that is, is because it must be. Even if your fate is not predetermined and your acts are not all fated—because they're not written beforehand in a bronze and parchment tome —they are nevertheless as necessary as everything else that exists in Nature.

VIII. MORNING

Morning of the next day. The neighborhood of Alzate sleeps, wrapped in fog. From the chimneys come the first tenuous wisps of smoke, the matutinal prayer of the humble life, and then the cocks begin to crow. Jaun desends to the stable, where he looks over the mounts.

JAUN: Hey, Basurdi! Get up, you animal!

BASURDI (*aside*): This man is always ready to hound me.

JAUN: Have you watered the horses?

BASURDI: No.

JAUN: Well what are you doing, stupid?

BASURDI (*aside*): This business of being a servant is a dirty deal, it's unjust and hateful to me. It's a case of being dependent at all times on the whims of the master, who always wants this or that. What a nuisance! What a bother! If I were only rich! I wouldn't do a thing. My servants would do everything for me!

USOA: Is the baggage well stowed?

JAUN: Yes. Basurdi, bring me my arms!

BASURDI: Here's your sword and javelin. Will I carry anything?

JAUN: Carry the horn.

BASURDI: The horn! This man is always trying to discredit me. (*Aloud*) I'll carry a sword.

JAUN: No, no. For all the help that you're likely to give me. . . When I was with Bildoch and we were attacked by the men from Zabaleta on the road to Sumbilla, you ran away.

BASURDI: Ah, naturally! Was I supposed to stay and get killed like Bildoch?

JAUN: Of course you were.

BASURDI: That's one opinion. It's not mine. I'm no friend of rows. I want to be left in peace, just as I leave others in peace.

JAUN: You're not the wild boar they call you. You're just a hog.

BASURDI: I'd rather be a live hog than a dead man. Not everyone can say the same.

JAUN: Who can't say the same?

BASURDI: Why, the dead men.

JAUN: Quiet, beast. I'm seized with an urge to kick you out of here. You're as much of a brute as you are an egotist, and as much of an egotist as you are an ingrate.

BASURDI: Where do you find wise and grateful and generous men? I'd like to meet them.

JAUN: Very well. That's enough. Pick up the horn and don't say any more.

BASURDI: There are others who could wear the horn better than I.

JAUN: You'll wear it sooner or later. Don't be in a hurry.

BASURDI: I won't.

JAUN: Take this horse by the reins so that La Pamposha can mount it at the door of her house in Balezta.

BASURDI: Is that girl coming with us?

JAUN: Yes, and be careful what you say.

BASURDI: Bah! That one's already heard anything I'd say.

JAUN: Whether she has or not, do me the favor of not saying anything piggish in front of her.

BASURDI: I'm not in the habit of saying anything piggish.

JAUN: Yes, you're a knight of the Round Table.

BASURDI: I know I'm not that. And this other nag, who's that for?

JAUN: That's for Arbeláiz, who'll join us at Erricoechea.

Jaun dons his brown wool cloak, and mounts his horse. Basurdi leads the other horses along by the bridle.

IX. ON THE WAY TO EASO

Jaun and Basurdi have halted along the Alzate road, at the door of a house known as Balezta (The Crossbow).

JAUN (*calling*): Eup! Eup!

THE CROSSBOWMAN: Who's there?

JAUN: It's me, Jaun de Alzate. Isn't your daughter going to Easo?

THE CROSSBOWMAN: Yes, she's coming down right now. Pamposha! Pamposha!

PAMPOSHA: I'm coming. What a hurry! Good morning, Jaun!

JAUN: Good morning, Pamposha! You're as fresh as a morning in Spring.

BASURDI (*aside*): Whether she's fresh or not is a matter would bear looking into. I wouldn't think so.

PAMPOSHA: Thank you, Jaun. . . Oh, I have to laugh. . . Ha, ha. . . Shall I climb up?

JAUN: Yes.

PAMPOSHA: Well, I don't know how to mount.

JAUN: I'll help you. Upaa!

BASURDI (*aside*): Just to be sure, the master is holding her around the waist.

THE CROSSBOWMAN: You'll take good care of my daughter, Jaun.

JAUN: Don't worry, nothing will happen to her on the road.

THE CROSSBOWMAN: She's a bit giddy. Well, she's in your hands now, eh?

JAUN: All right. Yes. That's all right. Basurdi!

BASURDI: What?

JAUN: Go and get Arbeláiz.

Jaun and Pamposha go on together, and Arbeláiz and Basurdi soon join them; they all head out along the road to Easo. When they pass in front of the town of Vera they stop to gaze at the church the Christians are building.

ARBELÁIZ: By all that's holy, our Basque ideas and customs are in great peril. Christianity is advancing on all fronts. These Christian cultists want to strip us of everything, and substitute something else for our practices. And why? To give us discourses in Latin, which none of us understand.

JAUN: You're right, Arbeláiz. They want to take away our venerable Basque traditions, and implant this new religion with Jewish dogmas. I intend to oppose them with all my forces, though they may not be much.

ARBELÁIZ: You're the lord of Alzate.

JAUN: Bah! A hundred houses and a handful of huts.

ARBELÁIZ: You've got good friends: those in Gamboa, in Spain, and those in Urtubi, in France.

JAUN: Yes, but they're all becoming Christians.

ARBELÁIZ: The truth is that these Christians are skillful. They take over everything and become more and more important. What churches! What convents! What golden cups! What cloths! We, on the other hand, who remain faithful to Urtzi, are satisfied with a wool cloak and a misletoe crown.

JAUN: Do you believe that our gods have any strength left, Arbeláiz?

ARBELÁIZ: Perhaps they've grown weary, but I believe they will once again enjoy a period of brilliance.

JAUN: And suppose they're dead.

ARBELÁIZ: I believe that Urtzi and Leheren and the others still have work to do. They will die, yes, but not so soon. For the time being, our gods are effective: they get us what we want. You've seen it yourself numberless times.

JAUN: That's true.

ARBELÁIZ: The Christians are busy praying and praying, repeating words of a language they scarcely understand. And what for? All for nothing.

JAUN: And yet they say we're the stupid ones, and that they know the only truth.

ARBELÁIZ: That's what they say.

JAUN: There must be some merit in their ideas.

ARBELÁIZ: Do you think so?

JAUN: Without a doubt. If it weren't so, why would Christianity be sweeping the world?

ARBELÁIZ: You must be right. It's something to worry about.

JAUN: The Christians in Easo are about to begin their Christmas ceremony.

ARBELÁIZ: Yes. First the feast of Oel, though, which is rather renowned thereabouts.

BASURDI: What a prospect! I can feel a river of wine pouring down my throat!

ARBELÁIZ: While the Christians celebrate their feast, we celebrate the birth of the Sun, and so we can join in both celebrations without starting arguments or arousing jealousies. After all, we're less demanding than they are.

X. LA PAMPOSHA GETS BORED

PAMPOSHA: Jaun.
JAUN: What's the matter, my child?
PAMPOSHA: I can't ride like this. I'll fall off.
JAUN: Do you want us to go slower?
PAMPOSHA: No. But couldn't your horse carry us both? That way
I'd have something to hold on to.
JAUN: All right. Get down from your horse, and when we get
to a large stone, you can jump up on mine.
   *La Pamposha gets down from her horse, mounts the other
   horse with agility, and holds on to Jaun's waist.*
JAUN: How light you are!
PAMPOSHA: When I want to be, I'm very light. . . Jaun, please
don't talk about those things any more.
JAUN: What things, Pamposha?
PAMPOSHA: Serious things. I get very bored.
JAUN: What do you want us to talk about?
PAMPOSHA: Of love affairs, and wonderful things.
JAUN: We're too old for that, Pamposha. Basurdi is still young
. . . but he's an animal.
PAMPOSHA: Basurdi . . . Ha, ha . . . what a laugh!

XI. SHAGUIT, THE MADMAN

   *The party passes through the suburb of Zalain. A tiny little
   man, wearing a red riding hood, sings as they pass.*
SHAGUIT: Arre, arre, mandoco;
                           Biyar, Iruñaraco.
                           Andic cer ecarrico?
                           Zapata eta guerrico
                           Oc guciac norentzaco?
                           Gure aur politarentzaco.
(Giddap, giddap, mule. Tomorrow you'll go to Pamplona. And
what will you bring me from there? Shoes and a fine wide belt.
And who will all that be for? For the littlest child, the prettiest
one.)
BASURDI: What are you up to Shaguit?
SHAGUIT: I'm singing to amuse myself.

BASURDI: How's your head, madman?

SHAGUIT: It's all right, though it hasn't grown as big as yours.

BASURDI (*raising his stick*): You're crazy as the devil, and I'm going to give you. . .

JAUN: Hey! Slow there, slow. For the time being it's not obvious that this man is any crazier than you.

SHAGUIT: Are you the lord of Alzate?

JAUN: Yes; and you, who are you?

SHAGUIT: Don't you know me?

JAUN: No.

SHAGUIT: I'm a singer, and a madman, so everyone says. I wander around the fields and through the towns, and sing happy songs at weddings and celebrations, and earn my bread.

JAUN: You're a poet, then.

SHAGUIT: You can call me what you like. I'm a poor but happy man. I haven't tried to make money, for money is of no use to me; I haven't tried to get a wife, and if I tried to be mayor of my town, people would laugh at me, and I would laugh too.

JAUN: Then you're a wise man.

SHAGUIT: Might be; but everybody says I'm mad.

JAUN: Where are you going now?

SHAGUIT: I'm on my way to Easo. Why don't you invite me to go along with you?

JAUN: Climb up on the horse with the saddle bags.

SHAGUIT: Thank you, my lord. (*Pointing at Pamposha*) Is that your wife?

JAUN: No; my wife is older.

SHAGUIT: Yes, she is your wife.

JAUN: No, though I wouldn't lose in the exchange.

PAMPOSHA: Ha, ha. . . ! Isn't that funny!

The travelers proceed along the road and arrive at one of the the suburbs of Easo, where the road is closed off with a chain, so that they are forced to dismount. They are at a toll station. Basurdi mixes with the people gathered about, and suddenly puts his arm around the waist of one of the local girls.

JAUN (*yelling*): Basurdi! Come here. I'll crack your skull open if I see you grab another girl by the waist.

BASURDI: But they like it.

JAUN: They like it! You animal!

SHAGUIT: Animal! Animal!

Basurdi gives Shaguit a shove.

JAUN: Basurdi! You're too much of a brute to go with us to Easo. I'm going to make you go back to Alzate.

PAMPOSHA: Let him stay. He makes me laugh.

JAUN: If this man is as an example, you can't say that travel broadens the mind, because he gets more and more brutish, vulgar, and coarse.

ARBELÁIZ: Well now, the business with the toll office is done. Let's head for Easo!

JAUN: Let's go.

XII. DISCUSSIONS

Jaun, Arbeláiz and La Pamposha have taken up residence in the house of Andria, sister of Jaun and married to the lord of Choriburu. Basurdi has been sent to stay in a neighboring hamlet. Jaun has noticed that his daughter, his sister and his brother-in-law are always whispering aside and talking mysteriously. Concerned about this, he makes inquiries and finds out that they have all become Christians.

JAUN: So you've all become Christians?

CHORIBURU: Yes, we've gotten baptized.

JAUN: My sister too?

CHORIBURU: She too.

JAUN: And my daughter Ederra?

CHORIBURU: She's one of the most enthusiastic Christians in Easo.

JAUN: Did you indoctrinate my daughter?

CHORIBURU: It was by her own will, you can believe me, that she came to the bosom of religion. When she gets home from mass, you can ask her yourself.

JAUN: That's just fine. Just dandy. We've really outdone ourselves!

CHORIBURU: You'll join the fold of Catholicism too.

JAUN: Not me, not me. And what does that mean, by the way, Catholic?

CHORIBURU: Universal.

JAUN: I'll never be universal. I'm happy to be from Alzate.

CHORIBURU: When you learn the truth, you'll join the Church. Right now you're living in idolatry, in a world full of error and vice.

JAUN: What errors? And what vices are practiced in Alzate? Would you be so kind as to explain what you mean?

CHORIBURU: You worship the sun, the moon, and the stars.

JAUN: And why not?

CHORIBURU: You pay homage to the beasts.

JAUN: That's not true.

CHORIBURU: You hold the he-goat to be a divinity.

JAUN: It's the symbol of a pasturing people. You Christians, don't you have the Lamb as symbol?

CHORIBURU: You people are barbarians; you're behind the times.

JAUN: On the other hand, you people are more hypocritical and fanatical than we are.

CHORIBURU: This rustic has an answer for everything. Very well. Here you have your daughter, back from mass. And don't call her Ederra. Her name now is Maria.

Ederra enters.

JAUN: Ederra, my daughter! Is it true that you have abandoned our creed and have turned Christian?

EDERRA: Yes, father, I have been baptized. My name now is Maria.

JAUN: To me you will always be Ederra. And why have you abandoned our old Basque traditions?

EDERRA: Because I've been taught the truth.

JAUN: The truth! The truth! Every people and nation has its truth. Catholicism may be the truth of foreigners, of outsiders, but it's not ours.

EDERRA: Father, don't blaspheme; you don't know Catholicism.

JAUN: I don't know it! Neither do I know the religion of China, but I tell you that wherever the Christian gods go, the Basque gods, Urtzi, Leheren, and the others, are good enough to go too.

EDERRA: All that is idolatry, father. We Christians have only one God, the only God, the Eternal, the Omnipotent. Today, Father Mamertus is coming, and he will explain the principles and mysteries of our religion, the true religion.

JAUN: What? Your religion has mysteries? I thought the truth had no mysteries.

EDERRA: You will be convinced, father. I'm going to pray for your conversion.

XIII. SOLILOQUY

JAUN: I'll not be convinced, for I don't plan to listen to him. I won't have any monk coming around to preach to me. If he shows up, I'll give him a thrashing. This is what comes of sending a daughter to town! She's abandoned her religion; she'll soon forget her own language and talk only Latin. I'll probably forget it myself, and we can all join together to decline Muse, *Musa, Musae,* and sing:

Those in u, without exception
are neuter gender, and no question.
And we'll all fall under the domination of those eloquent
monks, with their Jewish gods, and the day will come when
Alzate will have its cult church, bells and all, to wake us up
when we're asleep. The end of the Basques! *Finis Vasconiae!* . . .
O! Even I am seduced by Latin words. What a fate!

XIV. EDERRA'S FUTURE

JAUN: Andria, my dear!

ANDRIA: Call me Ana. That's what they call me since I was baptized.

JAUN: None of you want to preserve even your own Basque names! All right, then, Ana.

ANDRIA: What?

JAUN: Give me a second cup of wine.

ANDRIA: Why, you've already drunk six.

JAUN: I might be mistaken in my count; for me, it's the second. What do you think of what my daughter has done?

ANDRIA: Very well done. You should do the same: get baptized.

JAUN: Baptized! What for? First they would have to prove to me that my religion is false and that yours is true.

ANDRIA: But that's obvious.

JAUN: I don't see it that way.

ANDRIA: Get baptized and you'll see it.

JAUN: Not I. And do you think that perhaps now Ederra won't want to marry anyone unless he's Christian?

ANDRIA: I'm sure of it. And more than that: I believe that she has taken up with a young Castilian Catholic called Anselmus.

JAUN: With Anselmus! That ass! That fatuous foreigner!

ANDRIA: I've heard Ederra say several times: I won't marry anybody but Anselmus; either that or I'll enter a convent.

JAUN: But it must be a joke! I'll find suitors of more worth and social standing for my daughter, and I'll convince her to leave Anselmus.

ANDRIA: I believe it will be impossible.

JAUN: Well, we'll see!

XV. THE SUITORS

ARBELÁIZ: I've thought over what you told me the other day, and I've uncovered some non-Christian suitors for your daughter.

JAUN: Who are they?

ARBELÁIZ: I'll introduce them to you.

JAUN: Have you spoken to them?

ARBELÁIZ: Yes.

JAUN: Then bring them here, if you will, so that I can meet them. I'll talk to them and find out what they're like.

ARBELÁIZ: I'll bring them here right now.

Arbeláiz goes out and returns shortly with a skinny, sallow youth dressed in a black tunic.

ARBELÁIZ: Here you have Zechariah Pepper, the Jew of Tudela.

ZECHARIAH: I've heard from your friend Arbeláiz that you have a daughter to wed. I'm the owner of a banking house in Tudela which brings me in a fat profit. I've bought up a number of lots in that town, and I also make loans, to rich and poor, at the modest profit of 150 per cent per month. If you're rich, as your friend Arbeláiz says, tell me what dowry, in cash, you're willing to settle on your daughter, and, if it suits me, I promise you, by father Abraham, that I'll marry her.

JAUN: Friend Pepper, what will you have? I've got no sympathy either for Jews or for business.

ZECHARIAH: You're incapable of understanding us Israelites. You're a member of an inferior race.

JAUN: It must be very low if it's lower than yours.

ZECHARIAH: You're all as bad as Kaffirs.

JAUN: All right, all right! Go poison the world with your promissary notes and your commercial swindles.

ZECHARIAH: May the birds of ill omen devour you, you wicked man! May the light of your eyes fail you and may you fall to earth and the earth burn you and. . .

JAUN: I'm about ready to give this good Jew the end of my shoe.

ARBELÁIZ: Don't do it. Afterwards you'd have to pay him heavy damages.

JAUN: Then, let him get out.

ARBELÁIZ: I'll bring you another one of the suitors.

Arbeláiz goes out and returns with a Turk.

JAUN: A Turk!

ARBELÁIZ: A Turk all over. Suleiman Mustapha.

SULEIMAN: May God grant you, sir, the strength of the lion and the prudence of the snake.

JAUN: May Urtzi Thor give you the flight of the eagle and the calm of the snail.

SULEIMAN: May your heart be as a flowering rose bush.

JAUN: Thank you!

SULEIMAN: I've been told that you have a daughter to marry off, and that you do not have the prejudices of those Christian dogs in regard to the marriage state. If this is the case, and if I inspire confidence in your eyes, then give me your daughter. I'll marry her, and take her to the harem, where she can live a peaceful life of pleasure with my other wives.

JAUN: Honored Suleiman: I suspect that with you Ederra would not be happy. Our Basque girls want to be sole queens in their husbands' hearts, and I even think that your very name alone, O Suleiman, would be as welcome to my daughter as poison.

SULEIMAN: You mean that I don't suit you.

JAUN: You don't suit me.

Arbeláiz next brings in Harold, the Viking. Harold is dressed like a warrior and wears pagan decorations.

HAROLD: Since childhood I have battled and fought, and seen my lance steaming with red blood on the fields of war. With my own hand I have killed hundreds of enemies; I have drunk black ale from cups carved from human skulls, and have sung the battle hymn of the Scandinavian King Ragnarus Lodbrok:

Bibemus cerevisiam brevi
Ex concavis craniorum poculis
In proestantis Odini domicilio.

My cry is: Thor, aid us! I don't take orders from anyone, and I don't respect a single soul. I have a corsair ship filled with booty. My ideal is to die in the heat of battle, and when Odin calls me to his palace, I will go there with a smile on my lips. If you also are a warrior and your daughter has a stout heart, give her to me.

JAUN: I'm not as ferocious as you, Viking, nor is my daughter. That business about drinking from a human skull doesn't arouse my enthusiasm. You're a furious warrior, and I'm a stolid farmer. We wouldn't understand each other.

ARBELÁIZ: You just can't find a tree to hang yourself on, Jaun. Let's see if this suitor suits you. This is Manish, from Laborta.

MANISH: My parents are bent on getting me married, by force if necessary, to a rich and ugly heiress, but I refuse. I've seen your daughter and I like her. Will you permit me to talk to her?

JAUN: Why not?

MANISH: I come from Suraide, where I have a fine farmhouse, immense meadows, cornfields and cows. . .

JAUN: So you're from Suraide, the town where the people are famous for eating onion salads?

MANISH: Don't think that we eat more onions than anyone else.

JAUN: And even if you did! Yes, Manish, I should like it if my daughter were to marry you, and went to live in your country, which is splendid and admirable. You people are Basques, like us. And while we're infected with Castilian haughtiness and pride, you are contaminated by the vanity of your Gallic neighbors. If my daughter and you come to an understanding, I give my consent.

ARBELÁIZ: There is one more suitor, Jaun.

JAUN: Let him come in.

ARBELÁIZ: Here you have him.

ANSELMUS: I am Anselmus, the Castilian, and I've come to tell you that these interviews and conferences of yours for the purpose of marrying off your daughter are completely useless.

JAUN: What? Do you mean to interfere in my affairs?

ANSELMUS: This is not your affair alone, but also your daughter's, and therefore it is of interest to me as well.

JAUN: What cheek!

ANSELMUS: You may say, Jaun, that I am an outsider, a blusterer, and an insolent meddler; and you may believe that I come from a nation of poverty-stricken loafers, who give themselves the airs of princes though they're really beggars; but, nevertheless, I am Anselmus the Castilian, and Anselmus the Castilian is your daughter's choice, and whether you want it or not, she will be mine.

JAUN: You speak with a great deal of arrogance.

ANSELMUS: No, I speak with assurance.

JAUN: So sure are you of her?

ANSELMUS: Yes. She and I have sworn eternal love and no human force can ever separate us.

Intermezzo

CHORUS: Urtzi Thor, Urtzi Thor the strong, with his fierce eyes and red beard, has climbed up Mount Larrun and gazes out over the complicated terrain of Spain, the sharp peaks, the humid valleys, the green slopes of the hills. Where are you going, Urtzi Thor? Whither are you bound?

URTZI THOR: Farewell! Farewell Pyrenees beside the Sea! Rolling luminous mountainsides! Green and temperate valleys! Sonorous resounding towns! Farewell proud and ancient Basques and joyous youth with eagles' beaks! Farewell joyful, dancing girls! I'm returning to my frozen wastes. Farewell! Farewell!

Between the Feast of Oel and Christmas

PROLOGUE OF THE TWO DEVILS

CHIQUI: Perhaps some of you know me. Perhaps not. I'm part gnome and part devil. For some time now I've been employed in the cave of Zugarramurdi, and I've come to Easo with the mission of watching Jaun de Alzate, lest my man get the humorous notion of turning Christian. I'm here with a fellow devil who, in all truth, is rather a boor, and who is assigned to watch over Basurdi. I'll have my pal speak to you a bit, so that you can get to know him. Hey, you, Martín, speak!

MARTÍN ZIQUIN: I don't know why I'm supposed to speak in front of people. I don't know why. But here we are, as you know, in Easo, a Romanized Basque city, and the Christians are about to celebrate first the feast of Oel and then Christmas. At the same time, the Basques will be celebrating the winter solstice, the old feast of Joel, and my wise colleague Chiqui and I, naturally, like the devils we are, will be on the side of the idolators and against the Christians. The celebrations here are pretty fast. Chiqui and I excite people and get them to sin. It's not very difficult, scarcely any effort. The taverns breed vice faster than the bushes by the river. When they dance the *zirri,* the Paternoster croaks. The girls in this town are such . . . warm little muffins—warm as boiling water. Some jokers compare them to potatoes—cool to the naked eye, but once they're heated a bit, they burn your fingers when you pick them up. Our mission, as my honorable colleague Doctor Chiqui has told you, is to see that Jaun and his manservant don't get themselves baptized. With this in mind, Chiqui "cultivates" Jaun, while I "cultivate" Basurdi. In short, you know me now, and so that you'll know me better, here's my song:

> Martín Ziquin
> Erregueren sorguin
> Tipula eta gatz
> Ipurdian atz.

(Martín the Dirty, wizard to the king; onion and salt, and itch in the arse.)

SOMEONE IN THE AUDIENCE: What a filthy fellow!

AN OLD WOMAN: What a scandal! I believe you said "arse," did you not?

ANOTHER OLD WOMAN: Yes, he said "arse."

AN OLD WOMAN: The end of the world is approaching!

THE CHIEF OF POLICE: This is a piece of immorality. Officers, keep an eye on the spectator's hands, male . . . and female. The Society of Fathers is watching us. The Catholic Dames are sniffing around. If Martín Ziquin pronounces the word "arse" once more, throw him in jail at once, devil or not.

I. INVITATION

BASURDI: Master!

JAUN: What's up?

BASURDI: You'll let me out tonight, won't you?

JAUN: Well, why? Where are you going?

BASURDI: A few friends are giving a supper in Polus' wine cellar.

JAUN: You mean you have friends here?

BASURDI: Yes. A fellow named Chiqui is standing treat. He's an apprentice to Zugarramurdi, very distinguished. The supper's to be special.

JAUN: It is, eh?

BASURDI: We're to have *cocochas* of hake.

JAUN: The devil you say!

BASURDI: Tuna fish and onion.

JAUN: By god!

BASURDI: Some eels fished up this morning in the cove, very succulent.

JAUN: You make my mouth water.

BASURDI: And suckling lamb brought especially from Pampeyopolis.

JAUN: Why, that's a banquet!

BASURDI: And then, of course, there'll be anchovies and sardines. . .

JAUN: What a thought!

BASURDI: As for the wine, we'll have a steady stream of a Rioja claret, superior; and then, we'll have a second wine from Alicante, very superior; and last, a brandy that blows your lid off.

JAUN: Good heavens! You'll get drunk.

BASURDI: Oh, by the way, Chiqui told me that if you and Arbeláiz want to come to the supper, they'd be honored . . .

JAUN: Why, I'll tell Areláiz.

II. IN POLUS' WINE CELLAR

*Polus' wine cellar is near the central plaza in Easo. Inside it,
in a private chamber, are seated Lecochandeguius, Martín
Ziquin, Jaun, Arbeláiz, Basurdi, Shaguit, and two pedagogues,
Master Macrosophos and the Licentitate Sabihondus. The two
pedagogues wear threadbare cassocks and caps. Macrosophos
has bulging eyes and a long nose that has become red and
thick; Sabihondus is pompous and pedantic.*

LECOCHANDEGUIUS: Gentlemen, We are enchanted to receive into
the bosom of our Society two such illustrious foreigners as Jaun
de Alzate and the venerable Arbeláiz.

JAUN: Oh, is this a Society?

LECOCHANDEGUIUS: We are the Capelomagnicos of Vidaso, or in
the vulgate, Chapelaundis of the Bidasoa.

JAUN: Don't tell me any more.

LECOCHANDEGUIUS: Yes. We're the Chapelaundis of the Bidasoa,
the people of the big heart and the big beret. Among us there is
no bickering and no cheating. To live and laugh, to drink hearty
and laugh again, that's the motto and program of the Capelomagnicos.

CHIQUI: Comrade, you've spoken mightily, and I, though I'm no
more than a poor devil, am in agreement with you.

MACROSOPHOS: Me, too. Bibere et vivere; that's the great secret.

JAUN: Who is that fellow?

CHIQUI: That's Master Macrosophos, the great pedagogue, most
sapient in letters, human and divine, Doctor from Salamanca,
Alcalá, Paris, Pavia, etc. etc. He knows Latin as well as Cicero
himself; but his specialty is wine. Give him one of those coins
minted at Tours, big or little, and you'll see him in the tavern
at once. His red nose is the compass of the vinicultural science.

JAUN: What is Master Macrosophos working on at the moment?
What is his opinion on the important issues of the day?

MACROSOPHOS: My opinion is that we ought to start eating as
soon as possible.

SABIHONDUS: This Macrosophos is endowed with a penetration,
a sapience that is truly extraordinary and marvelous.

*They all start on the food, and for a long time silence reigns;
only the sound of eating is heard.*

CHIQUI: How do you like the supper?

SABIHONDUS: More than succulent.

CHIQUI: And this tavern wine?

MACROSOPHOS: Most excellent. With Salimbenus I can only say:
Mihit sapit dulcius vinum de taberna.
Quand quod aquae miscuit praesulis pincerna.

Do you understand Latin, Jaun?

JAUN: This Latin I do, since it's particularly Low, almost Castilian. Only I don't know what *pincerna* means.

MACROSOPHOS: The wine-pourer, or, in this case, the tavernkeeper.

As the supper draws to an end, a bevy of local beauties enters the chamber.

CHIQUI: Friend Jaun!

JAUN: What is it?

CHIQUI: I'd like you to meet Miss Napper, the seamstress; just call her Thimble; she dances the fandango like the angels themselves.

JAUN: Charmed to meet you.

CHIQUI (*to Arbeláiz*): This is La Gashina of Ciburu, from the tinkers' quarter in St.-Jean-de-Luz. A little devil in skirts. Watch over her lovingly.

ARBELÁIZ: With a thousand loving details.

CHIQUI: This is Choralda, the fisherwoman.

MACROSOPHOS: *Pulchra et satis pinguis,* or, in the vulgate, pretty and plump. She reminds one of the Venus Calipiga.

CHIQUI: This is La Erua, and this is La Ariña. And now, my vestal virgins, you may have whatever you want, be it a pastry, or a cup of wine, or anything you'd like.

The girls eat and drink.

LECOCHANDEGUIUS: Giddyup! Let's get going. On to the music.

SHAGUIT: Chomin, jozac trompeta;
                    Pello, non dec conqueta?

(Chomin, play the trumpet; Pello, where's your cup?)

MACROSOPHOS: I've still got some work to do here. (*He points to a large creampuff and some full bottles.*) I want to be left alone for a moment with this handsome pastry, made of artolagamum, or, to use the vulgate, puff paste.

SABIHONDUS: We can't move. *Non possumus.*

BASURDI: I don't see why we should leave this cozy corner. We're in Easo, in the best tavern in Easo, in the best room of the tavern, at a good supper. I'm for staying.

SABIHONDUS: This syllogism in sorites, or chain argument, convinces me.

BASURDI: Sorites! I don't know what that is.

SABIHONDUS: I'll give you a good example, in Latin.

BASURDI: In Latin? For me?

SABIHONDUS: Yes, in the Latin of Seneca.

> Qui prudens est, et temperans est;
> Qui temperans est, et constans est;
> Qui constans est, et imperturbatus est;

MACROSOPHOS:

> Qui imperturbatus est, et sine tristitia est;
> Qui sine tristitia est, et beatus est;

SABIHONDUS:

> Ergo prudens beatus est, et prudentia
> Ad beatam vitam satis est.

BASURDI: Amen!

MACROSOPHOS: Just a moment. Give me time to finish off this bottle.

SABIHONDUS: We'll finish it together. . . There we go.

MACROSOPHOS: *Quod erat demonstrandum.* Let's go.

They all go out to the street, where people are rushing back and forth, shouting and screaming. Some men are drawing a wagon in which they have placed a straw puppet; the scene is lit by firebrands. The puppet is Olenzaro, a mythological figure, who represents the ancient olerías. *As he passes, people sing out:*

> Olenzaro, buru aundiya,
> Entendimentu gabia
> Bartarratzian eran emendu
> Amar erruco zaguia.
> Au urde tripa aundia
> Zagar ustelez bestia!
> Orra, orra, gure Olenzaro,
> Pipa artzendubenic
> Ishirita dago.

(Olenzaro, that big knucklehead, last night polished off a ten quart skinful of wine. What a big-gutted pig, stuffed with rotten apples! There he is, our Olenzaro, with his pipe in his mouth and seated on his butt.)

MACROSOPHOS: What is this business about Olenzaro, friend Arbeláiz?

ARBELÁIZ: I think it's a mockery of the Basque religion. Olentzar is old Oel, the one in the old feast of Joel.

MACROSOPHOS: I understand. Joel, Yoel, Oel, Oelzarra, Olenzaro. What you say is quite possible.

ARBELÁIZ: Olenzaro has been painted as a brutish type, lacking intelligence. He's been represented as a charcoal-maker, since he's connected with fire and Sun rites. The Christians have him become a convert to Catholicism.

JAUN: Let's go to the plaza, little Thimble. I feel as agile as a boy.

CHIQUI: Giddyup! Let's all go there.

SHAGUIT: Bat, bi, iru, lau,
                  Ezconduda mundu au
                  Bost, sei, zazpi, zortzi,
                  Diabruarequin. Ederqui.

(One, two, three, four: The world has gotten married: Five, six, seven, eight: To the Devil. That's good enough for us.)

LECOCHANDEGUIUS: Aufa! Aufa! Long live the Capelomagnicos!

SHAGUIT: Bederatzi, amar, amaica,
                  Fraile bat arratoya,
                  Amabi, amairu, amalau.
                  Ezcomberriyac mesa eman du gaur,
                  Amabost, amasei, amazazpi,
                  Ez gabiltza gaizqui.

(Nine, ten, eleven: A ratty friar: Twelve, thirteen, fourteen: Has said mass for the newlyweds: Fifteen, sixteen, seventeen: We're not doing so bad.)

SABIHONDUS: *Bene, bene.* This is a song to set the step. I see that, despite your being an ignorant man, friend Shaguit, you know some delightful songs.

CHIQUI: Well, here we are in the plaza. Everyone start dancing!

ARBELÁIZ: I, in truth, I don't know how . . . A holy man like me . . .

LECOCHANDEGUIUS: Just snuggle up close to your partner; that's all there is to it.

SABIHONDUS: Is that all you have to do? Get close?

CHIQUI: That's all.

ARBELAÍZ: Why, this is a fandango!

CHIQUI: Yes.

MACROSOPHOS: *Fandangus libidinosus . . . tripudius hilarius.*

CHIQUI: And now for the quadrille in the French fashion. Each man has a right to kiss his partner, but don't overdo it.

ARBELÁIZ: Why, this is a cancan!

SABIHONDUS: *Cancanis scandalosus.*

MARTÍN ZIQUIN: And now for the run around town. Each man with his mate. Hand around the wineskin! Beat the drum hard! Ju . . . ju . . . aufa!

III. CHRISTMAS EVE

A few days have elapsed and Christmas Eve has come.
Christmas Eve!
The bells ring out.
It is the day of the birth of the gods, Mithra and the Sun,
Jesus and Bacchus.
Joy! Joy!
Christmas Eve!
A light shines in the window of a humble house. The fam-
ily has gathered around the fireplace, in the light and love of
the fire.
The sacred mistletoe hangs from the ceiling.
Young men and the old sing and play the tambourine.
Joy! Joy!
Christmas Eve!
Someone has spoken of the absent ones, of the travelers who
travel the earth and sea, of the sadness of life.
Sadness! Sadness!
Christmas Eve!
Someone has persisted and has recalled the voyage to the
country from whence no traveler returns.
Sadness! Sadness!
Christmas Eve!
Joy of living. Christmas Eve. Sadness of life. Solstice of the
sun. The mystery of things. O birth of babies! O children's
crèche! O Christmas of Dickens!
Joyfulness! Joyfulness! Sadness! Sadness!

IV. IN THE CHURCH

JAUN: The truth is that we're splicing our ropes in a highly in-
decent manner, Arbeláiz.
ARBELÁIZ: Yes, we're not exactly shining with virtue. If they find
out in Alzate, we'll be in for it.
JAUN: And with good reason. But, in any case, this will all soon
be over.
They meet Ederra and Pamposha.
EDERRA: Father! Just visit the church! If you could see how pretty

they've made it! If you could see how the lights shine and could smell the incense! Today they're singing carols in Basque.

PAMPOSHA: O, yes Jaun, come with us. The church is very pretty. *Somewhat abashed, Jaun enters the Christian temple. The voice of women and children, accompanied by tambourines, are heard.*

CAROL   Olenzaro juan zaigu
Mendira lanera
Intenziyuarequin
Icatza eguitera
Aditu zubenian
Jesus jayozala
Etorrizan corrica
Parte ematera.

(Olenzaro has left us to go to the forest to make charcoal. As soon as he hears of the birth of Jesus, he comes running to announce the news.)

CHIQUI (*in Jaun's ear*): What lack of style! How they corrupt the language! What would the academicians at the University of Lezo say?

CAROL   Artzai buru zuri bi
Anthon eta Peru
Belengo portalera
Etorri zaizqui gu
Zartudira barrena
Manuelcho en gana
Presente eguindiyote
Arcumecho bana.

(Two white-haired shepherds, Antón and Pedro, have appeared and enter the gate at Bethlehem; once in the presence of little Manny, they each offer him the gift of a small lamb.)

CHIQUI: What vulgarity! What slop! I can't understand how Basques can get enthused at these oriental myths passed on by Jews and Africans!

CAROL   Ay au egunen
Zoragarriya
Au alegriya
Pechuan
Jartzac guerrico
Josi berriya
Chapel garbiya
Buruan
Capoy parea
Escuan

Onlaco gaba
Santuan.

(Ay, what an exciting day! What joy in my heart! Gird on the
new-made belt, put the new hat on your head, and take two
brace of capons in your hand, on this so holy night.)

CHIQUI: What lack of poetry! What heavy going! How common
is Christianity! How little art in all this!

CAROL   Arratz gozoa,
Nere Cathalin,
Oberic ecin
Arquitu
Artzan mantalan
Usa cumea
Caicu esnea
Neurritu
Gauza gueyago
Baneuque
Zuretzat Jesús
Liraque

(A more beautiful night, my Catherine, could scarce be found;
take two squabs to put in your apron, and put some milk in
the wooden jar. If I had anything else to give, it would be for
you, my Jesus.)

CHIQUI: Bah! Bah! What claptrap! What vulgarities! What ratty
music!

(*Catching sight of Martín Ziquin, who has come into the
church*): What's the trouble?

MARTÍN ZIQUIN: The fact is, the girls are waiting outside: The
Thimble and the others!

JAUN (*to Ederra and La Pamposha*): I'm going out a minute.
My friends are calling . . .

V. THE TWO PEDAGOGUES

*Larrechipius' tavern boasts a large cellar containing enormous
barrels of cider, and, at the back, a room with a window overlooking a garden. Gathered in this room are the same group
of people who had been at the supper in Polus' tavern a few
days previously.*

JAUN: Basurdi!

BASURDI: What?

JAUN: Try to conduct yourself in a more decent fashion. You're eating like a pig.

BASURDI: The same as everyone else.

JAUN: No; the rest are not doing it in such an ugly manner, nor with such anxiety as you display. You must understand that no manual on education or manners allows you to wash your face in the salad.

BASURDI (*aside*): I hope you blow up! You're always hounding me.

JAUN: Now that people of more quality and refinement than you accept you as a table companion, the least you can do is conceal the ever present thread of your gross and plebeian nature.

BASURDI: I don't know what it is I do wrong.

JAUN: That's enough! Shut up! Let me hear the discussion between these two wise men.

SABIHONDUS: Now I say yes, a man *can* decently and honestly invite another man to drink, *ab hoc et ab hac,* a glass *quod dicitur* mug, shot glass, cup, etc., etc., and whether it be of muscat, malmsey, fighting red wine, *et sic de coeteris.*

MACROSOPHOS: My rejoinder is no, that one must leave off drinking *ad arbitrium,* and that in the Capitularies of Charlemagne one is prohibited from forcing anyone to drink, for it states: *Ut nemini liceat alterum cogere ad bibendum.*

BASURDI: Amen!

JAUN: Quiet, you animal! Especially when scientific points are being discussed.

BASURDI (*aside*): I hope you drop dead! You're always against me.

SABIHONDUS (*offering Macrosophos a cup*): So that if I, Illustrious Magister, offer you this pulchritudinous cup, filled with generous wine up to the very edges, I thereby sin against amity?

MACROSOPHOS (*taking the cup*): I make distinctions, dear colleague, I make distinctions. If I did not happen to like the wine that you proffer me in this pulchritudinous cup and you forced me to drink it for friendship's sake, then you would be sinning; but, I like it, and I drink it . . . ergo you do not sin. (*He drains off the cup.*)

SABIHONDUS: *Per Jovem! Indubie,* or in the vulgate, indubitably. But, I could not know, a priori, whether you would like wine or not; I lack certitude, *adoequatio rei et intellectus . . . ergo* I err.

MACROSOPHOS: *Nego majorem* . . . You know well enough that I like wine.

SABIHONDUS: I know it, but only in an empirical manner, and a posteriori I do not have a knowledge of the universals.

MACROSOPHOS: No; you have the certainty . . . *certitudo.*

SABIHONDUS: *Per Jovem!* And how could I have it, *magister?*

MACROSOPHOS: Because *Natura abhorret vacuum,* and my stomach is always a vacuum.

SABIHONDUS: And supposing it were full?

MACROSOPHOS: It would always have empty places. How many classes of vacuums are there, after all? Two, isn't that so? The vacuum *concervatum* and the vacuum *disseminatum.* The vacuum concervatum is the vacuum pertaining to whatever is within walls, as for instance, my stomach. Well now, I ask: In my stomach is there or is there not movement? There is a movement of solids and of liquids. And wherever there is movement, there is a vacuum . . . *ergo* in my stomach there is a vacuum.

SABIHONDUS: *Per Jovem!* You carry your sharpness too far.

MACROSOPHOS: You simply want to teach a fish how to swim: *Piscem natare doces.*

CHIQUI: Macrosophos is a well of wisdom, a pit of science, or rather, a barrel of science.

JAUN: Yes, he seems like a wise man.

CHIQUI: He's a master of *trivium* and *quadrivium.*

JAUN: I don't know what that is.

CHIQUI: *Trivium,* that is, grammar, rhetoric, and logic; *quadrivium* comprehends arithmetic, geometry, astronomy, and music.

JAUN: That's a lot.

CHIQUI: He can teach them to you, if you like.

JAUN: I'm a little old for such chores. Besides, I don't live here.

CHIQUI: As far as your being old is concerned, that's not true. As for his being in Easo, that doesn't matter, for Macrosophos might just as well be in Alzate.

JAUN: But Macrosophos must have some occupation.

CHIQUI: No, at the moment he's without work. And even if you offered him only a small wage, he'd go, especially if you offered him plenty to drink.

JAUN: I don't know. I'm not carried away by the idea.

CHIQUI: It's an excellent chance to get an education. Do you know how to write, friend Jaun?

JAUN: More or less.

CHIQUI: And read?

JAUN: Yes, pretty well.

CHIQUI: Well, you can have a teacher in Alzate, if you want.

THIMBLE: Drop that stuff. The point is to have a good time.

JAUN: Ah, Thimble, Thimble; you've got the fire of youth about you; I'm too old already to keep up with you.

THIMBLE: But you're a pretty sporty type.

MARTÍN ZIQUIN: Wine! More wine! Let's see now, who's the queen here? Who rules in the tavern of Larrechipius? We're still short of combustible material to put us in tune.

BASURDI: Wine! More wine!

SABIHONDUS: Egregious Macrosophos!

MACROSOPHOS: What is it, most sapient Sabihondus?

SABIHONDUS: Do you know the Defense of the Drunks of Salimbenus, distinguished Macrosophos?

MACROSOPHOS: Yes: (*Reciting*):

> Tertio capitulo memero tabernam
> Illiam nullo tempore sprevi, neque spernam
> Donec sanctos angelos venientes cernam
> Cantantes pro mortuo requiem oeternam.

BASURDI: *Ora pro nobis.*

JAUN: This fellow has stuck his foot in it again.

MACROSOPHOS:

> Meum est propositum in taberna mori
> Vinum sit oppositum morientis ori
> Ut dicant cum venerint angelorum chori
> Deus sit proitius tanto potatori.

BASURDI: Amen!

CHIQUI: Let's go out into the street.

SABIHONDUS: *Pergamus deambulatum.*

THE DEMIJOHN (*addressing the empty tavern*): What a way to drink! What brutes! With people like that to contend with, there's no demijohn alive, nor a carboy either, that's capable of putting up a resistance.

THE CASK (*by way of answer*): You're right. I've noticed the same thing. And just look at what a belly I've got. It's not surprising that you complain.

VI. IN THE STREET

SABIHONDUS: Gentlemen: We must sing a Bacchic and yet suburban song. Let's see now, you, Shaguit! Let's hear a jocund Basque song.

SHAGUIT: Here goes:

> Tra, la, la, la, la, len,
> Instante bat egon gaiten.

Tra, la, la, la, la, la, lú,
Oraiño untsa guituzu,
Sarriño joanen dituzu,
Joan bear eta ecin parti
Erori eta ecin chuti,
Chacurrac! Guau!
Gatuac! Ñau!
Arnuac untala eman nu gaur.

(Tra, la, la, la, la, len: We're in this one spot for an instant:
Tra, la, la, la, la, la, lú: So far we're in fine shape: We're thinking of leaving at once: We must move on and yet we can't: We
fall down and can't stand up: The dog goes Guau!: The cat goes
Ñau!: Today the wine has worked this way.)

BASURDI: Hi . . . ju . . . ju . . . ju!

JAUN: Basurdi, you're a smart aleck. Shut up! Don't call attention
to yourself. We're disgracing ourselves. What will they say about
the lord of Alzate if they see him in this state?

BASURDI: They'll say he's drunk.

JAUN: And does that mean nothing to you?

BASURDI: Nothing at all.

JAUN: Is that the respect you show your master?

BASURDI: This is supposed to be a celebration. What the devil!
Every man for himself!

SABIHONDUS: How about another song . . . something satirical
and bold.

BASURDI: Chicharrua ta berdela,
                     Chicharrua ta berdela.

(Yellowjack and needlefish, Yellowjack and needlefish.)

CHIQUI: Friend Basurdi, you've got the voice of a calf . . . nice
and dull. . .

SABIHONDUS: That is a most base and vulgar song. It's true that
the Muses love alternating songs: *Amant alterna Camaenae:* but
let us not descend so far. Let's see now: Shaguit, you who are
propinquous and potent, or propinquiously potent, though you
may be ignorant, sing us a song, more obsolescent and less con-
suetudinous or common.

SHAGUIT: Ollarrac Jotzian cucurucú
                     Orduan echera juango guera gu:
                     Batzuec ala,
                     Bertziac onla;
                     Errana gatic acholaric eztugu.
                     Cucurucú!
                     Nor guera gu?
                     Alzatarrac guerade gu.

(When the rooster sings cock-a-doodle-do, then we'll know it's time to go home: some this way, some that way: We're not afraid they'll talk about us: Cock-a-doodle-do! Who are we, who? We're from Alzate.)

JAUN: We're disgracing ourselves.

CHORUS OF INVISIBLE SPIRITS: Jaun! Jaun! Your soul is growing dim and sinking into the mire. You must not fall into bestial vice; only think, reflect; life is more than wallowing in pleasures as in the muck. The spirit is a diamond that must be polished.

JAUN: I'm going to quit this quadrille of miserable drunks and go home. I've had enough!

VII. PAMPOSHA

As Jaun reaches his brother-in-law's house, he catches sight of Pamposha, who is standing at a window.

JAUN: What are you doing at the window, Pamposha?

PAMPOSHA: I'm looking at the stars.

JAUN: You look like the goddess of the night.

PAMPOSHA: Who knows? Perhaps I am.

JAUN: You have the same effect on me as a magical apparition.

PAMPOSHA: Well, I'm quite real, Jaun.

JAUN: I imagine you are. It's very cold to be standing there without moving.

PAMPOSHA: I'm not cold.

JAUN: I'm not either.

PAMPOSHA: Are you back for the night?

JAUN: Yes.

PAMPOSHA: Then I'll come down and open up for you.

Pamposha comes down, opens the door, and the two go upstairs.

JAUN: Are you going back to your window?

PAMPOSHA: Yes. It's such a beautiful night! Do you suppose it's true that each of us has a star of his own?

JAUN: I don't know. Have you found yours?

PAMPOSHA: I? Not yet.

JAUN: It will be hard to find. They don't have names!

PAMPOSHA: Even if they had them, I wouldn't know how to find mine. I don't know how to read.

JAUN: You can't read?

PAMPOSHA: No. I can't read letters. But I can read my own heart.

JAUN: And what do you read in your heart?

PAMPOSHA: I read that it's very sad. On this happy night for others, my heart is in mourning. It's like a bird imprisoned in a cage, trying to escape.

JAUN: Shall I leave you?

PAMPOSHA: Why?

JAUN: Do you believe in the Christian Devil, Pamposha?

PAMPOSHA: Why do you ask me that?

JAUN: Because I feel possessed by him. I see you like an ogre might see raw meat. Goodbye!

PAMPOSHA: You say goodbye, but you don't move.

JAUN: You can put me out. I haven't sufficient will to leave. Put me out, or let me kiss you.

PAMPOSHA: Kiss me, if you like.

VIII. DAWN

JAUN: What shall we do now? And you a girl that her father has placed under my protection! I've certainly betrayed my trust.

PAMPOSHA: It's not your fault, Jaun. I'm to blame for everything.

JAUN: I've taken away your honor, as the Castilians say.

PAMPOSHA: My honor? From where did you take it? I never noticed.

JAUN: It's a manner of speaking . . . figurative, you know.

PAMPOSHA: I would have been aware of it, if you'd robbed me of anything.

JAUN: I feel like a hawk who has pounced on a dove.

PAMPOSHA: I must say the dove is very happy in the claws of the hawk.

JAUN: Yes, but what shall we do?

PAMPOSHA: Well I shall go on to Sara, just as I planned.

JAUN: Aren't you in despair? Don't you hate me?

PAMPOSHA: No, why should I? I chose you as I might have chosen someone else. Do you think that men are the only ones who have a right to choose?

JAUN: What a marvelous lack of conscience! When are you leaving?

PAMPOSHA: The day after tomorrow.

JAUN: Would you like it if we were to see each other tomorrow and the day after?

PAMPOSHA: Yes, my dear Jaun, yes.

JAUN: Here?

PAMPOSHA: Here.

JAUN: Don't you hate me? Don't you feel any rancor toward me?

PAMPOSHA: What for?

JAUN: Because of . . . the question of honor.

PAMPOSHA: No, no. The only thing I feel now, you know, is a certain tiredness.

IX. PROJECTS

JAUN: The truth is that I'm committing atrocities, acts unbefitting my age. And that Pamposha has gone off so serene and easy. What confidence in destiny! I'm leaving too. I've reached a decision, and that's something. Following Chiqui's advice, I've decided to study. It's shameful that I should be ignorant of so many things.

I've purchased a number of parchments from a peddler. One is on Prognostics, and is in the vulgate. Another, in Latin, is titled *Secretum secretorum naturae,* and was written by an English monk, so they say, a certain doctor Mirabilis, who constructed a steel head that could talk. I don't understand very much of this *Secretum,* but it's given me a strange desire to know more.

There's nothing for it but to learn. I've got to get a closer look at Science. And it will help me to stop playing the fool. I'll find out how much truth there is in the ideas of the cultists. I'm humiliated by the way they look down on us.

Chiqui has spoken to Macrosophos, and Macrosophos will come to Alzate. He's a great pedagogue, and with him I'll be able to delve deeper into the most abstruse sciences, and magic, and alchemy, and astrology, and mathematics. What horizons stretch out before me! In Alzate, I'll have time to spare. I'll buy learned books in Castilian and Latin, I'll bring in spheres and astrolabes, I'll submerge myself in the profundities of science, and, like the bees, I'll suck knowledge from all the flowers of human wisdom, and distill a sweet and delicious honey for my own exclusive use.

X. LEAVE TAKING

EDERRA: Are you going already, Father?

JAUN: Yes, my daughter.

EDERRA: Tell mother to come here before my wedding, that I love her very much, and that I must talk to her.

JAUN: I'll tell her, my dear.

EDERRA: I'd like to ask you for a favor, though I don't dare.

JAUN: Tell me.

EDERRA: Father Prudencio, the rector of the church at Vera, ordered a standing cross made here in Easo, and I'd like you to bring it to him.

JAUN: That's a rather annoying request.

EDERRA: No, there wouldn't be any difficulty; you can carry the cross in your saddle bag, and the stick can go separately.

JAUN: All right. So that you can't say that I'm not obliging, I'll take it.

EDERRA: Goodbye, Father dear!

JAUN: Goodbye, little one!

XI. THE CAPTAIN

Jaun, Arbeláiz, Master Macrosophos, Chiqui, Martín Ziquin, Shaguit, and Basurdi set out, some on horseback, others afoot, along the Bidasoa road. It's a winter day, with a gray sky and a drizzling rain. As the party passes between Behovia and Biriatu, they are suddenly surrounded by numerous men. The strangers are a party of bandits.

THE CAPTAIN: Halt where you are!

JAUN: What's the matter?

THE CAPTAIN: I said: Halt!

JAUN: What for?

THE CAPTAIN: You're under arrest! Come now, your money!

Jaun takes out his sword and begins to rain two-handed blows on the bandit chief, who, however, wards off all the blows, laughing all the while. The chief at length disarms Jaun and throws his sword into the river. Jaun thereupon lays hold of the stick to the cross he has been carrying and showers blows on the robbers to the left and right of him.

JAUN: Damnation! Thunder-bolts on your heads! Loafers! *Jaun delivers so many blows that he breaks the stick, and is left with only a splinter in his hand. The chief wraps a gray cape which covers him up to his eyes around himself, gazes ironically around at the scene, gives vent to a strident though muffled burst of laughter, and gallops off. The robber band flees, leaving a few of its men strewn on the field. Chiqui lashes the backs of the fleeing thieves with a whip, calling them dirty pigs as he does so. Macrosophos and Basurdi have hidden.*

ARBELÁIZ: You're strong as ever, Jaun! Young as ever!

JAUN: No, I'm not. Ow! This arm hurts me. I've lost the habit of handling weapons.

ARBELÁIZ: Of weapons, perhaps; but as for what's left of that stick . . .

MACROSOPHOS: You manage, friend Jaun, in a pulchritudinous and prepotent manner the *argumentum baculinum,* or staff argument.

JAUN: How many down?

BASURDI: There are three or four on the ground.

JAUN: Are they dead?

CHIQUI: Stupefied by your stick, nothing more. You were irrepressible, untiring. What a way of flailing!

ARBELÁIZ: A specialist in flogging!

JAUN (*to Basurdi*): What are you up to?

BASURDI: I'm going to remove what's removable from the fallen.

JAUN: A coward at fighting and a hero at pillaging.

BASURDI (*aside*): Drop dead! When you're not looking, I'll get the goods. (*A moment passes before he dares to look around again.*) Where have they gone? Where are the thieves? What curs! They played dead, and then got away.

MACROSOPHOS: This bears the mark of diabolic art.

JAUN: Did they get away with anything of ours?

CHIQUI: The cross is the only thing missing; everything else has been recuperated.

JAUN: What a strange mischance! What a nuisance! And after Ederra had gone through such a rigamarole about it.

CHIQUI (*to Martín Ziquin*): We've gotten it away from him. Urtzi Thor, our master, can rest easy now.

Intermezzo

THE CHORUS: Urtzi Thor! Urtzi Thor! Why have you descended Mount Larrun? Why do you gaze in melancholy from Urruña over the French Basque land, so fair and smiling? What sorrows weigh upon your heart? Why do you wear an air of anger and sadness?

URTZI THOR: Farewell! Farewell Pyrenees beside the Ocean! Rolling luminous mountainsides! Green and temperate valleys! Sonorous resounding towns! Farewell proud and ancient Basques, and joyous youth with eagles' beaks! Farewell joyful, dancing girls! I am returning to my frozen wastes. Farewell! Farewell!

The Inhabitants Along the Bidasoa

THE AUTHOR: I don't rightly know who ever set me to writing a conventional fantasy which scarcely can look to real life for approbation. True enough, I don't feel any great enthusiasm for realistic literature, but I feel even less for rhetoric.

I like to take my characters and types and details from reality, and then organize and dispose of them according to an individual sentiment; now then, to take them from literature already made is sometimes a disagreeable duty. Nevertheless, considering my aims, there is no alternative. Under the circumstances, I will give free rein to the old myths that hover over the landscape of my locale, though I reserve the right to dress them up in my own manner.

I. ENDARLAZA

It is night time. The travelers, retarded in their journey by the battle with the highwaymen, have reached Endarlaza at nightfall, and have now taken refuge in a natural shelter. The road, running along the banks of the Bidasoa, has become a quagmire.

BASURDI: In all truth I'm very frightened in such a place as this, so sad and dark. We should have gone back to Easo; it would have been the best thing to do. Bugs and beasts, bandits and monsters . . . how do I know what's lurking here? To think that I could be stretched out in my bed! This Jaun never thinks of anything but impossibilities.

MACROSOPHOS: What a dramatic and melancholic landscape! I wonder why we are adventuring in such parts. I'm beginning to feel a certain fright that always unnerves me.

JAUN (*aside*): The road hereabouts is something to think about, and my companions, with the exception of Chiqui and his friend, are afraid. I'll pretend I don't notice their alarm. . . Well, gentlemen, we're going to spend a few hours here, and at dawn we'll go on.

They all stretch out on the ground in the shelter, while one man stands guard outside.

The place is sad, bleak, and wild looking. The river, running almost in a straight line, lies in the depth of the valley. The water of the river, deep in its narrow channel, sleeps, black and immobile, on its rock bed. On either side of the shelter stretch forests of swamp oak.

On the opposite bank of the river, that somber and magical mirror, lies an old abandoned foundry, covered now with vines, its flight of stone stairs running down to the water's edge.

The moon shines in the sky and illuminates half of the landscape, outlining the large boulders in the mysterious gorge, which is narrow and tall, full of a sinister peace and a somber immobility.

The water murmurs sadly. The noise of the wind is heard in the trees, and sounds like the distant rumor of the tide.

From time to time the shrill cry of the owl is heard, and sometimes the swift running steps of some animal or human among the trees.

There is something perfidious and terrifying in the ravine that yawns in the night, in the sky without wind or clouds, in the moon itself, which gazes down palely from the black sky, as if she too were alarmed and uneasy.

II. THE BIDASOA

THE RIVER: I am a small river, but of greater fame and grace than many a large river. I have been mentioned by Strabo, Ptolemy, and Pliny.

I have two brothers, the Nive and the Urumea, and a small sister, the Nivelle.

In me there is something of the severity of Navarre, something of the mildness of Guipúzcoa and the graciousness of France.

Alternately Navarrese, Guipúzcoan, French, from Chapitelaco-Arria to Cape Higuer de San Telmo I am international. The churches of Pamplona and Bayonne have attempted to dominate my banks. The one at Bayonne asserted that it encompassed *usque ad Sanctum Sebastianum,* and the one at Pamplona, *usque ad flumen quod dicitur Vidasao.*

I have merely flowed on, without looking into the claims of one see or the other.

I gather up the songs of my rivulets, who supply me with

water, rivulets of exotic and picturesque names, such as the Hell, the Hog's Tail, and the Chasm of the Lamias.

I can boast some miraculous fountains, such as the one at Santa Leocadia de Legasa and the other at San Jaun de Yanci, some clear springs, and grottoes where the water is filtered drop by drop.

I flow through wide and sunny valleys and through narrow ravines; I reflect the green sides of mountains, the palaces and huts on my banks, the small hamlets filled with old houses whose fronts are decorated with a coat of arms that takes up half the façade.

In winter I low like a bull and I hurl along in furious spume-filled waves; in summer I form into green, placid backwaters, and I advance among the rocks undulating like a snake.

At dusk, my surface turns blue, and thousands of stars sleep in my depths at night.

Tranquil and idyllic at Oyeregui and in Narvarte, I take on a tragic air when my waves, embittered by the waters of the ocean, contend off the bar in the Bay of Chingudy, between the cliffs of the shadowy Jaizquibel and the point of Santa Ana.

Along my banks and across me have traveled the peoples of Europe as they descended to Spain, and later, to Africa, and the nations of Africa have come this way as they ascended to Europe. I can recall men bearing stone axes and bronze axes; I also recall Iberians and Celts, Phoenicians and Greeks, Romans and Goths, Swabians and Franks and Moors.

I have known Pompey and Augustus' captains; Henry IV of Castile and Louis XI of France; Charles V and Francis I; Condé and the Duke of Alba; Louis XIV and Mazarin; the handsome Don Beltrán de la Cueva, who fructified the royal bed of Henry IV of Castile, and the no less handsome Admiral Bonnivet, the rival in love of Francis I, who laid siege to Gaste-zularra, the castle nearest Behovia. I have seen Napoleon confer with his generals, and Wellington with his; I have contemplated the feats of Soult, Longa, Jáuregui the Shepherd, Latour d'Auvergne, and Leguía; I have followed Mina, and Zumalacár-regui in his forays; and I have seen Fabvier and Caron; I have watched Armando Carrel hoist his republican flag in Behovia against the French of Angoulême; I have likewise saluted illustrious voyagers, like Goya and Velázquez, Madame D'Aulnoy and Victor Hugo.

True enough, I now offer very little enchantment along my banks, especially on the Spanish side, which is strewn with the ugly barracks of the border guard. Still, I have hopes for a better future, for a certain savant, the Bachelor of Arts and Sciences Juan de Itzea, has prognosticated that some day I will mark the site of an independent republic: a republic without flies, without friars, and without border guards.

Stronghouses of the Baztán, with the wooden top floor! Mossy convent of Arizcun! Palace of Reparacea! Massive tower of Ursúa! Black castle of Lesaca! Bridge of San Miguel de Vera! I contemplate you, for centuries now, by day and by night! I also see Biriatu, which spies on me from its height, and the island of the Pheasants, which I am slowly carrying away. And finally, I spread out in the Bay of Chingudy, in whose waters the blackish houses of Fuenterrabía and the white houses of Hendaye stare at each other, and from where Iparraguirre sang the wonders of his country, and where the French corsair Pellot de Montvieux lived.

But now I must be off. Today there is to be a gathering—which we call *batzarre,* in this our Endarlaza—of all the inhabitants along my banks, and I now yield them the word.

CHORUS OF BASQUE SPIRITS: Since you have arranged for our gathering, here we are, O Bidasoa! But you must understand that we lead a most fugitive existence, completely precarious, that we are in hiding, proscribed, fleeing always from the sound of the bells, and prayers, and holy water, and the Asperges and the hyssop. We no longer have a place to take shelter, and Latin pursues us relentlessly with its *saecula saeculorum* through all the corners of the world.

III. THE FOG

THE FOG: I am the advance guard of the Gulf Stream; I approach across the sea, traversing endless leagues; I pass through the narrow gap of the Bidasoa, between Mount Larrun and the Rock of Aya, and I halt briefly around the beech forests of Velate. I sport among the ravines reddened with autumn, and lay hold of the sharp peaks, and submerge in waves of fog the oak forests where Basque liberties and the sacred mistletoe were born.

I lend enchantment and poetry to the night with my blue veils; I stretch languidly across the waters of the river; and, under the caresses of the sun, I undo myself in the air.

IV. THE DRY LEAVES

THE LEAVES: Aufa! Thither and yon! To sport and play! To run! To whirl in whimsical round dances through upper air! For too long now we've been enslaved, forced to lie quiet!

Aufa! Aufa! Through the gray sky of autumn, over the tops of the trees, we'll sail through the air as if we had wings . . .

V. THE GLOWWORM

THE GLOWWORM: I am the star of the arbors and foliage; I shine among the leaves and the grass as Sirius might shine on a winter's night. I am the moon of the moor, the moon of the copse, and, in the wetness of dewy nights, my light shines forth white and blue like the mystery of a lamp.

VI. THE TOAD

THE TOAD: It seems that witches use us now for their spells. They often whip us, dress us in annoying little capes, and force us to swallow a consecrated wafer in order to manufacture supposed venoms with our blood. Men, those bloodthirsty animals, catch us and spit us on a stick, so that we can die a nice slow death.

We're actually easy going and sweet-tempered; our chief pleasure is to play the flute at twilight; we don't feel a bit diabolic or venomous; we'd like to be loved, and the truth is that solitude weighs upon us when we hear, in the little hole in which we chance to dwell, the beating of our own poor heart.

MACROSOPHOS: The opinion current among savants is that there exists an inflexible and insuperable hatred between the toad and the spider, and that combats between them are often held, in which the spider not infrequently emerges victorious.

JAUN: I've never seen such a battle. It must be pure fantasy.

MACROSOPHOS: No. *Magister dixit.*

JAUN: When I see it, I'll believe it.

MACROSOPHOS: To doubt in that manner is to lack the proper scholastic spirit.

VII. THE LAMIAS

THE LAMIA: Pst! Pst!

JAUN: I hear a kind of hissing among the branches. Basurdi, look and see if there's anyone there.

BASURDI: I'm going.

THE LAMIA: Pst! Pst!

JAUN: I hear it again. I told you to look and see who's there.

BASURDI: I won't go.

JAUN: Why?

BASURDI: Because I'm afraid.

JAUN: You're afraid! Pig! Coward! (*Aside*): The fact is that I'm afraid too. (*Aloud*): And why are you afraid, I'd like to know?

BASURDI: I saw a white-skinned blonde in the foam of the river, carrying a distaff. It must be a lamia, a *mamurra,* half woman and half snake.

JAUN: Liar! Loafer! Bum! I'll crack your head open, for being a coward and a false man.

THE LAMIA: Pst! Pst! Jaun! Jaun!

JAUN: They're calling me. I'm coming!

SHAGUIT: We'll both go.

JAUN: Who is it? Who knows me hereabouts? Who's calling me?

THE LAMIA: It's me, a lamia. Come!

JAUN: I don't trust you. Come closer to the river bank. The mist from the river is bad for me.

THE LAMIA: They tell me you're going to turn Christian, Jaun. Is that true? Are you going to abandon us?

JAUN: No.

CHORUS OF LAMIAS: Come, Jaun! Today is our day, Saturday, *nesqueguna,* the day of the young woman who dispenses happiness. We'll carry you to palaces of diamonds and pearls, and you'll see us dance roundelays with the gnomes and the sprites. We'll spin for you, on golden distaffs, the finest cloths of slenderest threads, and we'll embroider silver stars in the fabric. We have some threads that are made of the rays of sunlight and moonlight; we make the most perfect headdresses, children's clothes, finery for brides, kerchiefs for elegant dames, and shrouds for the old. You'll see our enchanted spindles, spinning in the air with frenzy. Come, Jaun! You come too, Shaguit!

SHAGUIT: Come on, let's go with them.

JAUN: No, no. I've heard the tale of the ironworker who married one of you. . .

THE LAMIA: And he was happy.

JAUN: I heard that he pined away, turned yellow as a candle, and died when he found he had married a witch.

THE LAMIA: We're not witches. How can you, who live on the banks of the Lamiocingo-erreca, say that? Why, we never associate with witches. Near here, by the riverside, we have our stone Lamiarri, and at Zugarramurdi we have a special cave called Lamien-Lezca. In the French Basque country they think more highly of us every day. There, our gathering places are Atherey, the grotto at Isturitz, and the sacred fountain of Atharratz. Come!

JAUN: All your phrases haven't convinced me. Farewell!

MACROSOPHOS: What was it?

JAUN: A lamia.

MACROSOPHOS: The masters say that the lamias can take out and put back their eyes when they want. The lamia is a symbol of curiosity and self-love. In his treatise *De curiositate,* Plutarch speaks of a blind lamia who, when she wished to come out of her cave, took her eyes out of the box in which she always kept them.

JAUN: A strange whim.

MACROSOPHOS: Philostratus, the elder, represents lamias as being very lascivious, and he says, in his Life of *Apolonius of Tyana,* that they lure young men whom they wish to devour to their hiding places, and that they like sprightly lads who are good and fleshy.

VIII. THE BASA-JAON

BASURDI: Another monster! What a night! It's filled with phantoms.

Some glittering red eyes are seen peering from amid the foliage.

JAUN: Who are you, red-eyed monster?

BASA-JAON: I'm the terrible Basa-jaon.

JAUN: You seem a little timid to be so terrible.

BASA-JAON: The fact is I find myself in a precarious situation. Sometimes I think I'm a giant, with an enormous head, burly arms, and a mountain of a body; other times I think I'm nothing but fancy and smoke. I don't know whether I have any objective reality, if I exist in the world of phenomena, as a

disciple of Professor Kant would say, or if I'm a figment of
Monsieur Chaho's fantasy. I'm not accepted in any reunion of
Basque spirits; they laugh at me because I can't produce documents of identification. In such circumstances it is really *so*
disagreeable not to have any documents!

The Basa-jaon goes off sobbing.

JAUN: The poor devil!

MACROSOPHOS: I think this Basa-jaon is an impudent faker. He is,
at best, a sylph, a faun or a wood sprite who has gotten lost in
these latitudes and picked up the Basque language.

IX. THE SIRENS

THE SIRENS: We come from the Valley of Bertizarana, where
we are represented on the escutcheons of the houses, half-women
and half-fish, carrying a mirror in one hand and a comb in the
other.

Despite our being completely aquatic, we have adapted ourselves to life on land: we've forgotten our palaces of rock, foam,
and emerald, where we sang our mysterious antique songs, as
old as the world; forgotten, too, is the tumultuous dance of the
green waves, the dim islands of clouds, the thunder and lightning, and the whistle of the wind.

Our wild escapades on the backs of dolphins and tritons are
finished.

Now we sing along with the mermaids, to the accompaniment
of the rumor of fountains, on the banks of rivulets, in the midst
of the cane-brakes among the reeds and water lilies. We live in
open grottoes, behind curtains of clematis, perfumed with
sandalwood, and there we loll langorously.

Some call us seductive and false; we are no more so than are
your own women. As an ancient Castilian poet once wrote:

> Merely by their singing
> The siren, they say, deceives;
> Though 'tis past my conceiving
> What manner of gay deceiving
> Is not sweet to all Eves.

MACROSOPHOS: Who are they?

JAUN: They are sirens.

MACROSOPHOS: Sirens with wings?

JAUN: No, without.

MACROSOPHOS: True sirens have wings. Head, breasts, and arms of a woman; the rest, bird.

JAUN: Well, then, these are counterfeits; either that, or they've forgotten their wings.

X. WITCHES

THE WITCHES: We are Basque witches, persecuted by the Spanish Inquisitors, burned by the magistrates of Lancre and d'Espaignet. We are the Basque witches made famous by the rhetoric of the historian Michelet. We concoct potions and unguents, philters for love and philters for hate. We know all the wiles for deceiving a man; we know how to snuggle into the wool of a mattress, change ourselves into frogs and cats, and fly through the air on a broomstick as we sing: "Black stick, white stick, take me to the Sabbath!" We are put out of sorts by the rosemary branches of Holy Week, by scissors opened in the form of a cross, and by holy water. Wouldn't you like to come with us, travelers?

JAUN: No. We're in a hurry.

XI. THE LAMENT OF THE AGOTE

THE AGOTE: I am the *Agote,* the despised *Agote,* one of the despised race from the valley of Baztán, in Navarre. I come from the Arizcun side, and wherever I go, along the bank of this river, I am despised. I don't know what they have against me, or why I'm reproached. They accuse me of being the descendant of lepers, but my breath is no more poisoned than is that of other men. I am forced to wear a bit of red cloth, in the form of a bird's foot, sewn to the miserable rags that cover me. The old pre-Christian Basques hate me, and the Christian Basques do too. Why? I don't know. I can't correct my faults since, if I've done something wrong, I don't know what it was or when I did it. My crime is to have been born in this house and not in another. A strange crime.

MACROSOPHOS: Listen to that wretch complain.

JAUN: He has good reason.

MACROSOPHOS: He has not. He is a descendant of heretics. His punishment is merited. The sons must pay for the sins of the fathers, and the sins of one generation be expiated by the generation that follows.

JAUN: What an absurdity!

MACROSOPHOS: Absurd, not at all. Don't we have to pay for the fault of our father Adam?

JAUN: We'd do enough by paying for our own faults! Anything beyond that would be unfair and unjust.

MACROSOPHOS: Human justice can never be strictly just; it's even more convenient that it not be.

JAUN: Why?

MACROSOPHOS: For various reasons: *prima, secunda, et tertia.*

JAUN: Very well. Let's see what they are.

MACROSOPHOS: *Prima,* because if human justice were strictly just, there would be no need for divine justice, which would be a bad thing; *secunda,* because if human justice had to descend to judging all the particulars, causes and concauses that determine an act, it could never judge, which would be most prejudicial; and *tertia,* because this inquisitorial labor would sap the morale of society, which would be a bad, not to say dangerous, thing.

JAUN: So that we may say: Long live justice, most especially when it is unjust!

XII. THE VOICE OF THE GYPSY

THE GYPSY: I have my house on the banks of this river; I speak the same language as the Basques; I wear the same clothes; but, despite all this, they don't trust me. My eyes flash with a fire that gives me away, and my soul is dominated by appetites that are not theirs. I feel myself a sensualist, I love pleasure, and I love to steal; and I hate all narrow regimentation. I have a taste for the nomadic life, an enthusiasm which these people, who have been living in this same land for thousands of years, can not feel. I don't know which country is my fatherland, for wherever I go I find myself a stranger.

XIII. THE IRONWORKERS

THE IRONWORKERS: Lay on, Machín! Let the song of our hammer resound day and night: tin, tan, tin, tan!

Everything is due to us; the very name of our age is the Age of Iron. The artificer is artificer because of us; the farmer is a farmer because of us; and because of us the soldier is a soldier, the farrier a farrier, and the quarryman a quarryman. And, yet, the world disdains us, and sings the praise of butcher-kings who have shown an ability to cause the death of numerous people and who dress in ermine. O cruel and stupid world! You will never learn to appreciate us. You will ever show more enthusiasm for your silly vanities than for those who contribute everything.

Lay on, Machín! Let the song of our hammer resound day and night: tin, tan, tin, tan!

XIV. THE SMUGGLER

THE SMUGGLER: I'm Ramuntcho, I'm Ichúa, I'm any one of those adventurers brought into the light of day by the dazzling and charm-encrusted prose of that old French siren named Pierre Loti. I inhabit odd corners of Hendaye and Fuenterrabía, of Behovia and Biriatu, of Vera and Urruña, of Ascain and Sara. My enemies are the revenue officers and the border patrol.

Loti, the ex-commander of the "Javelot"—a small French warship out of action in the Bidasoa—attempts to make out, like a good Gallic patriot, that our sole enemy is the sallow Spanish border guard; but just as bad, and usually worse, is the big-bellied French customs officer, with his yellow mustache and red nose.

XV. THE SEAGULL

THE SEAGULL: I, too, know your Bidasoa. My nest is on the Jaizquibel cliff, the craggy promontory which the waves pound with a fury. I visit the beaches of Ondarraitz and Fuenterrabía, looking for food on the sandbanks and sea muck at low tide; but my real element is the open sea, where everything is gray and blurred and there are no clear lines. I am a daughter of chaos; in the tempests, in the middle of the fog, I breathe most freely in the thick salty air, and there, like a war whoop, my wild sharp cry resounds. In the abyss of the glaucous ocean I sway with the waves and avoid the whirlpools of spray. Amid the whining and lamentation of the northwest wind I fly with

a mathematical precision, and I sport and dally above the
storm. . . But I know your Bidasoa, I visit there to look for food
in the running muck at low tide, and I know the beaches at
Irún and Ondarraitz.

XVI. THE SAILORS OF FUENTERRABÍA

THE SAILORS: We are the sailors of Fuenterrabía. We're happy-go-
lucky, never a worry and nothing to fear.

We've worked on fishing boats, and overseas merchantmen, and
done a bit of piracy as well.

Good wine, good loot, good girls in every port, and on we
sail!

The river is the father of our people, and the sea our mother.
In the old days we used to go fishing for whales; then we went
to the cod banks of Newfoundland; now we make more modest
expeditions. We've fought against the French with courage and
constancy; we've made our long and dangerous voyages.

We've known storms and reefs, anguish and terror; Kraken,
the monster of the Maelstrom, and the isle of Satan. None of it
scares us now.

Good wine, good loot, good girls in every port, and on we
sail!

We've seen sirens and marine serpents, harpies and octopus,
fire islands and mysterious volcanoes; we've gone ashore in the
most exotic lands, where dwelt dwarfs or giants, blacks or yellow-
skins, amazons or one-eyed men.

We've witnessed bloody rains and feather snowfalls; we've
seen countries without day and countries without night, and
crystal cathedrals in the middle of the sea.

Danger lurks about us all the time. A gust of wind, a gash in
our nutshell, and down we go! And that's exactly why we're
always gay.

Good wine, good loot, good girls in every port, and on we sail!

XVII. THE ADVENTURER

THE ADVENTURER: I'm the Basque adventurer, neither Spanish
nor French; I serve whoever pays me, and I serve him faithfully.

I'm not interested in ideas or fatherlands; my only fatherland is my house, and after that, the wide world.

Hurray! Hurray for adventure! Hurray for chance!

All my property lies a sword swipe to the left of me and a sword swipe to the right of me, as a musketeer or a horse dragoon, in the service of God or the Devil.

Hurray! Hurray for adventure! Hurray for chance!

Charles V or Francis I, John of Austria or the Bourbon Constable, the Pope or Luther, Pizarro or Pedro de Ursúa: they're all fine with me, if they lead me to success. I'd just as leave be a sailor as a soldier, a Turk as a Christian. The only thing I *don't* want is to toil away at some obscure job.

Hurray! Hurray for adventure! Hurray for chance!

Since I'm an adventurer, I naturally like to travel. I dream of some day finding a treasure to make me rich, or that I'll be like the Inca or even some minor king, or that I'll be surrounded by women and slaves.

Hurray! Hurray for adventure! Hurray for chance!

If I should lose an arm or leg in battle, I'll pass the rest of my life smoking at my ease in some barracks for disabled soldiers; if I'm killed, a brave roll of drums will see me to my grave, and I can't get sad thinking of my fate either way.

Hurray! Hurray for adventure! Hurray for chance!

XVIII. THE HAWKER AND HIS DOG

THE HAWKER: The prognastics of the weather! The eulogy of cuckolds! The deceptions of women! The rivalry between Carnival and Lent! Follies to sing to the sound of the rebec! Songs of all kinds! Who wants one? Who'll take another?

I pass along this road, as I've passed along many another, alone with my dog. I sell rosary beads, scapularies, medals, histories of the saints written in Latin, stories of purple love, and sultry tales in Castilian.

The prognostics of the weather! The eulogy of cuckolds! The deceptions of women! The rivalry between Carnival and Lent! Follies to sing to the sound of the rebec! Songs of all kinds! Who wants one? Who'll take another?

I'm arrested and hauled off to jail for any old reason by the mayors of tiny towns, by aldermen, provosts, bishops and abbots. . . None of the mighty has use for my ware; everyone

distrusts me and takes me for an impious unbeliever. I go on
dauntlessly trying to bring culture to the world, and my broad-
sides will eventually overcome the unreason of my powerful
adversaries. Come on, hound dog, let's move on!

The prognostics of the weather! The eulogy of cuckolds! The
deceptions of women! The rivalry between Carnival and Lent!
Follies to sing to the sound of the rebec! Songs of all kinds! Who
wants one? Who'll take another?

XIX. PELOTA PLAYERS AND VERSE MAKERS

PELOTA PLAYERS AND VERSE MAKERS: We're also products of the
banks of the Bidasoa. We, too, are adventurers and wander from
town to town and from tavern to tavern. Some of us play pelota,
and play it well; the rest of us make verses in Basque, and do it
ill enough; but all of us gain our objective, which is simply to get
out of the house often and wander from fiesta to fiesta. That's
all there is to it. That's the secret. For, as one of our verse-
makers says:

> Bordariyari chardiñ erdiya
> Eure ollasco osua
> Eperrac eta usuac
> Edari generosuac
> Ondo beteric basua.

(For the countrymen in cottages, half a sardine. For us, a whole
chicken, partridge and dove, plenty of wine in a glass brimful.)

XX. THE POLE FISHERMAN

THE POLE FISHERMAN: Tranquillity! Tranquillity! I'm all tranquillity. I wait for the trout and the salmon, hour after hour,
without getting impatient. I watch the cork floating in the water,
and my brain turns to cork, and my nerves do too.

The water flowing by tells me a thousand vague tales that I
can forget on the spot. The eddies in the stream murmur their
many confused secrets, and they float on in my soul, sweetly
and contemplatively.

Tranquillity! Tranquillity! I'm all tranquillity.

XXI. THE SEA

THE SEA: You people are a part; I am the whole. You are a line; I am the sphere. You are a note; I am the symphony. You are an isolated sign in Space; I am Alpha and Omega, the beginning and the end.

Your life of mountains and valleys is the fruit of my restless abyss, the issue of my boiling spray; your life-force comes from me, and your life-force will return to me. Sooner or later I will undo your mountains, your walls and bulwarks, your cliffs and escarpments. Sooner or later, organic matter and the matter of life will return to the laboratory from whence they came, and I will indulge a whim to create a new terrestrial fauna and a new Humanity.

You are a part; I am the whole. You are a line; I am the sphere. You are a note; I am the symphony. You are an isolated sign in Space; I am Alpha and Omega, the beginning and the end.

XXII. DAWN

Dawn is near. The fog is beginning to clear.
JAUN: Well, let's go!
ALL: Let's go!
The travelers cover a league or so before the sun comes up.
MACROSOPHOS: At last we've left that dark corner behind. And what most fertile valley is that in the distance?
JAUN: That's the valley of Zalaín.
BASURDI: We could eat a bite here.
CHIQUI: We can drink the magnificent water of the fountain of *Cherri-buztango-erreca,* or in Castilian, the arroyo of the Pig's Tail.
BASURDI: Pooh! What a sad thing is water!
MACROSOPHOS: Is this the site of the great Academy of *Cherri-buztango-erreca,* where the Capelomágnicos of the Bidasoa are wont to gather?
ARBELÁIZ: The very same.
CHIQUI: A site celebrated in history.
MACROSOPHOS: *Celeberrimus.* What minds! Christormius, in

physics; Schudurrus, in metaphysics; Mandasahius, in geography; Merluzius, in the study of communications; Chacursulus, in Zoology; Tipithus, in botany. What a pleiad!

XXIII. IN ZALAÍN

JAUN: Basurdi!

BASURDI: What?

JAUN: Go and knock at the door of this house and ask if there is anything to eat.

BASURDI: I'm going.

Basurdi enters the courtyard of the house, and reappears shortly afterwards.

ARBELÁIZ: No wine?

BASURDI: No. There was only a bit of cider.

JAUN: Where is it?

BASURDI: I drank it.

JAUN: You're a damnable ass.

MACROSOPHOS: One mustn't speak badly of asses. Ammonius owned an ass so erudite that it left off feeding to listen to verses in hexameter.

BASURDI: No doubt you're the same kind of brainy ass; I'm one of the other kind.

CHIQUI: Not bad, Basurdi. So you'd all like a little wine?

ARBELÁIZ: Cider is so hard on the aged!

CHIQUI: I'll bring back some wine. Hand me the jug.

Chiqui pretends to bore a hole in a tree and extract wine therefrom; actually he fills the jug from his own wineskin. They all drink.

CHIQUI (*to Martín Ziquin*): This old sinner of a Jaun is back home now, and he won't be going back to Easo. There's no danger that he'll get himself baptized. He'll go on being faithful to Urtzi Thor. I think we can leave him safely for the present.

MARTÍN ZIQUIN: I think so, too.

CHIQUI: Well, then, that's that; take half a turn, and Away!

The two imps disappear, and Jaun, with Arbeláiz, Macrosophos, Shaguit, and Basurdi ride on to Alzate, where they trot down the main street of the hamlet.

Intermezzo

THE CHORUS: Urtzi Thor has gone to be near the sea. He is standing on the cliff at Socoa contemplating the furious waves as they dash themselves into spray. The wind lows like a bull, and the rain-filled gusts soak the red beard of the cauldron hero. What are you looking at, Urtzi Thor? What do you have in mind? Whither are you bound?

URTZI THOR: Farewell! Farewell Pyrenees beside the sea! Rolling luminous mountainsides! Green and temperate valleys! Sonorous resounding towns! Farewell, proud and ancient Basques, and joyous youth with eagles' beaks! Farewell, joyful, dancing girls! I am returning to my frozen wastes. Farewell! Farewell!

Follies and Realities

THE AUTHOR: I here enter the fourth part of my legend, and for this part I have erected a certain scientific, philosophic and religious superstructure. Perhaps this idea doesn't suit you, and you feel that my work will now become clearly and frankly dull and boring. You don't seem to like it. What do you expect? What is it you'd like?

Yes, it would be better if you went to see a film. You can watch shy little girls, who are brazen underneath; impeccable gallants wearing impeccable duds; traitors with masks and traitors without masks; Indians galloping along like galloping consumption; credulous and candid clergy; everything fixed for you just as you like it, the moral arranged to your taste, as in a serial. I myself have a penchant for serials; but not for that kind. So go on, go to the movies.

Go to the movies, if you like. I, as I say, am going to construct, in the fourth part of my legend, a scientific and religious structure which I will erect on the basis of my studies of magic, angelic or demonic art, alchemy, astrology, palmistry, geomancy, necromancy, hydromancy, catoptromancy. I see that you raise your eyebrows. All right. Go to the movies. It would be the best thing all around. I'll finish the *Legend of Jaun de Alzate* for myself and two friends.

I. SALIVARY NOSTALGIA

At the entranceway to Erricoechea, a house on the street of Alzate.

ARBELÁIZ: What's Jaun doing?

BASURDI: Nothing. He's always stuck in his library reading; reading and arguing in Latin with Master Macrosophos, who seems to me a big fool, except in drinking wine, where he's a real Master.

ARBELÁIZ: What a man, Jaun!

BASURDI: When he's not in his library, he's out in the garden, standing on the lookout and staring at the river for hours on end.

ARBELÁIZ: How he has changed!

BASURDI: He no longer thinks about eating, or drinking, or looking at the girls. He's getting musty from spending his life with books.

ARBELÁIZ: He must have a lot of books.

BASURDI: More than the Christian priest, who has at least ten or twelve. And then he's hung some maps on the walls, where he's drawn in some figures and some stars; if I had to look at all those things very long I'd go crazy.

ARBELÁIZ: And is it true that he's also taken up medicine?

BASURDI: Yes. He makes miraculous cures. He looks a sick man in the eye and then he tells him: "You've got a broken tendon in your foot. Don't eat fat and you'll get better." And the man gets well.

ARBELÁIZ: What a genius! What knowledge he has! And he no longer thinks of going to Easo?

BASURDI: Hardly!

ARBELÁIZ: What a shame! Do you remember those *shalchas* at Larrechipius' tavern?

BASURDI: Do I remember! What *cocochas* of hake he made!

ARBELÁIZ: And what tuna fish and onion!

BASURDI: And the suckling lamb brought in from Pompeyopolis?

ARBELÁIZ: The sauce was something sublime.

BASURDI: And what sardines!

ARBELÁIZ: My mouth waters to think of them.

BASURDI: And what needlefish!

ARBELÁIZ: And what yellowjack!

BASURDI (*singing*): Yellowjack and needlefish
       Yellowjack and needlefish

ARBELÁIZ: And what do you say about that yellowish liquor at Polus' tavern?

BASURDI: Great! Sabihondus called it nectar: I don't know what that is, but it must be something very good.

ARBELÁIZ: I suddenly feel melancholy, Basurdi.

BASURDI: Me too.

ARBELÁIZ: The trouble is that we've run out of fuel.

BASURDI: Fuel?

ARBELÁIZ: Liquid and solid.

BASURDI: The truth is that they live well in Easo!

ARBELÁIZ: I should say so; we could live well there, too.

BASURDI: It makes one feel like becoming a Christian and going there to live.

ARBELÁIZ: What's your opinion of the Trinity, that mysterious thing that is one and three, and three and one. Do you understand that?

BASURDI: Me? Not a bit of it. But I understand roast lamb. We'll never go to Easo again with the chief. It's all over. We're condemmed to cornbread and cider and an old lamb once in a while.

A WANDERING BEGGAR: Who'll buy my couplets in honor of the glorious prince Saint Michael the Archangel, first minister of God, who broke the chains of the penitent knight Don Teodosio de Goñi, on Mount Aralar!

> Since in the court of heaven
> You boast such high renown
> Send, Archangel Michael,
> Some comfort to this town!
> As the leading general
> Of our celestial host
> You vanquished daring Lucifer
> At every battle post,
> And drove the awful Vaunter
> With his hateful pride to Hell.
> Since in the court of heaven
> You boast such high renown
> Send, Archangel Michael,
> Some comfort to this town!

ARBELÁIZ: We aren't Christians here, friend, nor do we understand what you're driving at, so don't hope to sell any of your papers hereabouts, not even one.

THE WANDERING BEGGAR: That's all right. Give me some alms, then, instead.

ARBELÁIZ: All right. Here, take this, and be off.

II. THE OLD WOMEN OF ALZATE

OLAZÁBAL'S GRANDMOTHER: They say that Jaun, our lord, no longer leaves the house.

ZARRATEA'S GRANDMOTHER: They say also that he spends his life over books, and that now he knows so much that he makes miraculous cures.

OLAZÁBAL'S GRANDMOTHER: That's what they say, though I doubt it, myself, for they say he gets it all from books. I don't think there's much to be gotten out of books.

ZARRATEA'S GRANDMOTHER: I don't either.

OLAZÁBAL'S GRANDMOTHER: I don't know how to read, but that's what I think.

ZARRATEA'S GRANDMOTHER: That's how it seems to me.

OLAZÁBAL'S GRANDMOTHER: Some say that Jaun would like to become a Christian.

ZARRATEA'S GRANDMOTHER: What an outrage!

OLAZÁBAL'S GRANDMOTHER: I've said before that Jaun isn't any good. Turning Christian!

ZARRATEA'S GRANDMOTHER: In our time such things didn't happen, did they? We weren't made of such stuff.

OLAZÁBAL'S GRANDMOTHER: I should hope not. Would you ever become a Christian?

ZARRATEA'S GRANDMOTHER: Me? Never! I'd rather die!

OLAZÁBAL'S GRANDMOTHER: It's that Macrosophos who is putting foolishness into Jaun's head; and now Prudentius, the rector at Vera, is coming to instruct him.

ZARRATEA'S GRANDMOTHER: And then, Arbeláiz doesn't work for our religion. The sacred fire in the stone circle in the woods at Gentil-arri is untended. The horse consecrated to the Sun is dying of hunger; you can count his ribs. Just the other day he was found eating a sandal.

OLAZÁBAL'S GRANDMOTHER: A sandal?

ZARRATEA'S GRANDMOTHER: Yes.

OLAZÁBAL'S GRANDMOTHER: What a disgrace! The last time I saw him, he was eating a straw hat; and that, after all, is a healthier food.

ZARRATEA'S GRANDMOTHER: It's a scandal. That Arbeláiz is a fraud.

OLAZÁBAL'S GRANDMOTHER: It's in his family. The father was as big a fraud as the son.

ARBELÁIZ: I don't understand why these old women talk about things that are none of their business. Dirty hags! If I could, I'd put a torch to these witches and set them on fire.

ZARRATEA'S GRANDMOTHER: I've got four eggs here in my apron, and I'm taking them to sell at the store.

OLAZÁBAL'S GRANDMOTHER: I've brought some maize from my house.

ZARRATEA'S GRANDMOTHER: We'll trade the eggs and the maize for a little *thantha*.

OLAZÁBAL'S GRANDMOTHER: The same thought had occurred to me, because with this humidity! . . .

ZARRATEA'S GRANDMOTHER: And the sufferings and disillusions that one has had to endure. . .

III. ARBELÁIZ

Jaun de Alzate's library is a large room with a fireplace. Be-
side the fire stands a small oven with retorts on it. Against the
whitewashed wall there is a wooden stand filled with vellum
books. A stuffed alligator hangs from the ceiling, and the skulls of
various animals line the shelves of a cabinet.
Symbols and amulets are seen on the walls: the ancient
inverted swastika, emblem of fire and of the god Thor; various
Gnostic signs; the seal of Solomon, the Trutenfuss *of the*
German magicians, which is formed of two interjoined equi-
lateral triangles.
*   It is night, and Jaun is seated before a table, a book in hand,*
in the light of a lamp.

BASURDI: Jaun!

JAUN: What is it?

BASURDI: Arbeláiz is here. He wants to see you.

JAUN: Show him in.

ARBELÁIZ: Jaun, old friend! We never see you any more. What
are you up to?

JAUN: I'm searching for the truth.

ARBELÁIZ: And are you finding it?

JAUN: Sometimes I have hopes; I seem to see a light from afar,
and I set out in search of it; but then the light dims and darkness
descends.

ARBELÁIZ: And after having read so much, haven't you found
anything?

JAUN: Nothing. All this stuff is nothing but a mash of words.
Chimeras! Vain chimeras!

ARBELÁIZ: And Macrosophos, doesn't he know?

JAUN: Yes, he knows the chimeras that all the others know.
That's his function. But whether or not a thing is true doesn't
interest him.

ARBELÁIZ: What? He doesn't care whether it's the truth or a lie?

JAUN: No.

ARBELÁIZ: What kind of a man is he? What type of bird is such
a fellow?

JAUN: He belongs to that class of bird they call scholastics. . .
And what's the news in Alzate?

ARBELÁIZ: That's what I came to talk to you about. Catholicism is upon us like a flood. Yesterday, which was a Christian holiday, the church they're building in Vera was filled. They say that their saints perform more miracles than our gods; that the priests pass around a kind of white bread. . . These Catholics are such fanatics that they're calling us idolators and gentiles, and they want to have us arrested and burned.

JAUN: And you, what are you going to do?

ARBELÁIZ: I don't know. It depends on you, on what you do. If you submit, I'll submit.

JAUN: I won't submit, unless I'm first convinced.

ARBELÁIZ: As long as you stand firm, I'll be at your side.

There is a knock at the door.

JAUN: It must be Prudentius, the rector at Vera who is coming to catechize me. You can stay, if you like, and listen to our conversation.

ARBELÁIZ: All right, I'll stay.

IV. A STORM OF WORDS

PRUDENTIUS: Good and holy evening!

JAUN: Good evening, rector. Sit down.

PRUDENTIUS: Ah! Is my rival in religion here?

ARBELÁIZ: No, I'm not your rival. You charge, and make money; I'm a mere amateur, a devotee. You're powerful, and I'm powerless.

PRUDENTIUS: You admit that?

ARBELÁIZ: Why not?

PRUDENTIUS: And beholding power settling on me, a miserable sinner, does it not occur to you, unfortunate heathen, that Catholicism will blow you along like a feather in a wind?

JAUN: Whether or not it blows me along has nothing to do with it. Force is not reason or right.

PRUDENTIUS: In Catholicism, force is reason.

JAUN: Very well. Convince us of this proposition.

PRUDENTIUS: Have you read the Exposition by Saint Thomas?

JAUN: Yes.

PRUDENTIUS: And what do you think of it?

JAUN: I didn't follow it very well. Whatever can't be understood the author calls a mystery, and whatever can't be reasonably believed must be believed as a mystery. One mystery, well and good; but so many . . . ?

PRUDENTIUS: Pride. Satanic pride!

JAUN: Why do you say that? I have no interest in not believing. It would be a lot more convenient to go along with the general current, the strongest impulse; but I don't believe. What can I do about it? I have either to be furnished clearer ideas or given a denser skull.

PRUDENTIUS: I also gave you *De unitate intellectus,* written against the Averroists by this same Thomas.

JAUN: True enough.

PRUDENTIUS: And did you read it?

JAUN: Yes. And I was left with the impression that in such obscure matters, it is just as fitting to defend the pro as the con.

PRUDENTIUS: And have you read in the Bible?

JAUN: Yes. I can't understand how such a vulgar race can be the one chosen by God! They're wrangling people, completely lacking in a sense of loyalty, and all the other races have denigrated them. I found the fable about man's being created in the image and likeness of God in six days a puerile story. Is it possible that God has a stomach and intestines, a nose and ears? Did he have to rest, like some mason's helper? It all seems perfectly absurd. And the punishment of Adam more absurd than the rest, since God sets a trap at his feet and then punishes him —and all his descendants as well!—when he falls into it. What a hard man your God is! It's easy to see that he's king of a mean and cruel people! What an implacable despot! Just because some boys make fun of Elisha's baldness, he sends two bears to eat them up! This seems to me, if I may say so, enormously ridiculous.

PRUDENTIUS: Your arrogance is ludicrous. Your audacity is ludicrous. For people like you, miserable and obscure peasants, with your repugnant cult of a billy-goat and the most vile superstitions, to look down on the nation of Moses, which understood the Eternal, the Omnipotent Will! . . . Allow me to laugh!

JAUN: Laugh if you like. The Jews, and the first Christians, their successors, placed the lamb under a divine sign because they were pastoral people; and we've done the same with the goat because we have many goats and because we've made the goat a solar symbol. If our goat is an idol, so is your lamb.

PRUDENTIUS: What pain it gives me to listen to you!

ARBELÁIZ: We Basques worship the Sun, the Moon, the Lightning, the Thunder, the Fire, the trees, the forces of Nature, the fountains . . .

PRUDENTIUS: Quiet, quiet, senseless old man! Do you think I don't have information on your demoniacal councils? Do you think I'm not aware of your witches' sabbaths, your dancing on the mountains under a full moon? Do you think I'm not informed about your drinking horse's blood and burying your dead in the woods as if they were animals?

JAUN: I don't know that there's much difference between the way the body of a man rots in the middle of the woods or in your consecrated cemeteries.

PRUDENTIUS: I am aware that you have an idol, a likeness of Jupiter or the God Mars, with his head surrounded by rays, that you call Urtzi Thor and sometimes Jaun Gorri, the Red Man.

JAUN: That's true. It's a symbol of the Sun. The twelve rays are the twelve months of the year.

PRUDENTIUS: It's the same idol that Saint Leon saw at Bayonne when the Norman pirates carried him off to one of their temples. At the foot of the idol there was a sheep and a billy-goat, and the saint blew on them and the two perversely used beasts were whisked into the air and reduced to dust.

ARBELÁIZ: That's his story. There's no record among us of any such event.

PRUDENTIUS: Keep quiet, old man! It seems hard to believe that age has not given you more discretion.

ARBELÁIZ: Among our people there are also those who accept the idea of an unknown god.

PRUDENTIUS: The *"Deus ignotus"* of which Strabo speaks—whom some say is the Moon. . . But most of you live in idolatry. You preserve the cult of the horse and the billy-goat, of the fountains and the trees.

JAUN: Why be astonished that uncultured men like us feel admiration for the forces of Nature and give them human attributes?

PRUDENTIUS: It's not your ignorance that astounds me! I am simply astonished at your blindness, your rashness; I am astounded that you reject baptism, that you reject grace.

JAUN: Are you astonished, too, that we do not wish to submit to outsiders?

PRUDENTIUS: Yes. I am astonished that you do not wish to submit to a superior order.

JAUN: What order is that?

PRUDENTIUS: God's order.

JAUN: You Christians are as single-minded and unbending as savages!

PRUDENTIUS: Why wouldn't we be unbending, since we possess the truth? All truth is in the Church. Truth that is not in the Church is not truth.

JAUN: And the truth of Science, isn't that truth, either?

PRUDENTIUS: Not that either.

JAUN: Then you accept no collaboration in knowledge or in belief?

PRUDENTIUS: Everything has already been said: there is nothing further but to obey.

JAUN: It seems to me that there is religious intention and significance in a God as well as in an idol, or vice versa. If the religious intention of one or the other is good, why not accept it?

PRUDENTIUS: Accept an idol's intention? Accept the devil? No. For, as Saint Thomas has pointed out, all superstitions are founded upon a tacit compact with demons: *"Omnes supersticiones procedunt ex aliquo cum Doemonibus inito, tacito vel expreso."*

JAUN: Of our customs, then, our ancient ideas, nothing is to remain?

PRUDENTIUS: Nothing. As Saint Eloy, bishop of Noyon, said in his sermon *Ad omnem plebem,* it is necessary to withdraw from all pagan customs; there must be no thinking about the sun, or the moon, or observance of the solstices, or singing and dancing on St. John's Day, because all these practices are works of the Devil.

JAUN: You accept nothing of ours . . . only the cross.

PRUDENTIUS: The cross! What do you mean by that?

JAUN: The cross was Basque before it was Christian.

PRUDENTIUS: What an absurdity!

JAUN: It is not absurd. In many parts of our country the swastika cross is still to be found. Some suppose it to be the symbol of the two roads in the world; others that it symbolizes the four cardinal points; among us, in any case, it is the emblem of Thor, of fire, of flame, of the Sun.

PRUDENTIUS: It is a symbol that you have taken from the Christians, then.

JAUN: No. It is a symbol you have taken from us. When the first Christians of the Roman Empire put the cross on their standards, they called it Lábarum. Now *Lábarum, Laburu, lau buru* means "four heads," "four points," in Basque. Labarum is the Basque cross, the swastika, the Tetragrammaton, the symbol of Urtzi Thor, which the Basques carried with them to Lombardy, and which was taken over by Constantine.

PRUDENTIUS: Labarum probably comes from the Latin *labare,* to wave, for the standard that waves in the wind.

JAUN: My explanation is more logical. All standards wave in the wind, but not all signs have four points or four heads like the swastika cross of Lábarum. In addition to our swastika cross, you will find in many parts of our country, drawn in caves, the scaffold cross, which is nothing more than the hieratic representation of a man with his arms spread on a radiating disk, and therefore a symbol of the sun.

PRUDENTIUS: I see that you aspire to be a philosopher. A philosopher in Alzate! Ha, ha . . .

JAUN: Why not?

PRUDENTIUS: The philosopher, as Tertulian has asserted, is a glorious and haughty animal, interpolator of error. All his speculations are stupid and vain: *"Cogitationes omnium philosophorum stultas esse."* And this father of the Church has gone so far as to say: "Since Jesus Christ, we have no need for curiosity, nor need for investigation since the Gospels: *Nobis curiositate opus non est post Christum, nec inquisitione post Evangelium."*

JAUN: The blacks in the jungle might say the same, in terms of their religion.

PRUDENTIUS: Do not provoke heaven's wrath!

JAUN: You can unchain it against me, hurl it on my head. I don't believe you enjoy better relations with the lightning than does my friend Arbeláiz.

PRUDENTIUS: I pardon you, unfortunate man!

JAUN: Your pardon and heaven's wrath have the same affect on me. I used to believe that there were good and bad spirits, and that man could establish relation with them. I no longer believe it. I now believe that there is nothing else but Nature.

PRUDENTIUS: What, no angels, no devils? You deny all the evidence, unhappy man!

JAUN: An evidence nowhere evident. For me, there is no dualism in the world. Truth or falsehood, illusion or reality, infinitely variable or completely one, it's all the same.

PRUDENTIUS: The devil speaks through your mouth at this moment. You should be more humble. Only think that Tertullian, with all his great intelligence, has said: *"Prorsus credibile est, quia ineptum est . . . certum est quia imposibile est . . ."*

JAUN: What I don't understand, I don't understand. As far as I can see, no one knows, or will know, why we come into the world, nor our purpose in being here, assuming there is any prior reason for our appearance, something which I doubt.

PRUDENTIUS: The devil continues talking through your mouth. Get thee behind me, Satan! And I'm going. I must tell you both only that I am keeping a watch on you, for I will not permit this village to be condemned because of you. If you want war, you shall have it, and go to hell, to suffer torments without end, in an endless eternity.

Prudentius goes.

ARBELÁIZ: What a character! What a way of talking!

JAUN: And such a man is called Prudentius, "prudent"! A few years ago I would have thrown him out the window.

ARBELÁIZ: We'll be forced to yield.

JAUN: Not I. By conviction, yes; but merely for the sake of submission, no. They want to swap one fiction for another. Fiction for fiction, I prefer my own.

ARBELÁIZ: That man has such conviction!

JAUN: Yes, he's an actor. All these Latinists, and those educated in their schools, turn out to be actors.

ARBELÁIZ: Yes, but he's such a forceful talker!

JAUN: All right, you do what you want. I'm not yielding.

SHAGUIT (*outside, singing*):

Ay au fraile picarua
Galdu biardu mundua,
Precisamente naidu bela
Nescatillen zancua.

(O, what a roguish monk the world is going to lose! For all he says he really wants are the legs of girls.)

JAUN: Tell Shaguit to come up. Perhaps it's better to talk to madmen than to the prudent.

V. SORGUIÑ-ECHE

Jaun de Alzate has granted the witches of the neighborhood the right to use his mill at Errotazar—now in ruins—for their reunions. Errotazar is on the banks of the Bidasoa, near an irrigation ditch.

And so now the mill is also called Sorguiñ-eche: the house of the witches.

The ruins of Errotazar still have thick walls, though they have turned black with time and are covered with vines. There is also a wooden tower and arches span the river.

At night, the grounds around Errotazar undergo a transformation. In the words of the people, it becomes a country of magic and mysteries, peopled with monsters; a country illuminated by a yellowish and sickly moon. Everything there is irregular, deviant, monstrous.

In the fields, behind the eerie and strangely growing trees and vegetation, mocking sprites and goblins and insects with human visages appear on all sides.

Near the Errotazar ruins there is an abandoned hermitage and a road lined with stone crosses upon which are ranged, in the form of a pyramid, pensive groups of crows and owls; at a little distance stands a cross of rotting wood, hung with a Christ figure with twisted arms and an expression of hideous pain.

In the ruins themselves, inland from the water, three hanged men are suspended from a dead tree, and beneath them splendid mandragoras have sprung from their death-feces. Red and venom-filled toadstools abound: the amanita phalloides with its dirty texture and the amanita muscaria, the fly amanita; and there are luxuriant beds of henbane and belladonna.

At the entrance to the mill, a bat, nailed to a wall by one wing, utters hideous screams.

It is said that the Sabbath is celebrated at Errotazar with grand dances; that the women dance naked, and wear girdles of catskin around their middles.

On these days, if the people in the nearby farmhouses hear the cock crow in the first hours of the night, they throw a fistful of salt on the fire, for the early crow of a cock indicates the passage of witches.

VI. THE MOTHER WITCH

The night is overcast. Shreds of black clouds scud across the sky; the moon, as if in fright, runs before them with a face pale with terror. The dogs bark furiously. Jaun de Alzate, together with Macrosophos, Basurdi, Chiqui, and Timotheus, the sacristan of the church at Vera, are on their way to Sorguiñeche, to witness the Witches' Sabbath.

CHIQUI: Urtzi Thor has left us, friend Jaun.

JAUN: Where is he going?

CHIQUI: To the pantheon of dead gods, where the Christian gods will go in their turn.

JAUN: And is there nothing left behind in his passing?

CHIQUI: It's possible that the degeneration and passing away of Urtzi Thor is the fable of King Arthur. The famous Round Table is merely a symbol for the firmament, and Arthur's father is the god Uter, dragon head, god of battle, who lives in the sky

and whose shield is the rainbow; he is a sidereal god, like Urtzi.
And then, Arthur is a warrior, like Thor, and once dead rises
into the sky and shines as the Great Bear. Uter and Urtzi;
Arthur, Aitor, and Thor; Urtzi and *artza* (the bear), and the
Great Bear, all these are, without a doubt, part of the same
family.

JAUN: From which facts we arrive at the conclusion that we are
already under Christian sway.

CHIQUI: Does it irritate you?

JAUN: Yes.

CHIQUI: Of course I understand that Christianity is not congenial
to the Basques, since it's a Jewish swindle with a Latin varnish.

JAUN: Not congenial, you say! And yet everyone is turning
Christian.

CHIQUI: What would you have? Man's gaze is not stern enough
to contemplate nature face to face. . . Well, here we are at
Sorguiñ-eche. We'll get a good view of the Sabbath.

MACROSOPHOS: These celebrations are doubtless a species of Luper-
calia in which homage is paid to the Priapus-Bacchus-Sabasius
billy-goat.

JAUN: It's quite likely they've never concerned themselves hereabouts with Bacchus or Priapus.

MACROSOPHOS: How could that be? All this is nothing but a
reminiscence of Greek and Roman witchery.

JAUN: Why so? When I'm convinced that the man who eats
a fig in China is imitating a man who does the same in Athens,
I'll believe in this supposed unity of knowledge, ideas, and superstitions.

MACROSOPHOS: These ideas come from the same trunk. There is
unity in everything: in the bad as in the good.

JAUN: And also variation.

MACROSOPHOS: Does not man spring from a single pair?

JAUN: Perhaps. I don't think so.

*Chiqui knocks with his fist on the large splintering door to
Errotazar. His knock sounds like a hammer blow.*

A CRACKED VOICE FROM WITHIN: Who is it?

CHIQUI: Open up, in the name of ten thousand pairs of devils,
or I'll kick the door down!

*The door swings ajar, and Jaun and his companions go in.
Numerous corridors or pathways thread their way among the
maze of the ruins. In the middle, in the remains of a great
hall, stands the effigy of a he-goat between whose large horns a
torch is glowing. Around the walls of the hall numerous men
and women, come from far and near, are taking their ease;*

the old women among them are playing cards on boards laid across their laps. The corridors are filled with crazed chickens, ragged black cats, gaunt hounds, and toads dressed in velvet and wearing little bells at their throats. The shelves along the walls hold hangman's nooses, fetuses in alcohol, alligators, and the skulls of hogs, horses, monkeys, and dogs.

JAUN: This is all very unpleasant.

CHIQUI: Let's find the mother witch.

They make their way along one of the corridors and finally come to a tiny room.

THE MOTHER WITCH: How dare you enter here?

CHIQUI: It's me, Chiqui.

THE MOTHER WITCH: Ah! It's you, Chiqui? Ingrate! Traitor! You know how I feel about you, and yet you never come to see me.

CHIQUI: All right, grandmother: cut the sentiment!

The mother witch is very old and very wrinkled, bald and hook-nosed. Her eyes are mud-colored and cloudy, her mouth is toothless; her skin is coarse and dirty, and her chin sprouts long gray hairs. She is tending a boiling cauldron; two buzzards, as immobile as stone chimeras, keep watch. A black cat gazes over the scene with its yellow eyes, while rats run about the room in patterns.

CHIQUI: Who is that rat with red eyes, grandmother?

THE MOTHER WITCH: In this rat the soul of Lanzarote del Lago lives on.

JAUN: What an imagination!

CHIQUI: And who is that rat that spews fire from its tail?

THE MOTHER WITCH: That's my confidant. It's he who tells me the secrets of the neighborhood, and of everybody in town.

CHIQUI: What's your program for tonight?

THE MOTHER WITCH: The same as every Sabbath, my son.

CHIQUI: The usual vulgarities!

THE MOTHER WITCH: Would you like me to trot out some little imps?

CHIQUI: A review of imps! (*To Jaun*): How does that strike you?

JAUN: All right.

VII. THE CONJURATION

THE MOTHER WITCH: I conjure, I conjure: *Conjuro te Sabella, quae faciem habes multeris et renes piscis, caput tennes in nube et pedes in mari, septem ventos bajulas, doemonibus imperas. . .*

JAUN: Here we go with Latin again! Don't you know how to conjure in Basque?

CHIQUI: What do you expect! The Basques are such traditionalists that sometimes they know what their fathers have done but never what their grandfathers have accomplished. There used to be renowned masters of magic and witchcraft in Biarritz, Guethary, and Saint-Pée, but they've all forgotten their science. Someone should buy them a *Malleus maleficorum*. And now shall we let the mother witch get on with her conjuring?

JAUN: All right, let her finish.

THE MOTHER WITCH: It's already finished. They're coming.

Like shadows on the wall, gnomes and imps, grotesques and fools begin to appear; they breathe fire from their mouths, and the flames take the shape of bats, owls, vampires, larvae, lizards, frogs mounted on the backs of flying fish, and all announce themselves by name.

THE IMPS: Black Wind, Sad Belly,
                     Turkey's Ass, Lion Skin,
                     Cat's Eye, Goat's Horn,
                     Cock's Comb, Buck's Paw.

CHIQUI: These are vulgar imps, with no standing or responsibility.

THE DEVILS (*self-importantly, and wearing the melancholy air of starving schoolmasters*):
                     Samiaxas, Leutias, Bucella,
                     Barnaza, Sabella,
                     Agios, Celin, Celes, Potas,
                     Ibris, Palamitis, Aglotas,
                     Authos, Anostro, Nostro, Bay,
                     Afren, Oscazo, Uba, Glay,
                     Actiova, Baleztaco, Caudebat,
                     Easas, Celsus, Saudebat,
                     Acaos, Asmodeo, Cedón,
                     Achas, Alex, Zabulón.

JAUN: All this strikes me as a stupid nonsense. All I can see is some shadow play on the wall.

CHIQUI: The trouble is that you're too intellectual. (*To the others*): Didn't you all see the devils?

BASURDI: I did.

MACROSOPHOS: I did, too.

CHIQUI: And you, Timotheus?

TIMOTHEUS (*rousing himself from his stupor*): *Ab hoste maligno, liberanos Domine.* Out! Out, malign spirits! Run, we must run! Let us fly this place! A thousand monsters fly through the air and the fumes of sulphur and pitch will choke us. We must run for it! Satan lies in ambush!

CHIQUI: These Christians are cowardice made flesh. They have a fear of hell that is really ridiculous. What a laugh! The sacristan has no doubts about what he sees.

JAUN: Let him go, if he's so scared.

CHIQUI: Aren't you a little afraid?

JAUN: Me? Not at all. This business strikes me as a farce, and I accept it as a more or less entertaining one.

CHIQUI: A farce! The work of the devil a farce! (*To himself*): This Jaun is a hard man to shake.

VIII. THE SABBATH

The great hall is filled with male and female witches; they busy themselves reciting a litany around the billy-goat, the solar symbol converted into a representation of the Devil.

THE MOTHER WITCH: Lucifer.

THE CHORUS: *Miserere nobis.*

THE MOTHER WITCH: Beelzebub, the flyflap.

THE CHORUS: *Miserere nobis.*

THE MOTHER WITCH: Astaroth, of the Order of the Seraphim.

THE CHORUS: *Ora pro nobis.*

THE MOTHER WITCH: Sabaoth, of the ass's head.

THE CHORUS: *Ora pro nobis.*

JAUN: This isn't worth coming for. It's nothing but a stupid burlesque.

CHIQUI: Is that what it seems like to you?

JAUN: Of course it is! You were telling me that the Christianity which is sweeping over us is nothing but Jewish swindle with a Roman varnish. Well, your magic is also Jewish, and it also makes use of Latin. Really, these witches, these *sorguiñas* aren't worth anything. I think I'll tell them to get out of my ruins.

CHIQUI: Let them stay a while longer. Let's consult this fortune teller. Hey, old woman!

THE FORTUNE TELLER: What would you like, maestro?

CHIQUI: Would you mind showing us some of your tricks?

THE FORTUNE TELLER: What would you like me to do? Would you like me to show you your future in this cauldron of water?

MACROSOPHOS: This art is called lecanomancia.

CHIQUI: That's it exactly. (*To Jaun*): This has merit if it's done well.

JAUN: We'll see!

The Fortune Teller stirs the cauldron, and then plunges a burning torch into the container.

CHIQUI: Eh! Eh! Watch out for the flames!

BASURDI: I've never seen anything like this.

MACROSOPHOS: I never have either. Look how the fire comes out of the cauldron!

TIMOTHEUS: Get thee behind me, Satan! Get thee behind!

CHIQUI (*confidentially, to Jaun*): The flames come from potassium and sodium and other alkaline metals.

JAUN: What flame? I don't see any flame in that cauldron.

CHIQUI: What a man! There's no way of passing anything off on him.

THE FORTUNE TELLER (*gazing southward*): I conjure thee, Uriel Seraph, by the seventy-two names of the All-Powerful God, by Adonai, by Belial, by Astaroth, prince of Hell, let us see in this water, without fail or deceit, as I shall ask of thee. Abracadabra! . . . Now you can all look.

MACROSOPHOS: Good heavens! What monsters!

BASURDI: It's enough to scare me to death.

TIMOTHEUS: Get thee behind me! Get thee behind me! Out! Out, malign spirits!

JAUN (*gazing into the cauldron*): What's in there? I don't see anything.

CHIQUI: You don't see anything?

JAUN: All I see is the bottom of the cauldron.

CHIQUI: We're wasting our time with this fellow. So you don't see anything?

JAUN: Nothing.

They all troop back to the central hall.

CHIQUI: Everyone is gathering to celebrate the Sabbath.

Male and female witches come in on broomsticks.

THE MALE WITCHES: Monday, Tuesday, Wednesday: three.

THE FEMALE WITCHES: Thursday, Friday, Saturday: six.

BASURDI: Sun. . .

CHIQUI: Silence! Let no one pronounce the name of Sunday!

THE BROOMSTICKS: At last we've been emancipated. For century after century they used us in vulgar ways, making us rub shoulders with dust and filth. At most, we've appeared as objects of craft in the hands of maskers at carnival time. Our predisposition and natural attributes for aerial navigation have not been previously recognized. But now the day of our redemption is here: *le jour de gloire est arrivée.*

What splendid jaunts we take, at a hundred and fifty kilometers an hour! What whirls! What landings! No, no, we must never let them employ us again on vile chores! We no longer live in a time of obscurantism. We are definitely apparatuses for aerial navigation, not dust gatherers or floor wipers.

All the male and female witches dance a roundelay on their brooms, while a villager plays the bagpipe. Some of the old women carry the bone of a human in one hand; Basurdi and Macrosophos notice that these bones seem to diffuse light; Timotheus claims they give off sulphur vapors; Jaun announces that they give no more light than any other object. The old women, grown hot and flushed with their dancing, begin peeling off their clothes, until they are all in their chemises.

BASURDI: Ho, ho! What a sight this is going to be!

CHIQUI: Grandmother witch, we've had enough. The spectacle is beginning to tire us, and we're going.

THE MOTHER WITCH: You're going already?

CHIQUI: Yes, we're going.

Jaun suddenly recognizes a leper who lives in one of the outskirts of Alzate.

JAUN: What are you doing here?

THE LEPER: I come here, sir. . .

JAUN: Why do you come here?

THE LEPER: Because this is the only place where they treat me like a man.

Chiqui and his companions quit the abandoned mill.

IX. FAMOUS MEN AND MAGICAL MIRRORS

CHIQUI: The truth is that there's no way to deceive this fellow Jaun. He's interested in seeing only what is actually in things, as if this were a human condition. He's ruined my plans. I no longer know what to do to get the best of him. I think I'll show them some colored prints and those mirrors that deform one. (*To Martín Ziquin*): I say there, you, Martín, look sharp now. I'm going to show these people some prints by holding them up to the light, and I'll let you know who is represented; then, you embroider your description as best you can.

MARTÍN ZIQUIN: Very well; I'll do it.

JAUN: What are we going to see here?

CHIQUI: First we'll all have a drink.

MACROSOPHOS: Good enough. *Bibamus.*

They all drink; meanwhile Chiqui disappears.

MARTÍN ZIQUIN (*with the voice of a circus barker*): Step forward, gentlemen, step up! Here you'll see famous men and magical mirrors!

MACROSOPHOS: There are people who claim that it's dangerous to look into certain mirrors, because you can lose your soul that way.

JAUN: Bah! What rot!

MACROSOPHOS: Yes, yes. The science of catoptromancia has its principles. According to Varro, quoted by Saint Augustine in his *De civitate dei,* this science comes down to us from the Persians.

MARTÍN ZIQUIN: Step forward, gentlemen, step up! Here you'll see famous men and magic mirrors!

CHIQUI (*to Martín Ziquin*): This one is Julius Caesar.

MARTÍN ZIQUIN: This bald-headed man before you is Julius Caesar, the rival of Pompey, who was thus called because he was a man of such pomp. This Julius was the one who said *Veni, vidi, vici,* that is, "I've ventured along the way of vice"—for apparently this gentleman led a rather dissolute life.

MACROSOPHOS: What an outrageous statement!

MARTÍN ZIQUIN: The most famous thing that Julius Caesar did was to cross the Rubicon, which was a river four or five yards wide. Everyone used to say: Julius, I bet you can't jump it! So he took a running start and jumped it with his feet together.

MACROSOPHOS: Absurd! Absurd!

CHIQUI (*to Martín Ziquin*): This one is Nero.

MARTÍN ZIQUIN: This fat man crowned with laurel is Nero, who used to take a flute with him to play in the bathroom, where he was finally killed. Whereupon he said: "What an artist is lost to the world!" For, though before him there had been theater flutists, café flutists, and wine-tavern flutists, there had never before been a bathroom flutist.

MACROSOPHOS: What a barbarity!

CHIQUI: (*to Martín Ziquin*): Here's Charlemagne.

MARTÍN ZIQUIN: This fellow with the white beard is Charlemagne, who was called by this name because of his height. He's wearing a red cloak, a crown with black feathers, and has a sword in one hand and a globe of the world in the other.

MACROSOPHOS: This man doesn't know what he's saying.

MARTÍN ZIQUIN: Step forward, gentlemen, step up. Here you'll see famous men and magic mirrors!

CHIQUI (*to Martín Ziquin*): Here comes Mohammed.

MARTÍN ZIQUIN: Here we are face to face with the famous Mohammed, with his sharp nose and black, pointed beard. This is the man who said: Since the mountain won't come to me, I'll go to the mountain to hunt rabbit.

MACROSOPHOS: What an ignoramus!

CHIQUI (*to Martín Ziquin*): This is Attila.

MARTÍN ZIQUIN: Here we have Attila, the famous Attila, who possessed a special system for trampling down the grass so that it would never grow again. His method was the forerunner of macadamization. As you see, Attila is low of stature, broad-chested, big-headed, flat-nosed, beady-eyed, sparse-whiskered, and copper-hued.

CHIQUI (*to Martín Ziquin*): This one is Roland.

MARTÍN ZIQUIN: This young man, with the woman's face, and carrying a broadsword in one hand and a shield adorned with a two-headed eagle in the other, is Roland, killed by the Basques at Roncesvalles. Here you see him once more, surrounded by the twelve peers of France and the giant Ferragus and the terrible Fierabrás.

JAUN: This is neither history nor legend, but the stuff of novels.

MARTÍN ZIQUIN: Novel or history, either way. In the long run, I think that everything is the stuff of novels, friend Jaun.

Step forward, gentlemen, step up! Here you'll see famous men and magic mirrors!

CHIQUI (*to Martín Ziquin*): This one is Merlin, the enchanter.

MARTÍN ZIQUIN: This old man, with his sad aspect, and placed in an uncomfortable position, is Merlin, the wise enchanter, caught in a hawthorn bush by the wiles of his beloved, Bibiana. Beware all women! The big blonde here is Melisande. And this fellow is Don Gayferos. . . I believe that's the end of the portraits.

BASURDI: I heard someone mention the Wandering Jew.

MARTÍN ZIQUIN: I'll show him to you right now. Hey, Chiqui! The Wandering Jew! Here he is, Isaac Laquedem, with his great beard, his thick stick, a cloth cap on his head, and sandals on his feet.

CHIQUI (*emerging once more*): Pray pardon the stupid statements of my companion. . . And now, if you all agree, I'll show you the Danse Macabre. One moment, please. Meanwhile, I'll leave you the bottle to while away the time.

X. THE DANSE MACABRE

BASURDI: The Danse Macabre! What's that?
MACROSOPHOS: That's what we men of culture call *Chorea Mac-chabaeorum.*
BASURDI: Now we know.
JAUN: You'll see it, Basurdi, you'll see what it is.
CHIQUI: It's about to begin.
A cemetery is seen in the light of the moon. The skull of a skeleton suddenly peers from beneath a gravestone. Another pushes at a great slab, and, on catching sight of the audience mutters: "And they still won't go away." Another skeleton, using two tibias, sounds the call to arms on a drum. Suddenly a bugle band of skeletons appears.
CHIQUI: Here are the trumpeters of death!
BASURDI: Listen to those damned skeletons play the bugles, lutes, and kettledrums!
CHIQUI: There's the Pope of Rome on his throne, wearing his tiara and holding his staff. Death is watching him, and will soon carry him off. Here's the Emperor with his sword—and the skeleton that spies on him. Here's the King in his palace—for whom the bony guest pours wine. Here's the Empress, the Queen, the Bishop, the Cardinal, the Duke, the Abbess, the coquettish woman looking at herself in the mirror, the Friar, the Nun, the Traveler, the Shepherd. . . The Skeleton representing Death acts jovial and gay. . . Here you see him crowned with laurel; there he is dressed in a cape; in one place he appears showing his victim a sand hourglass; in that street he is seen carrying, like a devout worshiper, the lantern for the viaticum; he shows a skull to an astronomer; he steals money from a miser; he runs a knight through with his own lance; he kills a soldier with a thighbone; and he goes along playing his flute, or drum, or lute, or bagpipe, and dancing joyously, grinning through his skull, and making his bones and ligaments creak. . .
MACROSOPHOS: Most interesting, indeed.
CHIQUI: And now, let's have a little something to drink.
BASURDI: I can't go on. My eyes are closing.
JAUN: The same thing is happening to me!
MACROSOPHOS: To me also.
TIMOTHEUS: And me too.
They all stretch out on the floor.

CHIQUI: Now we're going to make an aerial voyage. By way of test, we'll go first to Mount Larrun. I'll get the sails ready. Climb aboard the ship. One, two, three. . . Are we all in? Let's go! Listen to the sails shake!

BASURDI: I want to get off. I've forgotten to do something necessary.

MACROSOPHOS: My head is flying off!

TIMOTHEUS: Get thee behind me!

JAUN: I had too much to drink . . . my ears are ringing . . . none of this is true. . .

CHIQUI: Here we are at Mount Larrun.

BASURDI: What speed! What a climb!

MACROSOPHOS: What power!

JAUN: I suspect that all this is a lie.

XI. CHIQUI AND MARTÍN

CHIQUI: Here we have to make an effort, Martín. I've gotten all these people drunk. Now we'll have to carry them in a cart up to Mount Larrun. When they come to their senses up there, and when I tell them that we've flown up, they'll have to believe me.

MARTÍN: Fine. I'll go and find a cart, and be back in a minute.

He returns with a small cart. Martín and Chiqui load the four drunks aboard it, and they set out toward Larrun.

XII. THE AERIAL VOYAGE

CHIQUI: All right, gentlemen, prepare yourselves! Now we're going to make the great voyage. All aboard! Are we all ready?

ALL (*weakly*): All ready!

CHIQUI: Here we go! We're climbing! Careful with the sail! What a wind!

BASURDI: My hat will fly off.

TIMOTHEUS: My skull cap will get lost, and when I get back I won't be able to go to church.

MACROSOPHOS: Don't they have cap shops in Vera?

TIMOTHEUS: No. This cap was smuggled in to me from Bayonne.

CHIQUI: Look at the terrible abysses that lie below us!

BASURDI: I'm too frightened to look!

MACROSOPHOS: What tremendous concavities! *Horresco referens!*

CHIQUI: We're over the Mediterranean, parallel to the Pyrenees.

MACROSOPHOS: Just a moment! What do you mean parallel? That

can't be. Strabo affirms that the Pyrenees run north and south, parallel to the Rhine.

CHIQUI: Strabo is mistaken.

MACROSOPHOS: Strabo can not be mistaken.

JAUN: Well, he's mistaken all the same. Pliny the Elder understood that the Pyrenees run east and west, and Ptolemy marked the position of the two extreme points: one, the promontory of Easo, in the Ocean; the other, the temple of Aphrodite, of Portus Veneris, in the Mediterranean.

MACROSOPHOS: We must ascertain who has the most prestige and repute, Ptolemy or Strabo.

JAUN: No; we must ascertain who is telling the truth.

CHIQUI: In this case Ptolemy has the better of Strabo . . . Now we're going over the river Ebro . . . We're already into the Mediterranean Sea!

MACROSOPHOS: What waves! What pitching and rolling!

BASURDI: I just saw a whale.

JAUN: A whale in the Mediterranean?

MACROSOPHOS: It must be some Leviathan.

JAUN: There are no such things as Leviathans. That's a Biblical fraud.

CHIQUI: We're approaching the coasts of Italy. We're at Rome already!

MACROSOPHOS: I can see the seven hills and the Capitol. And near the Capitol, the Tarqueian Rock: *Saxum Tarpejum*. And I believe I also see the She-Wolf.

JAUN: And don't you see the famous geese?

MACROSOPHOS: No. Not yet!

JAUN: It seems to me that I am seeing them.

BASURDI: And the Pope? Isn't the Pope visible anywhere?

CHIQUI: He's the one with the tiara and staff.

BASURDI: Unfortunate man! And is he that poor?

CHIQUI: Don't you see that he's a prisoner, as the lay sisters say.

BASURDI: Hasn't he got a home?

CHIQUI: What does he want one for? Isn't he the representative of Christ, who was born in a stable?

MACROSOPHOS: O the grandeur of Rome!

BASURDI: What a town! What squares, all surrounded by streets! What good things to buy there must be in the markets! Not like Alzate, where we have to go to Lesaca or Saint-Jean-de-Luz for everything.

CHIQUI: I'd make the roofs of all the houses in the Eternal City transparent for you, by using a formula invented by my colleague Asmodeo, but, since everyone, clerics and laymen alike, are probably committing some abomination at this very moment, I'll desist. For I don't want to make misanthropes of you. Where do you want to go after Rome?

MACROSOPHOS: I'd like to see the countries famous in antiquity.

CHIQUI: Up we go then. There's Athens and the Parthenon. On the other side you have the Pillars of Hercules. That large river comes from the Land of Cinnamon and is called the Nile. Some savants claim they can taste a slight flavor of custard in the water. There's the land of the Amazons, and the island of Trapobana.

MACROSOPHOS: According to the authors there are two summers and two winters in every year on that island.

JAUN: That's a lie.

CHIQUI: Those are the Ethiopians.

MACROSOPHOS: Ah, the Ethiops! Of the Ethiops it is known that they imitate their king so closely, that when he is lame, they all limp, and when he is one-eyed, they all squint an eye.

CHIQUI: When the king of Ethiopia is foolish, which tends to be the case in kings everywhere, the Ethiopians will be able to go about with their tongues out, pretending to be stupider than they are normally.

MACROSOPHOS: Assuredly.

CHIQUI: Well this happens in every country in greater or lesser degree, friend Macrosophos. . . There's Babylon and its tower.

BASURDI: Damn! It's higher than the church at Vera.

CHIQUI: That lady is the Queen of Sheba, sword in hand.

BASURDI: What a fine wench! What a chest! But who could get near her with that sword sticking out?

CHIQUI: That's Egypt.

MACROSOPHOS: Here, according to what Dion Chrysostom says in one of his discourses, there is a city where all the men are bartenders and all the women barmaids.

JAUN: What rot!

CHIQUI: Are they also orators?

MACROSOPHOS: Why do you ask?

CHIQUI: Because if they are, this would be the ideal town for the Socialist Party. . . Those over there are the Atlantes.

MACROSOPHOS: Ah! The Atlantes! They are gigantic beings who inhabit a place by a salt mountain, and they have no individual names.

JAUN: And how do they distinguish among themselves? By numbers?

MACROSOPHOS: I do not know. That is a point I have not elucidated.

CHIQUI: There are the troglodytes, who live in caves.

MACROSOPHOS: And who call each other by such names as bull, goat, hog, ass. . . That is, according to Diodorus of Sicily.

BASURDI: We also call each other hog and ass.

MACROSOPHOS: Yes, but the difference is, friend Basurdi, that the troglodites thus call each other without offensive intention.

CHIQUI: There are the ichthyophages, who eat only fish, and the lotophages, who live off lotus flower. Now we'll head for the deserts of Scythia. That's the country of the pygmies, who, according to general belief, spend their lives in combat with cranes.

MACROSOPHOS: That's right. But we must observe that Aristotle locates the pygmies in Egypt, near the sources of the Nile. Philostratus places them in Asia, on the banks of the Ganges. Pliny puts them in Scythia. The majority of writers state that the pygmies wage war with the cranes, who are always attacking them; other authors, like Menecles, the Greek historiographer at Athens, maintains that they wage war with the partridges. Some assert that the pygmies go into battle mounted on birds; others say on sheep. According to Juvenal, the pygmies are not more than one foot tall: *Quorum tota cohoros pede non est altior uno*. The Fathers of the Church, Saint Augustine and Saint Jerome, attest to the existence of the pygmies; and Saint Thomas says that the men can reduce themselves to the size of ants. According to Philostratus, the pygmies are the sons of Earth and brothers of the giant Antaeus. They are a cubit in height; the women become mothers at three years of age, and old at eight. Their houses are made from the shells of cranes' eggs.

JAUN: What a lot of nonsense!

MACROSOPHOS: What do you mean nonsense? This is Science! Moreover there are nations of running people where the men have only one leg and foot.

JAUN: And they get about?

MACROSOPHOS: Of course they get about. Pliny calls them the Sciapodos.

JAUN: He may call them what he wishes. I don't believe such people exist.

MACROSOPHOS: The Sciapodos are so called—shadow foot, in Greek—because their feet are so enormous that when one of them wants to protect himself from the sun he uses his foot as a parasol.

JAUN: That's really the height of absurdity.

MACROSOPHOS: Why? Are there not cynocephalics? Are there not monocular beings? Are there not phanesians, who cover their bodies with their ears?

CHIQUI: They exist either in reality or in the imagination.

JAUN: Most particularly in the imagination.

CHIQUI: There are Gog and Magog.

MACROSOPHOS: Ah! Gog and Magog. They are giants without heads, with eyes in their chests and mouths in their stomachs.

BASURDI: Maybe that's the reason we speak of the mouth of the stomach.

MACROSOPHOS: No. You are mixing the species. Because they have eyes in their chests these individuals are called sternophthalmous.

JAUN: That's what they're *called!* But do they exist, that's the question?

CHIQUI: Gog and Magog are merely the Tartars and the Mongols. Here is King Bersebi, and the other one is the king of Cambaleth.

MACROSOPHOS: *Civitas Cambaleth magnis Canis Cathayo:* the city of Cambaleth of the Great Khan of China.

CHIQUI: Finally, we have the Anti-Christ, who, as you see, wears the apocalyptic number 666. And now, if you wish, we can ascend to the island of Thule and the island of Ierne, where, according to reports, people eat each other. But I suppose that it must be cold in these northern latitudes, and we don't have even a muffler between us, nor even a skimpy Bayonne waistcoat. So let's go back to our own country. . . Here we are in France already. And now we're passing over Aquitania tercia or Novempopulania. . . Here we are in Larrun again. . . Let's get some sleep. . . Good night! . . .

XIII. ON AWAKENING

Everyone wakes up in a cave on Mount Larrun.

TIMOTHEUS: All this has been nothing but diabolic art.

JAUN: Perhaps drunkenness more than anything else.

BASURDI: Didn't we go through the air?

TIMOTHEUS: No.

BASURDI: Didn't we pass over Rome?

TIMOTHEUS: No.

BASURDI: Then what did we do?

TIMOTHEUS: Lay here without moving.

MACROSOPHOS: The objection made by the sacristan leaves me stupified and dubitative.

BASURDI: The sacristan is a liar.

TIMOTHEUS: No, I am not a liar. The fact is that I see clearly through the wiles of the Evil Enemy, while you are all seduced by him.

BASURDI: I'm talking about what I've seen with my own eyes.

JAUN: See here, let's come to some conclusion! I have the impression that we have been traveling, that we crossed over the sea, and that it was white with foam.

MACROSOPHOS: How do you mean, white with foam? I disagree with the opinion of my predecessor. I saw it green.

BASURDI: It looked blue to me.

TIMOTHEUS: I thought it was more like black.

JAUN: It was the houses of Rome that were black.

MACROSOPHOS: I protest! Not black, but red, the color of stone.

BASURDI: They looked yellow to me.

XIV. SHAGUIT SINGS

JAUN: Nothing of the sort! All this has been nothing! Nothing but phantasmagoria: we have neither traveled, nor moved, nor sailed through the air, and the sacristan is altogether right. (*They go out of the cave.*) What the devil! We're on top of Mount Larrun! Who brought us here? How did we get here? There's Shaguit over there, singing a song.

SHAGUIT: Cucu micu,
                  Choriac sasian umiac ditu.
                  Shagusharrac jango al ditu,
                  Shagusharrac alcatia
                  Berac eguindu leguia.

(Cucu micu, the bird has little ones in the brambles. The bat will eat them up; the bat is the mayor, and he makes the law.)

JAUN: Hi, Shaguit, listen!

SHAGUIT: What is it?

JAUN: Did you see us come here?

SHAGUIT: Yes.

JAUN: Which way did we come?

SHAGUIT: Through the air.

JAUN: Through the air?

SHAGUIT: Yes.

JAUN: How?

SHAGUIT: With the cranes.

JAUN: I don't believe it. We must have been carried here, while we were drunk, in some wagon or other.

XV. MOUNT LARRUN

MOUNT LARRUN: I am one of the Pyrenees, the westernmost mountain. I am the king of this small Basque country, which is most pleasant and variable. In the middle of a carboniferous terrain, by which I am surrounded, I rest upon a base of primitive rock. I can boast some large rock crags, formed by enormous conglomorates, with green flanks and stony recesses where dwarf elders, foxglove and henbane grow.

Whenever I want to dream, I gaze at that far-off star, with whom I have been enamoured for millions of years; whenever I am melancholy, I contemplate the sharp and intricate mountains of Spain; if I feel like smiling, I gaze over the fertile plain of France.

Around me cluster Vera and Urruña, Hendaye and Saint-Jean-de-Luz, Echalar and Sara, Ascaín and Zugarramurdi.

I can look over into the nearby valleys of the Nivelle and the Bidasoa, joyous and sparkling. I can make out the basin of the Nive, which flows into the Adour at Bayonne; the woods of Saint-Pée; Point Mondarraín; and I can watch the waves of the sea, which leave a white line on the beach and which break into spray against the cliffs of Socoa, of Bidart, and of Guethary.

I am the lookout over this Gulf of Gascony, over this restless, turbulent, treacherous Gulf of Gascony.

From my lookout tower I have witnessed geologic cataclysms; I have watched the slow sinking of the coast into the ocean and the battle of the nearby rivers to open a passageway across the earth. I have been a witness to wars on land and sea; I have seen the Romans and the Vikings come ashore; I have observed the republicans of the French Revolution organize into the Croix du Bouquets and the Camp of the Sansculottes; I have descried the Spanish Carlists dig trenches at Peñaplata; and I have spied on Muñagorri in the fort at Pagogaña of Erláiz, and the monk Santa Cruz in the caves of Arichulegui.

On my crest rests the Hermitage of the Holy Ghost, which is Christian by day and given over to witchcraft by night. None of all this makes me uneasy; what concerns me the most is that far-off star, with which I have been in love for millions of centuries, and which has not yet taken heed of my sighs.

XVI. THE DOVE

THE DOVE: I come from Scythia, from the woods of Central and Eastern Europe. I fly across great forests and large lakes; in my passage I circle snowy cities with Byzantine bell towers in the form of onions, and fly over densely populated areas whose Gothic cathedrals rise into stone needles covered with fretwork and whose sides are illuminated by the pale sun of autumn.

XVII. THE NIGHTINGALE

THE NIGHTINGALE: I am a nocturnal *romanza,* which issues forth and is yet occult, and which enchants the darkness with its trilling. My music reflects the heart of solitude and of the fields and the poetry of nature; and it leaves a kind of joyful melancholy in the soul, a melancholy like a wound, and a subtle sadness resembling pleasure.

XVIII. THE OWL

THE OWL: I am an illustrious bird, consecrated to Minerva, as wise as Solomon, half-way between a cat and specter. Perhaps I am prone to melancholy; perhaps it can be said that my habits are antisocial and savage. I have been painted as a vampire that draws blood from children, and my feathers have been used in magical charms and spells. All that is sheer fantasy. I have a bad reputation, but it is undeserved. I have been treated unjustly. Nothing but eulogies for the dove, who is stupid, ungrateful, and self-centered, and nothing but scorn and slights for me! All because she is white, and I am black. I am a sacrifice to taste and aesthetics. And what taste and aesthetics! The manneristic and ridiculous aesthetic of a poet with bangs.
BASURDI: It's the owl, bird of ill-omen.
MACROSOPHOS: The presence of the owl is not baneful until the precise moment when it begins to sing.
JAUN: I don't believe it is any more baneful than that of the sparrow.

MACROSOPHOS: Owls and crows are, according to important authors, fateful and ill-omened. An owl made an appearance before the battle of Philippi, and foretold death and defeat to Cassius.

JAUN: Did Cassius tell you this himself?

MACROSOPHOS: No. This is something we know *de auditu*. The authors tell us.

JAUN: Bah! They tell so many lies!

XIX. THE SHEPHERD

THE SHEPHERD: Seated here, with my white crook between my hands, I gaze out over the valleys and the sea, watching over my flock, which is scattered across the meadows, while the cuckoo sings as if he were playing hide-and-seek in the distance. Sometimes I play simple melodies on my shawm, and the mountains themselves seem to dance to my tunes. I know nothing of what goes on around me; I don't know how other people live, not even the people in the villages that I can see. And so, when I see the cranes, flying along as a rearguard in the autumn migrations, as high as the clouds themselves, formed into a triangle and uttering piercing shrieks, I ask myself: Where do they come from? Where are they going? And, without knowing whether the countries they came from and the ones they are going to are good or bad, I look at them with envy.

XX. THE BILLY-GOAT

THE BILLY-GOAT: I am the billy-goat, and I preside over the witches' sabbaths. I am the favorite companion of Bacchus, Priapus, of Mendes, and the god Thor. I used to be looked upon as the symbol of fertility; and now they say I am the Devil; but I haven't noticed any change in me. I am a poor horned creature, like many another, whom they have converted into a solar myth. I symbolize tempestuous night fertilized by a lightning bolt.

XXI. URTZI THOR'S COMPLAINT

URTZI THOR: I am the god Urtzi Thor, the strongest of the gods. Only recently come from Scandinavia, I soon reigned as far as the Pyrenees, where the Basques paid me homage along with their local gods.

They called me Urtzi: the firmament, the front of the sky, the solstice of the year, the thunder.

I have heard talk of a certain Aitor, the father of the Basques; this Aitor is also my forefather.

I was happy to see my kingdoms extend to the southern regions, down to these Pyrenees, which were raised up, according to tradition, by fire. I was happy to have the homage of the Basques, and at the fact that together with the Germans and the Scandinavians they should have given Thursday over to my special advocacy, calling that day Urtz-eguna, Urtzi's day, and that they remembered my name by incorporating it in the word for thunder, which they called *turmoya*.

I have taught men the cult of heroism and bravery; I have battled with the giants and with death, and if I have not exactly vanquished them, that is merely because of some enchantment. I have come to the defense of the farmer and the forger, and of all creators and all workers in the earth.

And now men are abandoning me. The semitic cult of Jehovah is penetrating everywhere, and I must go.

You no longer love me, ingrates? I shall go, and take my thunder and my lightning bolts and my twelve stars; I shall go, with my hammer and my iron gloves and my cauldron on my head. You no longer like my fierce eyes and my red beard? You no longer care for my goats? You prefer the Jewish prophets, with their black curly hair that makes them look like figures in a barber-shop window? Well and good. I shall go back to my aerial kingdom. I shall no longer struggle with the monster serpent, enemy of gods and men, which you Basques called Leheren-Suguia.

I will not be a beggar. You don't want me? I shall go; I shall embark and disappear into the arctic seas, where the midnight sun holds sway.

Urtzi Thor approaches a Viking ship which is painted black and has a gilt figurehead on the bow. Urtzi Thor goes aboard taking his billy-goats with him.

Intermezzo

THE CHORUS: Your going grieves us deeply, Urtzi Thor. Why do you go? Why do you abandon us? Is it fatal destiny which forces you to leave our lands behind? If such is the case, Farewell!
THE OCEAN: Farewell, Urtzi Thor, valiant among the valiant!
MOUNT LARRUN: Farewell, agile Thor, master of the lightning!
URTZI THOR (*from aboard his ship*): Farewell! Farewell Pyrenees beside the sea! Rolling luminous mountainsides! Green and temperate valleys! Sonorous resounding towns! Farewell proud and ancient Basques, and joyous youth with eagles' beaks! Farewell joyful, dancing girls! I am returning to my frozen wastes. Farewell! Farewell.

Joy and Sadness

THE AUTHOR: Our friend Jaun has taken a bad road: the road to intellectualism. The wisest of men, such as Father Prudentius and Macrosophos himself, have tried to dissuade him from going down this fatal incline.

He closes his eyes: he wants to see the pro and con of all things, to observe them with an absurd impartiality before deciding. He demands to make things clear by means of a hateful criticism; he attempts to achieve common sense. In Alzate and at the very height of the Middle Ages!

The same thing happens to writers with regard to their characters as happens, through some kind of evil magic, to the creators of monsters and homunculi. At first, they, the fathers, decide and give the orders; then the children, that is, the monsters and homunculi, are the ones to impose their will and hold sway.

I was not planning to lead Jaun through such difficult paths, but he has hurled himself down these by-ways, and I have not been able to hold him back.

Poor Jaun! Unfortunate Jaun! How much better for you it would have been to have attended the novenas or the vesper services! To submit! For there is the true path of happiness.

Who could think of rebelling and attempting to act the eagle in a chicken hatchery?

Who could think of belonging to the school of the Portico while living among sacristans?

Poor Jaun! Unfortunate Jaun!

I. STREET CONVERSATION

PRUDENTIUS (*the Rector*): How are you Macrosophos? How is the illustrious pedagogue? Do you still drink at all the vinaceous springs of the neighborhood?

MACROSOPHOS: Yes, I continue my libations. And the honorable Rector, is he well?

PRUDENTIUS: Very, well, thank you.

MACROSOPHOS: And does the church continue to rise?

PRUDENTIUS: It will rise to the sky.

MACROSOPHOS: And the charity box for the souls of the dead, does it continue to be filled by the grace of God.

PRUDENTIUS: Fairly well, fairly well.

MACROSOPHOS: The tithes and first fruits, then, rain in like manna.

PRUDENTIUS: They do not let up.

MACROSOPHOS: Still, I suppose that that early epoch has gone forever, that millennium, when everyone turned over his property to the Church, thinking that the end of the world was approaching, *Limite mundo apropincuante.*

PRUDENTIUS: Everything passes. . . And your rebellious disciple Jaun, what is he doing now?

MACROSOPHOS: He's in a bad way. He's following an imprudent and mistaken course. And he is becoming a skeptic.

PRUDENTIUS: There you have the end to which science inevitably leads.

MACROSOPHOS: At Leyden we bought a copy of the poem by Lucretius, *De rerum natura,* and the reading of it has deranged his judgement.

PRUDENTIUS: Lucretius! Why he's worse that Averroes, *iste maledictus Averroes!*

MACROSOPHOS: My disciple is under the nefarious and lethal influence of Lucretius' book. It's from him that he got his skepticism, his atheism.

PRUDENTIUS: Frightful!

MACROSOPHOS: It's awful.

PRUDENTIUS: And what will you do?

MACROSOPHOS: I won't stay here much longer.

PRUDENTIUS: Then, goodbye, Macrosophos, illustrious pedagogue!

MACROSOPHOS: Goodbye, honorable Rector.

II. SOLITUDE

A Sunday afternoon in the fall of the year; the weather is warm and wet. Jaun is in his library, reading. From time to time he gets up and goes to the window, where he gazes out disconsolately. In a nearby meadow, a group of country people are dancing to the music of a bagpipe. Some old women can be seen playing cards under the porticoes of their houses.

Weary of reading, Jaun contemplates the passing of the nostalgic afternoon. Yellow leaves fly through the air and scatter down the walks and roads. Some of the trees still have traces of reddish leaves, curled and trembling, hanging along their black, dry boughs. The sky is leaden gray; the wind begins to whine, and it carries on it the acrid odor of dry fern. The jackdaws fly cawing in the sky, and a flock of cranes forms a black triangle along the horizon. From time to time some rain falls. The sound of the rainwater in the spouts by the attic can be heard, and it mingles with the rumor of the river of Lamiocingo-erreca, which has suddenly swelled to a yellowish flood. Smoke floats over the blackish houses of Alzate. In the street, a beggar sings to the accompaniment of his guitar.

THE BEGGAR: When the angel Saint Gabriel
Came on his embassy
To tell of Mary's election,
She fainting bent her knee.

And Mary said: I am the slave
Of the Eternal Father
Who to you this message gave.

JAUN: How sad this song makes me!
Jaun closes the window, lights the lamp, and puts some wood on the fire. Chimista, the dog, sighs beside the fireplace. The firelight barely illuminates the large room, and the corners remain in darkness. Jaun sits down once again.

JAUN: I am striving to tear both hope and fear from out of my soul. I do not know if I shall ever achieve calm. In this dark corner I have hidden myself from other mortals, so that no one comes to see me now but some sick man seeking help. The neighbors consider me eccentric. Only the owl comes at night to pay me a visit, and his sharp cry accompanies my vigil. I shall let Macrosophos go. I can no longer stand his pedantry and false science. All he knows are names and subterfuges. Well, on with my reading:

"Amethyst protects against drunkenness; coral is an anti-epeleptic; an emerald will hide if the person wearing it enters a conjugal bed; a diamond will uncover female infidelity; the sapphire is a preservative against magical charms."

What nonsense there is in these so-called occult sciences! They should really be called occult nonsense. But, I must go on.

"It is well known that the halcyon, which resembles the king-fisher, is a natural weathercock and that, suspended by its beak, it will point with its chest to the quarter from which the wind blows."

Another lie. Must it be a necessity for men to lie in this

fashion? Let's see if there is one sensible observation, something real, in this whole book:

"It is asserted that the plant called *sferra cavallo* possesses the power of breaking locks, and of causing the shoes of horses that walk on it to fall off. Pliny supposes that this power is also inherent in the herb called *aethiophis,* but then he later casts doubt upon it, when he recalls that Scipio was held up at the gates of Carthage though he had as much of the herb at hand as he could want."

The extravagance continues. Only you, Lucretius, saw clearly into the reality of things, of Nature, that blind Nature with its rigid and immutable laws! But I must continue my reading:

"It is also possible to open a lock without using a key by writing on a parchment the following signs and letters: '++ F.A.P.H.R.G. (A.P.H.Q.),' and then putting the parchment inside a newly made cloth and placing it on a Christian altar, where it must be left for nine days."

What simple-mindedness! How can people put such things in books? I will look for something more useful further on:

"It is said that in the royal palace at Venice there is not a single fly, while in the royal palace of Toledo there is only one, and it is asserted that this is due to the fact that metal idols have been buried in the foundations of both palaces. Gregory of Tours, in his *Historia Francorum,* asserts that certain people claim that the city of Paris had originally been built and consecrated in such a way that it was not subject to fires and that neither snakes or dormice were to be found there; but that in his time, when one of the Paris bridges, which was covered with mud, was cleaned, an iron snake and dormouse were turned up, and that, because they were immediately pried out and taken away, a prodigious number of snakes and dormice have ever since infested Paris and its environs, and the city has since then been subject to fires."

O Lucretius! What disdain would you feel to read such drivel.

III. MASTER AND DISCIPLE

MACROSOPHOS: Friend Jaun, you devour your books with too much voracity. One must live: *Primum vivere, deinde philosophari.*

JAUN: That's well enough for you, who search in books for means to a reputation, but it's not for me.

MACROSOPHOS: Well, then, what are you looking for?

JAUN: Spiritual utility, but still utility; something to resolve the problem of my life.

MACROSOPHOS: Why do you think that to seek a reputation is worse than seeking health or utility?

JAUN: I don't think it better or worse, but merely different. When a man like you and one like me meet each other, it is not likely or easy that they should be in accord. One desires to play with ideas; the other wants to live with them. One of the two is bound to say: This egotist looks to Science for his peace of mind. The other man will think: That fellow is an orator who thinks only of showing himself off.

MACROSOPHOS: Are you searching for peace of mind?

JAUN: Yes.

MACROSOPHOS: So that's what you're looking for?

JAUN: Yes, for I am looking for truth. I should like to know where truth lies, so that I might take refuge in its shade.

MACROSOPHOS: Aren't religion and science enough for you?

JAUN: Religion isn't enough, because I don't believe in it. Science isn't either, for I don't know in what it consists.

MACROSOPHOS: Why, in Physics, in Logic, in Astrology, in Alchemy. . .

JAUN: All this science of words in Latin, Greek, and Hebrew is an illusion. All these disquisitions over ideas and things whose reality is in question are mere phantasmagoria. Chimeras! Pure chimeras! Vain chimeras!

To talk about the Trinity and Grace, the Word and the Pneuma, the Demiurge and astral planes and philosophic stones and hypostasis and metempsychosis . . . all that is to play games in a vacuum. Nothing exists but Nature.

MACROSOPHOS: Ah, now the nefarious influence of Lucretius begins to appear.

JAUN: I have made experiments and tested the emptiness of this pretended science.

MACROSOPHOS: How?

JAUN: By experimentation, by experience.

MACROSOPHOS: Experience is deceptive, as Hippocrates said. I have more faith in dialectic, in the syllogism.

JAUN: The syllogism is a framework without any value. That two universal and affirmative propositions should yield a consequent particular affirmative is true; but, what does this teach me? All men are mortal; I am a man; therefore I am mortal. There is no need for me to state these propositions, for I know I am mortal without the aid of a syllogism.

MACROSOPHOS: This is the way to ruin Science.

JAUN: The kind of Science that isn't science, you mean. The science of words.

MACROSOPHOS: Duns Scotus, known as Doctor Subtilis, has made notable discoveries by the use of the syllogism.

JAUN: I don't believe it.

MACROSOPHOS: Words can possess a great importance. *Carmina de coelo possunt deducere lunam:* The moon can be made to fall from the skies with words, as Virgil said.

JAUN: I don't care if Virgil said it, or if my servant Basurdi did, it's all one to me.

MACROSOPHOS: What a blasphemy!

JAUN: What possible effect on nature can the arrangement of certain words or certain letters in a certain order have? Or the fact that they are spoken in a certain way? None at all. Words are just so much noise, as far as nature is concerned.

MACROSOPHOS: Origen and Saint Clement of Alexandria have demonstrated in the most evident manner that the names of God placed in a certain order can produce miracles . . . with the co-operation of the Devil, naturally.

JAUN: My own experiences and experiments have shown me that nothing of the sort is true.

MACROSOPHOS: How have you verified your experiments?

JAUN: In accordance with all the rules.

MACROSOPHOS: Neither experiments nor experiences can invalidate the truths that the masters have asserted. Aristotle, Pliny, the Fathers of the Church, Saint Augustine, Origen, Saint Thomas, have all believed that words were something more than *flatus vocis.*

JAUN: As far as I'm concerned only the facts count.

MACROSOPHOS: The facts! What have they got to do with it?

JAUN: The facts are everything. Beyond the facts everything is theory and hypothesis, and even these must be based on facts; when hypotheses can not be supported by facts, they are nothing but fables; and thus, magic and astrology are nothing but fables.

MACROSOPHOS: And the authority of the masters, the *Consensus Omnium,* have no value, then?

JAUN: Not for me. *Magister dixit* means nothing to me.

MACROSOPHOS: What are these experiments that you have carried out, that make you believe that the methods of the masters are worthless?

JAUN: They are many and of every kind.

MACROSOPHOS: Let's see. . .

JAUN: My experiments are principally related to magic.

MACROSOPHOS: Very well! Let's see, then! Prima . . . secunda
. . . tertia.

JAUN: I have observed, for example, that the moon exercises no
influence over the growth of plants; I have observed that bought
bees do the same work as borrowed bees; I have observed that
the word *Ananizapta* works no effect at all on persons suffering
from the plague; and that dog bites are not to be cured by repeating *Hax, pax, max, Deus adimax.*

MACROSOPHOS: These are minutiae without importance.

JAUN: For science, there is no such minutiae.

MACROSOPHOS: What else have you proven to be false?

JAUN: I have verified that no purpose whatsoever is achieved by
wearing a necklace bearing a triangular piece of parchment on
which is written the word *Abracadabra* in accordance with the
instructions of Serenus, the ex-doctor and upholder of Basilides,
the Alexandrian Gnostic, which are contained in his verses beginning: *"Inscribis chartoe quod dicitur Abracadabra."*

MACROSOPHOS: None?

JAUN: None. And it is equally useless to write the word
Avigazirtor on a piece of new parchment before sunrise.

MACROSOPHOS: So that, according to you, phylacteries have no
effective action?

JAUN: They have no effective action. I have taken a piece of red
parchment and written on it the phrase *Omnis spiritus laudet
Dominum.* This is an infallible recipe in magic for achieving
whatever one wants. Well, I gave the parchment to Basurdi and
entrusted him with three or four errands. He didn't carry out a
single one.

MACROSOPHOS: Perhaps Basurdi said some Christian prayer that
invalidated the magical effect of the phylactery.

JAUN: He doesn't know any prayers, Christian or otherwise. He
didn't do what I asked him to do because he's naturally lazy, and
that's the only reason.

MACROSOPHOS: What other tests have you made?

JAUN: I placed the hearts of a black chicken, a bat, and a frog
in a flask. This is a sure-fire method for becoming invisible, according to magicians. I gave the flask to several people in turn
and had them carry it about in their right hand.

MACROSOPHOS: And nothing happened?

JAUN: Nothing. I could see them just the same as always. And
then I've gathered herbs on the eve of St. John's and they've dried
up just like any other herbs and haven't cured a single infirmity.
I've tested to see if the needle used to sew up the clothes of a

dead man prevents people from eating if it be placed on the table where they are to sit, but it does no such thing.

MACROSOPHOS: That's strange!

JAUN: I've proven to my own satisfaction that bread baked on Christmas Eve dries just as quickly as bread baked any other time, and that to fill the cider barrels on Fridays has no more effect than filling them on Monday or Saturday. Moreover, it's been more than a year now since I transplanted some parsley, and I'm not dead yet.

MACROSOPHOS: That doesn't surprise me. It's only a popular superstition about parsley.

JAUN: I've cut the head of a bat with a silver coin, I've stuffed the dead bat into a hole, left it there three months, then I've asked it for money, and—nothing doing. It's all a pack of lies, and what isn't a lie is a game, like your syllogisms and your logic. The only truth is in mathematics.

MACROSOPHOS: In short, you don't need me any more.

JAUN: Now there is an exact conclusion that you can deduce without the aid of a syllogism.

MACROSOPHOS: Fair enough. I was beginning to get tired of living here anyway.

JAUN: I'm happy to hear it. Thus the two of us will be satisfied.

IV. THE CHILD

Some weeks later.

BASURDI: Master!

JAUN: What is it?

BASURDI: There's a French woman with a child at the door.

JAUN: And what does she want?

BASURDI: She wants to talk to you.

JAUN: Talk to me?

BASURDI: Yes.

JAUN: All right. Show her in.

The woman comes in, hand in hand with a boy of about five.

THE WOMAN: Are you Jaun de Alzate?

JAUN: Yes, that's me.

THE WOMAN: Do you remember Pamposha, the girl from Balezta?

JAUN: Yes. How could I forget her? What's new with her?

THE WOMAN: La Pamposha lived in Sara, with her husband; but the husband didn't treat her very well and she's run away. They say she's gone off to Paris to live with a marquis.

JAUN: How easy life is for a girl like that! Is she as lovely as ever?

THE WOMAN: Enchanting! . . . Before she went away from Sara, La Pamposha stayed in my house, and she told me: If my husband treats the child well, leave the boy with him; but if you see that he is treating him badly, spirit him away and take him to the house of Jaun de Alzate, in Vera, and give Jaun this paper. I saw that the boy was being badly treated and I've brought him to you. And here's the paper.

JAUN (*reading to himself*): "Jaun: I send you your son. Remember Christmas night in Easo. Pamposha."
And this child? Is he the son of Pamposha?

THE WOMAN: Yes.

JAUN: What's his name?

THE WOMAN: Bihotz.

JAUN: This child is my son! I am overcome with emotion! . . . Basurdi! Call my wife here!

THE BOY (*to Jaun*): What a lot of books! Have they got pictures in them?

JAUN: Yes.

THE BOY: I want to see them.

JAUN: I'll show them to you. Look! (*He hands the boy a book.*)

THE BOY: This one doesn't have many pictures in it. I want another one!

JAUN: Here, take this one.

THE BOY: What's that big animal hanging from the roof? Is it a big lizard?

JAUN: Yes, it is.

THE BOY: I want to touch it.

JAUN: I'll lift you up so that you can reach it. Aren't you afraid that it will bite you?

THE BOY: No, because it's dead.

USOA (*entering*): What is it, Jaun? A child! What a pretty boy!

JAUN: Yes, he really is pretty; but he's a bit of a tyrant.

USOA: He's a love, a precious little boy. What's your name?

THE BOY: Bihotz.

USOA: Would you like to sit on my lap?

THE BOY: Yes.

JAUN: He's already making himself master. (*To Usoa*): Well, do you know whose boy this is?

USOA: Whose?

JAUN: He's the son of La Pamposha, from Balezta. La Pamposha has gone away to Paris. She heard that I was a wise man, and she tells me in a letter that she would like us to keep the boy for a few weeks and teach him something. (*Aside*): How one lies when it's a matter close to one's heart!

USOA: If you don't have any objections . . .

JAUN: On the contrary, I think it would be amusing.

USOA: In that case, let's keep him.

JAUN: Will you give this woman who has come all the way from Sara with the boy something to eat, then, and give her whatever she asks for her work.

V. SCANDAL

OLAZÁBAL'S GRANDMOTHER: And now what's Jaun doing?

BASURDI: He's changed completely. Since La Pamposha's child came here, he's not the same man. He's forgotten his books, and he runs and plays in the orchard, and he acts like a little boy. The other day Bihotz tore one of Jaun's favorite maps in the library and Jaun didn't even complain; instead he began to laugh.

ZARRATEA'S GRANDMOTHER: And Pamposha from Balezta, where is she?

BASURDI: They say she's in Paris, living like a queen; they say she has a palace and servants galore. . . But I can't stay any longer, I've got to go. Goodbye!

OLAZÁBAL'S GRANDMOTHER: What a scandal! Usoa is a fool. That boy is Jaun's son.

ZARRATEA'S GRANDMOTHER: Do you think so?

OLAZÁBAL'S GRANDMOTHER: Of course he is! The boy's grandfather lives here, doesn't he, at Balezta, and, nevertheless, he's been sent to Jaun's house.

ZARRATEA'S GRANDMOTHER: Why, that's true! Poor Usoa! Men! What bandits they are!

OLAZÁBAL'S GRANDMOTHER: And women! Just look at Pamposha! In Paris . . . with palaces . . . and manservants and lovers. . .

ZARRATEA'S GRANDMOTHER: Do you think she has lovers?

OLAZÁBAL'S GRANDMOTHER: Certainly! Who else would support her?

ZARRATEA'S GRANDMOTHER: What a scandal! This life is full of nothing but disillusion.

OLAZÁBAL'S GRANDMOTHER: It's no longer possible to be an honest woman.

ZARRATEA'S GRANDMOTHER: Isn't it the truth?

OLAZÁBAL'S GRANDMOTHER: Don't you think we should have a little *thantha?*

ZARRATEA'S GRANDMOTHER: Won't it do us any harm?

OLAZÁBAL'S GRANDMOTHER: No, no, none at all. It's very good for one. And with this humidity! . . .

ZARRATEA'S GRANDMOTHER: And the pains and deceptions one has to endure! . . .

VI. THE SICK BOY

A year has passed by. Bihotz, the child of La Pamposha and Jaun has been sick for some days now. Jaun has been diagnosing and studying the boy's illness in his books: in Hippocrates, Galen, and Avicenna; he has called in a witch, who has the reputation of being learned in medicine; they have already put the boy through a hole in an oak tree; they have used all the magical and medicinal recipes one after the other; and Bihotz is getting worse. On this very night he has taken such a bad turn that Jaun tells his wife Usoa:

JAUN: I'm going to France to fetch a doctor.

USOA: At this hour?

JAUN: Yes, right now.

Jaun descends to the stable, where he slips into a cloak and mounts a horse. He sets out, in the black night, along a narrow path, in search first of the Inzola waterway. His dog Chimisa, follows along behind him. Rain begins to fall. The horse sinks into the mud of the road. Soon he comes out on to a rocky path that climbs along the mountain; the horseshoes strike sparks on the rocky ground and make a noise like dull bells. In the Inzola pass, high in the mountains, the wind howls fiercely, as if some giant bull, terrible and menacing, were hidden in a nearby ravine. The next morning, Jaun is back with a French doctor. The boy's condition has not changed.

VII. THE DOCTOR

JAUN: Have you examined him thoroughly?

THE DOCTOR: Yes.

JAUN: What do you think?

THE DOCTOR: I think that it is a desperate case. Any child I have seen in this condition has died.

JAUN: What could we do? Wouldn't a strong revulsion in the region of the feet drive the disease to some other part of the body and clear the head?

THE DOCTOR: You can try.

JAUN: Don't you think it would yield any result?

THE DOCTOR: I think not, but you can try.

JAUN: What have you done in other cases like this?

THE DOCTOR: I have tried various procedures and remedies, but none has worked. That is why I don't prescribe anything now.

JAUN: Your truthfulness is cruel.

THE DOCTOR: What would be the use of trying to deceive you?

JAUN: You're right. If you can't do anything, you may as well leave him alone. At least we won't torture his poor little body. Goodbye, then! One of my servants will accompany you back to your home.

THE DOCTOR: Goodbye! I am sorry to have visited you for the first time at such a sad hour.

VIII. DEATH

JAUN: He's worse every minute. He can no longer see. (*Jaun goes to the window.*) Urtzi! Urtzi! God! God! . . . It's all one. There's nothing but the noise of the wind or the fall of the rain in the dark night. How sad it all is! How painful! How useless is Science! Everything I've studied is worth nothing, and I haven't even been able to lengthen this boy's life by a single moment. What shall I do now? Where shall I go for help? . . . Nothing, nobody. These shall be henceforth my only meaningful words. O Urtzi! I was happier when I believed in you.

USOA: The poor boy is like a little bird dying.

JAUN: Wretches! Madmen! There is nothing above us, nothing beyond our lives but a cold, blind nature, which neither sees nor cares.

USOA: He's dead.

JAUN (*sobbing and clasping his wife's hand desperately*): Go and rest, Usoa.

USOA: And you?

JAUN: I can't.

IX. LAMENTATION

JAUN: Unfortunate wretch! Why did you put all your old man's enthusiasm in this weak little creature? And now the world is blacker than ever. But why did you have to place all your hopes in this boy? To die, to die! There is no longer any other course for me, there is no hope left in me. I want to leave this anguish behind me as quickly as possible, quit this scene, go off into nothingness, escape from this deaf and blind universe!

CHORUS OF INVISIBLE SPIRITS: Jaun! Life is not a whim of mankind. Destiny wields blind rule. Seek further, follow your course to the end with courage and energy.

JAUN: Yes, we are merely poor puppets moved about by Fate. Our tragedy is not even original; we wail with the gestures that others have invented, we repeat the grimaces of others before us, and we quit our place in this wretched theater to leave it to some other fool who will repeat our very gestures and wails. Awful fate!

CHIMISTA (*the dog*): Look at me, humble, easygoing, resting by the fire. That's life!

JAUN: It was wanting to know that killed me. But who could have guessed that Science would have led to a blind universe, to a nature deaf to our cries, to an empty heaven? (*He gazes out the window; the light of the dawn is beginning to appear.*) The entire world is nothing but a lifeless body, a great cadaver, and we men are but sad worms, gnawing away at the carcass, until death does away with us too.

I hear voices. Who could it be?

X. THE PILGRIMS

THE PILGRIMS: We are pilgrims, on our way back from Santiago de Compostela. Give us a little something in charity, for the love of God, for we have earned it!

We have made our way across this brambly land so as to avoid the Summus Pyrinoeus and the Crucem Karoli, for the Gascons rob us, threaten our lives at the ends of their pikes, and even make us work for them like mules.

We are Wallachians and Germans, Franks and Bretons, Normans and Picards. Some of us go on pilgrimages from faith; others, from hunger; and there are those who go to play the vagabond; others, to live a more intense and varied life than is possible in small towns lorded over by a great landlord or abbot. In the old days, we used to be guided on by an angel or a star; nowadays we are led by cupidity or a taste for adventure.

We live in the midst of perils: hunger, thirst, fatigue, cold, snow, tempests, rainstorms, wild animals.

In short, we are pilgrims, on our way back from Santiago de Compostela. Give us a little something in charity, for the love of God, for we have earned it!

We wear numerous shells on our pilgrim's cloak, for we need more shells for our shell game than so many tortoises, and we carry a large gourd, not precisely for the transportation of holy water. We also sport a knapsack, and a staff, and a wide-brimmed hat, and we sing religious songs in chorus as we go. Whenever we find a good night's lodging, in some monastery, for instance, life is sweet; when we don't, life is a torture.

In short, we are pilgrims, on our way back from Santiago de Compostela. Give us a little something in charity, for the love of God, for we have earned it!

> Dum pater familias
> Rex universorum
> Donaret provincias
> Jus apostolorum
> Jacobus Hispanias.
> Lux, illustrat, morum.

JAUN: Wait! Wait for me! I'm going with you.

ARBELÁIZ: Where in heaven's name are you going, Jaun?

JAUN: I am going in search of truth. Farewell!

XI. FIFTEEN YEARS LATER

Jaun has come again to the neighborhood of Alzate one winter day's dusk. He is near death, and he struggles along with the aid of a cane.

JAUN: I am losing strength with every step forward, and I fear I will die before reaching my house. The icy wind makes my whole body tremble and shiver. I would lie down here, at the edge of the road, and die, but I want to reach home . . . Ah! . . . I'm drawing near . . . I'm almost there!

He knocks at the gate.
USOA: Who's there?
BASURDI: It's a beggar.
JAUN: No, Usoa! It's me, Jaun!
USOA: You! My poor friend! What tatters! O what sorrow to see you like this!
JAUN: Yes, it's me. Take me to my room, for I can no longer see.
USOA: My poor Jaun!
JAUN: Are you all well?
USOA: Yes, we are all well.
JAUN: Is Arbeláiz still alive?
USOA: Yes, he's still alive. Do you want me to call him?
JAUN: Well, all right.
USOA: He'll come right away.
JAUN: What did you do with my books?
USOA: We burned them.
JAUN: Why did you do that?
USOA: Father Prudentius ordered them burned, so that other people would not lose their minds reading them.
JAUN: And the belvedere in the orchard? And are my trees still kept up?
USOA: No, Father Fanaticus had them cut down.
Arbeláiz enters.
ARBELÁIZ: Have you come home, Jaun? I didn't ever expect to see you again. Did you find the truth you were looking for?
JAUN: There is no single truth, Arbeláiz, none. . . Urtzi is as true as Jehovah or as Christ. Have you all become Catholics?
ARBELÁIZ: Yes.
JAUN: I guessed it when I heard that my books had been burned and my trees cut down.
ARBELÁIZ: The Franciscan monks have built a monastery just opposite, in Celaya.
JAUN: But that house is mine!
ARBELÁIZ: Your wife deeded it to them; from there they catechized the town.
Everyone has been baptized, except Shaguit, the madman.
JAUN: And so he and I are the only two madmen left in town?
ARBELÁIZ: It looks that way.
SHAGUIT (*singing in the street*):
          Iru chitu izan ta
          Eta lau galdu.
          ¿Nere chituaren ama
          Zenec jan du?

Acheriyac jan diyo lepoa
Eta erretora jauna troncoa.

(To have three chicks and lose all four! Who ate the mother of my chicks? The fox ate the neck, and the Rector the trunk.)

JAUN: Isn't that Shaguit's voice?

ARBELÁIZ: Yes.

JAUN: Tell him to come up.

USOA: Wouldn't you rather have Father Prudentius come, Jaun? Don't you want to confess to him?

JAUN: No, no. Just open the windows so that I see my beloved mountains and let Shaguit sing and let me die in peace. . .

Epilogue

Our poor Jaun is dead. He had come and gone about the world; he had wandered too far, and his hour had come.

In his house in Alzate, some of the ceremonies of the old religion have been secretly performed. A coin has been placed in the dead man's hand; the coffin, as it was being transported, has been rapped smartly against the angles of the house. Moreover, the death of the master has been communicated to all the domestic animals, and to the bees as well. Some faithful friends are thinking of repairing to Gentil-arri to offer libations in honor of the defunct lord.

Jaun's body has been brought out, and the priests are moving along with it now, taking it, amid much pomp, to be buried in the Christian cemetery, which is laid out around the new church. The priests are singing the funeral chant, the gorigori. *The church bells go din, dan, din, dan.*

PATER PRUDENTIUS: This man whom we are about to bury was a rebel, a man who tried to go along on his own, to think for himself, without paying attention to the Church. If it were not for the scandal, I would have been in favor of burying him outside consecrated ground.

PATER FANATICUS: That would have been best. This man's soul must already be in hell.

PATER ANGELICUS: God will pardon him.

PATER FANATICUS: He refused the sacraments.

ARBELÁIZ: He probably didn't think he was so badly off.

PATER FANATICUS: He didn't think! When one has faith, one never neglects these things; but he had no faith and he deserves eternal punishment.

PATER ANGELICUS: God's mercy is infinite.

PATER FANATICUS: Jaun was a reprobate, an impious rebel against all the rules of the Church.

THE YOUNG MISTRESS OF OLAZÁBAL: Fie, fie! They say that Jaun didn't die like a good Christian.

THE YOUNG MISTRESS OF ZARRATEA: Jesus, Mary, and Joseph! The things one hears! And we ladies of Alzate must hear them, we who have always been such good Christians!

ARBELÁIZ: Poor Jaun, my old friend! You were valiant and good; you would have kept up the fight against these little men in skirts who are out to be our tyrants.

THE INNKEEPER: What a magnificent wake for the lord of Alzate! The men of his quarter have eaten up two dozen lambs and drunk down a barrel of wine. The old women have done away with all the hot chocolate and spirits. It would be something to have a man like that die every week!

SHAGUIT: Poor Jaun! Poor old friend! Who will protect me now, a madman among all these sane folk.

CHIQUI (to Arbeláiz): Do you know what I'm going to say now?

ARBELÁIZ: What?

CHIQUI: I'm going to say that Jaun hasn't died. That I've filled his coffin with dirt, and that Jaun is alive, that he'll never die; that I've hidden him in a cave in Mount Larrun, and that he will stay there as long as the Basque country is enslaved by the Catholics, and that when the moment comes, Jaun will appear with the hammer of Thor in his hand, to smash to pieces the world of hypocrisy and servility and to implant the cult of Liberty and Nature.

ARBELÁIZ: And who is going to believe that?

CHIQUI: You people. Don't you believe even more absurd things? Don't you believe the tales the Catholics spread about?

ARBELÁIZ: Yes, but do you dispose of jails, gallows, bonfires, judges, hangmen, and soldiers to drive the message home, like the Catholics?

CHIQUI: That's true; you're right there.

Final Farewell

THE CHORUS: From here we can still hear your powerful voice, Urtzi Thor. The stress of your words carries this far. Come, come back to these southern shores! Leave that land of midnight sun! Everything turns, everything returns; you, too, will return to us!

URTZI THOR: Farewell! Farewell Pyrenees beside the sea! Rolling luminous mountainsides! Green and temperate valleys! Sonorous resounding towns! Farewell proud and ancient Basques, and joyous youth with eagles' beaks! Farewell joyful, dancing girls! I salute you for the last time from my frozen wastes. Farewell! Farewell forever! Farewell!